A Charlton Standard Catalogue

Royal Doulton Animals

Third Edition

By
Jean Dale

Introduction
by
Louise Irvine

W. K. Cross
Publisher

The Charlton Press

Toronto, Ontario • Palm Harbor, Florida

Canadian Cataloguing In Publication Data

The National Library of Canada has Catalogued this publication as follows:

The Charlton standard catalogue of Royal Doulton animals
Biennial.
ISSN 1195-5384
ISBN 0-88968-218-6 (3rd edition)

1. Royal Doulton figurines—Catalogs. 2. Porcelain animals-Catalogs.
I. Charlton Press II. Title: Royal Doulton Animals

NK4660.C502   738.8'2'0294   C94-900404-9

**Printed in Canada
in the Province of Ontario**

The Charlton Press

Visit us at www.charltonpress.com

EDITORIAL

Editors	W. K. Cross, Jean Dale
Editorial Assistant	Susan Cross
Graphic Technician	Davina Rowan
Colour Technician	Marina Tsoukis

ACKNOWLEDGEMENTS

The Charlton Press wishes to thank those who have helped and assisted with the third edition of "The Charlton Standard Catalogue of Royal Doulton Animals."

SPECIAL THANKS

We would like to thank the staff at Royal Doulton Limited, on both sides of the ocean, for all their help and assistance: **Janet Drift,** Director of Retail Sales U.S.A.; **Ian Johnson,** Operations Manager, Giftware and Collectors (UK); **Fiona Hawthorne,** General Manager, Direct and Relationship Marketing (UK); **Maria Murtagh,** Senior Product Manager (UK); **Tricia A. Gadsden,** Brand Manager - Giftware and Collectables (Can.).

CONTRIBUTORS TO THE THIRD EDITION

The Publisher would like to thank the following individuals or companies who graciously supplied photographs or allowed us access to their collections for photographic purposes. We offer sincere thanks to:

Veronica Alvarado, Pascoe and Co., Coral Gables, Florida; **Anthony Cross,** The Englishman, Blackburn, England; **Alan Blakeman, BBR Auctions,** Barnsley, England; **Don and Betty Blubaugh,** Walnut Creek, California; **William T. Cross,** William Cross Antiques & Collectibles Inc., Toronto, Ontario, Canada; **John Fornaszewski,** Granite City, Illinois; **Harriman-Judd Collection,** Los Angeles, California; **Tony Kent,** Faulconbridge, Australia; **Mr. S. Marsden,** Berkshire, England; **Leone L. Monroe,** Stillwater, Oklahoma; **Mark Oliver,** Bonhams, London, England; **Lee Piper,** Boston, Massachusetts; **Raymond Portman,** Barnoldswick, England; **Arron Rimpley and Gregg Whittecar,** Whitley Collection, North Miami, Florida; **Steven Ross,** Munsey Park, New York; **Joseph Schenberg,** St. Louis, Missouri;

A SPECIAL NOTE TO COLLECTORS

We welcome and appreciate any comments or suggestions in regard to "The Charlton Standard Catalogue of Royal Doulton Animals." If any errors or omisions come to your attention, please do not hesitate to write to us, or if you would like to participate in pricing or supply previously unavailable data or information, please contact Jean Dale at (416) 488-1418, or e-mail us at **chpress@charltonpress.com**.

Editorial Office
P. O. Box 820, Station Willowdale B
North York, Ontario M2K 2R1
Telephone (416) 488 1418 Fax: (416) 488-4656
Telephone (800) 442-6042 Fax: (800) 442-1542
E-mail: chpress@charltonpress.com www.charltonpress.com

PRICING OLD, NEW AND THE INTERNET

The Old System

The first edition of Royal Doulton Animals, introduced in 1994, was priced in a manner similar to all the other catalogues we have published over the years.

We had developed four main streams of information upon which we relied for pricing.

(1) Auctions: Auction catalogues and their prices realized provide a wealth of information on what a collector or dealer is willing to pay for an item. We, of course, subscribe to and receive a variety of auction catalogues from all over the world.

(2) Dealers' direct mail catalogues: There was always a number of active dealers in the direct mail field publishing and distributing detailed price lists. Incorporating these lists in to our analysis was another important factor in arriving at a market price.

(3) Request: Two or three months before a print date pricing requests were mailed to various dealers in different parts of the world requesting their opinion on market prices. These replies were tallied and incorporated into the above data.

(4) Newsletters: We subscribe to every and all newsletters that appear on the subject for which we are producing a price guide. Newsletters give a wealth of information on current happenings in various hobbies, but they also supply goodly quantities of pricing information,

The four streams were compiled into one, extreme high and lows removed, and the results averaged to arrive at a market value. After a while a trend would emerge indicating the direction of the market. We were then ready to build a pricing model that would allow us to arrive at a suggested evaluation.

Over the past three years dramatic changes have taken place in collecting, especially collectables produced in the 20th century which have continuity between similar items. Posters, art pottery, art glass, Royal Doulton Animal figurines, coins and stamps all belong to this category. They all fit the same mould, all have the same properties in common. They all have high artistic design content, produced in small but reasonable quantities and widely distributed throughout the world. They started life as ornaments or decorations for the home.

The Evolution

The impact the internet would have on collectables was not fully anticipated. All the old avenues such as fairs, shows, dealer stores, retail outlets, direct mail and auction houses would come under severe pressure by the lowering of margins which the internet fostered. This would have a direct impact on pricing.

When Royal Doulton Animals, 2nd edition, was up for revision in the winter of 2001, the process began of gathering prices to generate the 3rd. Our method of collecting pricing information had to change.

Why! Simply because of the tremendous growth of the internet, and looking deeper, the rapid growth of on-line auctions in which 20th century collectables fit so well. Our auction results multiplied more than a thousand fold.

Dealers' websites have all but replaced direct mail. The direct mail house of five years ago is now the virtual store of 2002.

Items, prices can all be changed daily, with little effort or cost.

Land based auctions still contribute to pricing for they, through their historical connection with the collectors, gather in the scarce and rare pieces. The value of which is helpful in establishing an overall price trend. Seldom does the rare trend higher, without the basic items being carried along in unison.

Now, following this far, you are starting to wonder what has changed from the old model to the new, it is the internet component comprising two parts: on-line auctions and virtual stores, which were not available previously, but must now be inserted into the equation.

Average items daily

Category	Jan. 2001	Jan. 2002	Nov. 2002
Beswick	625	825	1400
Bunnykins	350	475	650
Coins	6,000	7,200	8,900
Disney	37,500	51,500	83,900
Harry Potter	2,300	12,000	12,900
Lalique	650	400	1,000
Moorcroft	250	300	400
Royal Doulton	**3,500**	**3,700**	**5,700**
Royal Worcester	600	800	1,150
Stamps	12,700	13,700	22,500
Star Wars	19,000	23,500	37,700

From the above table, which is based on only one on-line auction site, it is obvious that the growth being experienced in the collectable market is increasing at a rapid rate. Using the table, converting from a daily to an annual basis, clearly emphasises the magnitude of the numbers involved.

Centering on Royal Doulton, by January 2001 the projected annual rate of items offered for sale was 1,277,500. By January 2002, the number projected had risen to 1,350,500 and by November 2002, had increased again to over 2,000,000. Assuming only 25% sells, the number is still extremely large, 500,000 plus, when compared to a Royal Doulton Specialist Land-based auction which may sell 500 lots per auction twice a year.

The New System

(1) Auctions:

A. Land-based auctions: As before, we continually moniter auction results capturing the pricing data.

B. Virtual auctions. With the new on-line auctions, both dealers and collectors participate. Prices become a true indication at that moment of the value of the item.

(2) Virtual Stores: Dealers' virtual stores have replaced our previous direct mail component and dealer requests, for now their offerings are available 24-hours-a-day and are possibly changed on a daily basis.

(3) Newsletters: Newsletters still contribute in the previous way and must not be overlooked.

The price gathering process has changed dramatically. The ana lizing of the data remains the same.

TABLE OF CONTENTS

HOW TO USE THIS CATALOGUE

THE LISTINGS

Like the other Standard Catalogues in Charlton's Royal Doulton family of price guides, this book has been designed to serve two specific purposes. First, to furnish the Doulton enthusiast with accurate listings containing vital information, and photographs to aid in the building of a rewarding collection. Secondly, this publication provides Royal Doulton collectors and dealers with current market prices for the complete line of Doulton animal figures.

Royal Doulton produced in excess of 1,400 animal figures over some 90 years so a note on the organization of this catalogue is in order.

The Royal Doulton animal figures are listed in this catalogue in the following Series order: Stoneware Series, HN Series, K Series, D Series, Royal Adderley Bird Studies, DA Series, Art Is Life Series, Flambé Series, Dog Heads and Brooches and Advertising Animals.

Within the individual listings, animal figures are listed in order of their HN, K, D, or DA numbers. After this number comes the figure's Name. Next comes the Style Designation (Seated - Style One, etc.). When animal figures have the same name but different physical modelling characteristics they are listed as Style One, Style Two and so on. The Model Number of the figure appears next. This number was assigned by Royal Doulton and usually appears impressed in the base of the figurine. However there are figures which do not show the model number. Only varieties of a particular animal figure can have the same model number.

Next, where known, comes the Designer, next the Height, Size (if more than one of the same mould type), Colour, and the date of Issue and Withdrawal. The Series to which the figure belongs is listed next. Varieties of the figure then follow. Only colour differences, minor decorative alterations and slight changes in size due to firing constitute genuine varieties. Different physical modelling characteristics constitute different styles.

Lastly, the suggested retail price is given in American, Canadian and British funds.

A NOTE ON THE PHOTOGRAPHS

In some cases, photographs of models have been used to represent unobtainable varieties of that particular piece. The reader is cautioned that all photographs so utilized are to be used for model characteristics only. More specific details concerning a figure (i.e. colourway) should be determined from the information listed below the photograph. Readers are cautioned that colours, patterns and glazes may differ within individual figurines. Due to the number and variety of figures represented in this catalogue, readers must assume that photographs are not to scale.

A NOTE ON THE INDICES

At the back of this book the reader will find both an alphbetical index and a model number index. These will allow readers to locate and identify virtually every figure. In the alphabetical index, naturally, figures are listed alphabetically by name. Exceptions, however, exist for figures with more detailed names (barn owl, snowy owl, tawny owl for example). These figures are listed under the generic name of the animal (owl, in this instance). When a figure has a name that does not connote the type of animal represented (Spirit of the Wind, for example), that figure is listed alphabetically under 'S' for "Spirit."

The model number index allows readers to correlate model numbers with both the names and the various other numbers of the figures.

FIGURE NUMBERING SEQUENCING

In this catalogue an asterisk (*) in the lower left corner of a listing indicates that one or more of the following numbers was either unassigned by Royal Doulton or used for a piece other than an animal figure.

INSURING YOUR FIGURES

As with any other of your valuables, making certain your figures are protected is a very important concern. It is paramount that you display or store any porcelain items in a secure place - preferable one safely away from traffic in the home.

Your figures are most often covered under your basic homeowner's policy and there are generally three kinds of such policies - standard, broad and comprehensive. Each has its own specific deductible and terms.

Under a general policy, your figurines are considered 'contents' and are covered for all of the perils covered under the contractual terms of your policy (fire, theft, water damage and so on).

However, since figurines are extremely delicate, breakage is treated differently by most insurance companies. There is usually an extra premium attached to insure figures against accidental breakage or the carelessness of the owner. This is sometimes referred to as a 'fine arts' rider.

You are advised to contact your insurance professional to get all the answers.

In order to help you protect yourself, it is critical that you take inventory of your figures and have colour photographs taken of all your pieces. This is the surest method of clearly itemizing, for the police and your insurance company, the pieces lost or destroyed. It is also the easiest way to establish their replacement value in the event of such a tragedy.

INTRODUCTION
by Louise Irvine

THE HISTORY OF ROYAL DOULTON ANIMALS

THE LAMBETH STUDIO

The Doulton factory was founded in London in 1815 and in the early years they made drainpipes for the growing sanitary industry and domestic stonewares, such as bottles and jars. Occasionally useful items took the form of animals, for example a crocus pot in the shape of a hedgehog, but it was not until the Lambeth Art Studio was flourishing in the late 19th century that animals began to inspire a wide range of models. Often they continued to fulfill a practical purpose: owls serve as tobacco jars or perch on the edge of ashtrays; bears dip their paws into honey pots; rabbits crouch into little paperweights and mice hold menus aloft. Most bizarre of all, a life-size kangaroo obligingly holds umbrellas.

Waits Water by George Tinworth (c.1885)

This last piece was modelled by George Tinworth, the first full-time artist at the Lambeth Studio. He made his reputation as a sculptor of monumental religious works but, in between his major commissions, he sought inspiration in the animal kingdom. Water birds and marine creatures were incorporated into his fountain designs and, on a smaller scale, he produced paperweights depicting incidents from Aesop's fables. His most famous animal studies, however, feature the cheeky mice which occasionally invaded his studio. In his imagination they assumed human personalities and he modelled them enjoying many popular pursuits of the Victorian period. Frogs often join in the fun and together they participate in sports, play musical instruments and, on one scandalous occasion, get drunk! Tinworth's little mouse and frog groups were moulded in salt glaze stoneware during the 1880s and, as the editions were very small, they are extremely desirable today.

Fellow artist Mark Marshall preferred weird and wonderful monsters which seem to spring from the pages of a Gothic horror story. Slimy reptilian creatures claw their way around his vases or slither over rocky crags to form free-standing sculptures. A fish transmutes into seaweed to form a jug whilst a rabbit shaped vase is half lettuce. Marshall's preoccupation with monstrous hybrids and mutations was shared by many Victorians and literature of the time abounds with strange creatures, notably Tenniel's Alice in Wonderland, which inspired Marshall to produce paperweights of the Cheshire Cat and the Mock Turtle as well as a strange vase in the form of the pig-like Rath. One of his most hideous monsters was intended as a garden seat, obviously for those undeterred by lurid warts and fangs!

Garden ornaments were often modelled in the form of animals and the Lambeth factory catalogues show a wide range of species in terracotta and, to a lesser extent, salt glaze stoneware. Marshall was responsible for some of the designs, notably the 'Lizard' (R31) and the 'Pelican' (R19), but most were by the younger artist Harry Simeon and include studies of a 'Squirrel' (R36), a 'Fox' (R16), a 'Rabbit' (R22) and other garden visitors. Simeon became the most prolific modeller of animal subjects at the Lambeth Studio, producing several colourful stoneware ornaments which could also be used as bookends. He also contributed to a range of ashtrays, soap dishes and trinket holders adorned with birds and animal models. These colourful stoneware bibelots, as they are known, were introduced in the mid 1920s and are now widely sought after.

Royal Doulton also advertised their own products with animal models, choosing a polar bear, a cat and a stylised horse to promote their white Carraraware architectural glaze. The polar bear was the work of Leslie Harradine, who is better known to collectors as a figure modeller. In the early 1900s he was apprenticed at the Lambeth studio and produced several animal models for their slip cast stoneware process. His studies of parakeets on a rock (H58) and polar bears on an ice floe (H35) are illustrated in a Doulton catalogue of 1914 and presumably they were reproduced in some numbers but they are not easy to find today. Some of his designs were reissued in the animals collection produced at the Burslem factory, notably the 'Polar Bear on a Cube' and the 'Cuddling Monkeys' and it is possible that he also designed pieces specifically for this range. However, attributions can only be made on stylistic grounds as records about the Burslem animal designers are virtually non-existent.

Collecting Lambeth Animals

Of all the animals made at the Lambeth studio, Tinworth's mice and frog groups have most appeal to collectors. They have been sought after by Doulton connoisseurs for the last twenty years or so and prices reflect their desirability.

Few can fail to be amused by the idea of frogs and mice earnestly engaged in activities usually reserved for humans. Some of the groups are inspired by aspects of Tinworth's own life, such as his family's wheelwright business and his childhood enjoyment of the regular Punch and Judy show held in the streets of London. Others reflect his strict moral code, such as the companion group for 'Going to the Derby' who return looking down-hearted with the inscription 'Lost and serves them right.'

Tinworth's first mice models were produced for the 1884 Exhibition of Inventions and Music. Forty mice playing a wide variety of musical instruments were exhibited and proved so successful that Tinworth embarked on lots of other amusing activities for his friendly mice. Henry Doulton was particularly enthusiastic about the mice groups and commissioned models for his friends and family. He also ordered a selection to be made for display in the showroom.

It would appear that most of the groups were made to order in small editions with Tinworth putting the finishing touches to models produced by the assistant artists. Many different colour treatments are to be found with white, brown or olive green mice and occasionally, the same groups have different titles. Several designs are recorded in the pattern books with an X reproduction numbers but these do not appear on the piece. Usually George Tinworth's monogram can be found on the back or side of the piece. He was the only artist in the studio allowed to mark the body of the piece as opposed to the base. Some of the mice models are dated and it would appear that most were produced between 1885 and 1890.

The mice models were often adapted for practical purposes and the same designs can be found incorporating little vases or attachments to hold menus and place cards. It is possible that the free-standing models were used as paperweights but, first and foremost, they are conversation pieces to amuse and entertain.

Other artists at the Lambeth studio continued Tinworth's anthropomorphic tradition but their figures are extremely hard to find today. Francis Pope portrayed 'Mr Toad,' the hero of 'The Wind in the Willows' and Mark Marshall endowed rabbits with human attitudes in 'The Yawn and The Waning of the Honeymoon' which was made in Doultonware and Silicon ware.

Collecting Bibelots And Useful Animals

As many of the Lambeth animals have a practical purpose, this could be a novel theme for a collection. Look out for the various tobacco jars and match holders in the form of owls or the cruet sets incorporating brown bears, baboons or marmosets. The majority of useful animals, however, are incorporated in the little trays modelled by Harry Simeon. Known today as bibelots, a French word meaning trinket or knickknack, the trays could be used for cigarette ash, pins or trinkets. Some of the designs, such as the 'Mouse,' were offered in two sizes whilst others, notably the 'Kookaburra,' have different shaped trays in the form of a shell and a boat. The 'Dragonfly' dish was commissioned as a promotional piece for Wright's Coal Tar soap and they were given away free in exchange for tokens collected from soap packs. A price list for 1930 indicates that the other bibelots were quite reasonably priced at 9/9d for the 'Polar Bear' and 6/9d for the 'Koala.' Although the slip cast stoneware technique allowed the bibelots to be reproduced in considerable quantities between the wars they are increasingly hard to find today and there is stiff competition from discerning collectors.

Collecting 'Designer' Animals

During the 1920s and 30s, the Art and Industry movement encouraged famous artists to get involved with commercial potteries and Doulton worked with a number of independent sculptors, some of whom produced interesting animal models. Frederick Roth, an American artist, commissioned the Lambeth factory to reproduce models of a dog and a hippopotamus plus some polar bear bookends. The polar bears seem to have been the best sellers and have appeared a couple of times in the market-place. Richard Garbe, the Professor of Sculpture at the Royal College of Art, worked closely with Doulton on the figurine collection but he also modelled an impressive sealion which was reproduced at Lambeth as a bookend and also as a garden ornament. However, the most fruitful collaboration of the period was with Gilbert Bayes, a very distinguished British sculptor, who designed a series of animal models which were used as finials for washing line posts in London housing estates. Many of these have now been removed from their original sites and occasionally they appear at auction sales in the U.K..

Garden Ornaments

The Lambeth studio has a long tradition of producing animal sculptures for the garden but examples are very hard to find today. Perhaps most of them have disintegrated after years of exposure to frost and damp. Trade catalogues from the turn of the century feature terminals and fountain heads in the form of birds and animals and these were produced in terracotta and salt glaze stoneware. By the 1920s, the catalogues illustrate a wide range of free standing garden ornaments modelled by artists such as Mark Marshall, Francis Pope and Harry Simeon. Only a few of these have come to light in the Doulton world, notably the 'Owl,' 'Lizard,' 'Pelican' and 'Persian Cat,' but examples could still be lurking unrecognized in the undergrowth!

Pelican and *Beast* garden ornaments by Mark Marshall

Essentially the story of Lambeth animals ended with the outbreak of World War Two but there is one notable exception. Agnete Hoy, who briefly revived Doulton's London studio in the 1950s, modelled a very special stoneware cat, which was one of the last pieces to be fired in the Lambeth kilns. The edition was limited to just twelve models and each cat is coloured differently. One is owned by the artist, another is in the Doulton museum and one came on to the market recently which leaves nine still to find. Happy hunting on your Doulton safari!

THE BURSLEM STUDIO

Doulton's factory at Burslem, Stoke-on-Trent was established in 1877 and a few years later the first animal subjects began to appear. John Slater, the first Art Director, introduced a range of vases with models of birds perched on the sides but these strange designs were short-lived. In 1889 he recruited Charles Noke from the Worcester factory as his chief modeller and Noke's earliest vases are dominated by fabulous oriental-style dragons which writhe around the surface in high relief and leer down from the top. Dragons continued to be an important feature of Noke's work when he began experimenting with the Chinese rouge flambé glazes in the early 1900s as they were appropriate subjects for the fiery red effects achieved with his Sung and later his Chang glazes.

It was for the new flambé range that Noke first considered producing free-standing animal models and a catalogue page of 1908 shows four tiny flambé creatures squeezed in between exotic vases. These early designs have four digit model numbers - 'The Frog' (1162), 'Three Finches' (1163), 'Mouse on a Cube' (1164) and 'Lop-eared Rabbit' (1165), but a new modelling system for figure and animal sculptures was introduced around 1910. By 1912 more than 60 different animals had been modelled for the flambé process and a dozen of them were included in an article which appeared in the Connoisseur magazine in 1912. Noke also experimented with vivid monochrome glazes on these early models including blue, yellow, orange, red, brown and black.

Unfortunately the modellers responsible for this menagerie are not recorded although it is believed that Harry Tittensor and Leslie Harradine assisted Noke on the early development of the animal collection. It is known that Charles Noke was responsible for the Elephant (65) as it was one of his favourite animals. He started modelling them as a boy and continued throughout his life, producing huge fighting elephants in flambé and naturalistic colours, a small stylised example for the Chinese Jade range and some cute character elephants in humanistic poses. Charles Noke frequently endowed animals with human personalities, sometimes even dressing them in clothes, as with the very first model in this book, 'Pedlar Wolf' HN7, which was probably inspired by a character in Fontaine's fables. A succession of amusing characters followed, including 'A Fox in Hunting Dress' HN 100, 'A Rabbit in Morning Dress' HN 101 and a 'Granny Owl' HN 173 wrapped in a cloak. The animal which provided him with the most scope for caricature was the bulldog, symbolising the spirit of Britain at war, which appears in battle dress or patriotically draped in a Union Jack and bearing a marked resemblance to Winston Churchill. Examples of these very collectable bulldogs can be found in both the HN and the D series.

There are only a few animal models listed in the D series of earthenware models which was usually used to record Series ware patterns or Character Jugs. The vast majority of animals, whether they be in an earthenware or china body, were included in the HN series along with all the Royal Doulton figures. The HN pattern numbers record the different colours used to decorate each figure or animal and models can be produced in many different colourways. The first animals in the HN collection tend to be subtly decorated with muted naturalistic tones. Subjects range from domestic pets, notably dogs and cats, to wild animals including foxes, rabbits and the

Pedlar Wolf (HN7) by Charles Noke

more exotic monkeys and bears. Birds seem to have been very popular, whether it be chubby chicks, dabbling ducks or sleek penguins.

In the 1920s miniature animals predominated; some have the tactile qualities of Japanese netsuke, for example HN 820, 834 and 837, whilst others are of a humorous nature, notably HN 913-918. 'Bonzo,' the popular cartoon dog of the period, was modelled in several guises together with his feline friend 'Ooloo' HN 827, who was later renumbered K12 as part of a new series of miniature animals. The K series, which was introduced in 1931, included a number of tiny dogs, birds and hares, some of which stayed in production until 1977. Tiny dog's heads were modelled for use as brooches and larger busts were mounted on alabaster or wooden stands to serve as pen holders. Practicality was obviously an important consideration at the time as several other dog models adorn ashtrays and tobacco jars and birds were incorporated into flower holders.

Models of dogs became increasingly popular in the late 1920s and many different breeds were introduced in a variety of poses. In 1930 Frederick Daws, the celebrated animal sculptor, was invited to model a collection of Championship Dogs, mainly in show stances. He visited the kennels of award-winning dogs to work from life and his sculptures were approved by the owners before being reproduced in the HN collection. Most breeds were offered in three sizes and different colours and many stayed in continuous production for over 50 years. Daws also produced a very successful model of a famous racehorse of the day called 'Merely a Minor' HN 2530 but most of the horse studies in the Royal Doulton collection were the work of another freelance artist, William Chance.

Chance was a regular exhibitor at the Royal Academy and his work was equally well known and respected in North America. Most of his horses were offered in different colourways and sizes and they continued in the collection until the 1960s. 'Monaveen,' his most prestigious commission was not available in the general range as it was made specially for presentation to Princess Elizabeth during her visit to the Royal Doulton factory in 1949. It is a particularly complex action model of the famous steeplechaser, which the Princess owned jointly with her mother, and Chance spent a lot of time working with the horse's trainer to ensure it was an accurate portrait.

The freelance artists usually liaised with resident designer Cecil Jack Noke, who ultimately succeeded his father as Art Director. He commissioned Raoh Schorr, a well known animal sculptor with work in the national art galleries, to produce a collection for reproduction in ceramic. The Schorr subjects were launched in 1937 and most were available in white and black matt glazes, simulated green bronze and natural colours. Although they were favourably reviewed in artistic circles, they did not appeal to the general public. Consequently all the lively lambs, goats, calves, horses and donkeys were made for about five years only so they are not easy to find. Even more elusive are his unusual wild animals, such as the 'Cerval' HN 2500, 'Lynx' HN 2501 and 'Asiatic Elephant' HN 2506 which do not appear to have been produced for any length of time.

From 1939, Jack Noke was fortunate to have the services of a new resident modeller, Peggy Davies, who had joined the company to assist Noke senior in his modelling studio. Although she is best known today for all her crinoline ladies, she concentrated initially on animal studies and produced a delightful collection of kittens in playful poses which were introduced in 1941. Peggy went on to model several collections of little animals, including the six piglets, HN 2648-53 and the K series of penguins. She probably modelled many other series, including the character puppies HN 2585-90, but unfortunately there are no surviving records of designers to clarify her role. Shortly before she died in 1988, she talked about some of the prestige birds she had modelled including the 'Indian Runner Drake' HN 2636 and a falcon for display in the company showrooms. She also remembered working on the range of Championship Dogs and she assisted the new Art Director Jo Ledger on his Chatcull range of animals.

Jo Ledger joined Royal Doulton in 1955 and began experimenting with many new design directions for the company. For the animals collection, he envisaged a stylish new range, which he named after his house of the time, Chatcull Hall. Modellers Peggy Davies and David Lovegrove worked from his detailed drawings and produced some very elegant studies, mainly of exotic wildlife, which were launched in 1960. Perhaps the choice of species was too obscure as the collection was not a commercial success and soon withdrawn, with the exception of the 'Siamese Cats,' HN 2655, 2660 and 2662 which stayed in production until 1985.

It was many years before any new animal collections were commissioned but, in 1972, freelance artist Robert Jefferson was invited to model some large, prestige porcelain sculptures of animals and birds in their natural habitats. Jefferson had enjoyed a distinguished career at the Poole Potteries, where he produced many successful animal models but the impressive scale of the new Royal Doulton sculptures was an exciting new challenge for him. He spent many hours in field study, observing, taking photographs and making drawings before embarking on the original models, which were executed in wax to preserve the fine detail of the animal's coats and the bird's plumage. Jefferson later produced some studies of otters for the Images of Nature collection, which was launched in 1982. These highly stylised sculptures represented a radical new design direction for Royal Doulton. The streamlined silhouettes of the animals, fashioned in white bone china, have proved particularly effective in contemporary settings and new

subjects by a variety of modellers have been introduced to the collection on a regular basis. In 1987 the Images of Fire collection combined these trend-setting sculptures with a traditional Doulton finish, the dramatic flambé glaze. To date four large size models have been available in either white or flambé, and new smaller subjects have been modelled especially for the flambé treatment, for example the 'Elephant and Young' HN 3548 by Art Director Eric Griffiths and Robert Tabbenor's 'Dragon' HN 3552 which was an exclusive offer to members of the Royal Doulton International Collectors Club.

In 1985, the success of the Images animals encouraged Royal Doulton to withdraw all the naturalistically coloured animals remaining in the HN collection. As many of the models had been in continuous production for over 50 years, it was felt that all the potential customers had been satisfied and it was time for something different. The DA series of animals, featuring the work of Design Manager Graham Tongue and his team at the John Beswick Studio of Royal Doulton, was launched in 1989. These artists take a highly detailed, realistic approach to animal modelling. The textures of fur and feathers are painstakingly reproduced as well as the gnarled wood and mossy stones of their environment.

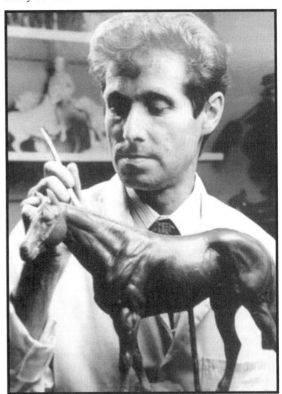

Graham Tongue at work

All the young artists in Graham's team were encouraged to be versatile and they spent a lot of time visiting aviaries, stables, kennels, farms and zoos to study their subjects, returning with copious photographs and notes from their encounters to ensure accuracy. In 1990, Warren Platt modelled some fine birds to raise funds for the World Wide Fund for Nature whilst Martyn Alcock has produced a delightful collection of puppies and kittens in appealing poses, such as 'Give Me A Home' DA 196. A more unconventional pet Martha, the 'Vietnamese Pot Bellied Pig' DA 189, has been immortalised by Amanda Hughes-Lubeck and she followed this with the equally unorthodox 'Nigerian Pot Bellied Pygmy Goat' DA 223.

Most of Graham Tongue's own models of birds, dogs, cattle and horses are featured in the prestigious Connoisseur collection and he has a considerable reputation for his portraits of famous racehorses, such as 'Desert Orchid' DA 134 and 'Arkle' DA 227. Graham has worked in the John Beswick modelling studio since 1966, a few years before it was taken over by the Royal Doulton group. During his long career he has modelled a wide variety of animals for the Beswick backstamp and many of these were transferred to the new DA range in 1989, together with models by earlier Beswick artists, such as Arthur Gredington and Albert Hallam. This is not the first time that backstamps have been changed on products made by other companies within the Royal Doulton group. In 1979, a series of birds produced at the Royal Adderley studio were given Royal Doulton backstamps but they only remained in production in this form until 1982.

BUILDING A COLLECTION

Since 1908, more than 1,000 animals have been introduced to the HN, DA and K series and these are now avidly collected in many parts of the world, Most collectors specialise in one category or another as it would be virtually impossible to acquire them all. Fox collectors can have a field day chasing more than a dozen models in various sizes, whilst elephant collectors can look out for at least ten types in lots of different sizes, colours and glazes, including flambé and Chinese Jade. No doubt there are other collectors pursuing rabbits, monkeys or pigs but some of the most popular collecting categories are discussed in detail below.

Collecting Dogs

Dogs are by far the most collectable animals in the Royal Doulton range. Appealing puppies cocking their ears, playing with bones or rolling on their backs were amongst the first models and it would appear that Art Director Charles Noke was more concerned with the character of the dog than its pedigree. This has led to some confusion in identifying the various breeds represented in the early years, for example HN 127 has often been listed as a Pekinese but Noke's notebook describes it as a Blenheim Spaniel, in other words a liver and white coloured Cavalier King Charles. The conformation of this breed has altered over the years and in the early 1900s it had a flatter muzzle like the Pekinese hence the confusion. Another puzzle is HN 231 which some dog experts say looks most like an English St. Bernard and others a foxhound. To confuse matters even more the pattern books describe it variously as a setter and a bloodhound. Whatever the breeds, these early models are hard to find and would be welcomed in most dog collections.

The most desirable Royal Doulton breed is undoubtedly the bulldog, which has been portrayed in many different guises. During the First World War, the breed symbolised the dogged determination of the British people and is now regarded as the country's national animal. Bulldogs, patriotically draped with the Union Jack, were introduced at the end of the 1914-18 war and they were reintroduced during World War Two in three sizes, D5913A, B & C. Cartoons of the period picked up the breed's resemblance to Winston Churchill and Charles Noke responded with new versions of the Union Jack bulldog smoking a cigar and wearing a derby hat or Trinity cap in the manner of the great war leader. The popularity of the great British bulldog has ensured its widespread use in advertising and there are several rare Royal Doulton models promoting various brands of drinks. Bar accessories, such as ashpots and match holders, were modelled in the form of bulldog's heads and sometimes complete miniature dogs are posed on top of bowls or pintrays. Keen canine collectors often seek out all the different types of dog derivatives which were produced in the 1920s and 30s. Various breeds were adapted to decorate tobacco jars, ashtrays, bookends, calendars, pen holders, wall plaques, and brooches and they are all hard to find today.

Terriers seem to have been the most popular type of dogs with Doulton artists in the mid 1920s and from HN 900 onwards they produced a succession of Fox Terriers, Scottish Terriers, Sealyhams and Airedales in standing or seated poses. Most were offered in a choice of colourings and, although they might not have the same amount of detail as the later Championship series, they are still very collectable and it is quite a challenge to complete the series as most had disappeared from the range by 1946. The rarest terrier of all is the white 'West Highland Terrier' HN 1048 which seems to have been produced for one year only in 1931. It is very similar to the 'Cairn Terrier' HN 1104 in the Championship series but the head is at a different angle and the ears are smaller.

New standards were set for Royal Doulton dog sculptures when the celebrated animal artist Frederick Daws became involved in the collection. He strove for complete accuracy in his representations of named champions and he liaised with the breeders on precise details of conformation. Most of his portraits are in show poses but occasionally he modelled the same dog sitting or lying, although these were not promoted with the champion names. The first show dog to join the range was 'Lucky Star of Ware' HN 1000, a blue roan Cocker Spaniel, which was twice overall champion at Crufts in 1930 and 1931. Later models feature the name 'Lucky Pride of Ware' - perhaps the owner had reservations about the change of colouring to plain black. Another name change occurred with the Rough Haired Terrier 'Crackley Starter' HN 1007 who is also known as 'Crackley Hunter.'

When Frederick Daws retired, other artists contributed to the series. Peggy Davies modelled the Doberman Pinscher 'Rancho Dobe's Storm' HN 2645 and the French Poodle HN 2631, which was originally going to be offered in a plain white decoration in three different sizes HN 2625-7, but in the end only one model was introduced. Perhaps Peggy was responsible for the Chow champion 'T'Sioh of Kin-Shan' HN 2628-30 but judging from the scarcity of this model it is doubtful if it actually went into production. The last championship dog in this series was the black labrador 'Bumblekite of Mansergh' HN 2667 modelled by John Bromley in 1967.

After a gap of some years, dogs are once again an important part of the Royal Doulton range. Many breeds originally modelled for the Beswick backstamp were transferred to the DA series in 1989 and the design team at the Beswick studios are regularly introducing new subjects, including a charming series of dogs and their puppies. In 1993, Graham Tongue revived the idea of modelling famous dogs with his portrait of 'Mick the Miller' DA 214, the famous 1930s racing greyhound, which has become the first ever limited edition dog in the collection

Collecting Cats

Feline fanciers are well served in the Royal Doulton collection with around 40 cat models to find in various colours and glaze effects. The earliest is model number 9 which was issued in flambé in 1908 and was also offered for a while in naturalistic colours as HN 109. Collectors can choose from miscellaneous moggies or pedigree Persians (HN 999) and Siamese (HN 2655). There are playful cats about to pounce on unsuspecting mice (HN 203) as well as studies of these popular pets in an equally familiar pose, catnapping on the best seat of the house (HN 210). The antics of a kitten inspired one of the most popular series ever (HN 2579 - 84) and the artist, Peggy Davies, recalled that her model threatened to cause havoc in the studio, weaving in and out of Charles Noke's precious flambé vases. Fortunately he was an animal lover and welcomed the kitten's invasion.

Two of the cats in the HN collection were inspired by famous cartoon characters; 'Kateroo,' the creation of David Souter, who appeared in the Sydney Bulletin and little 'Ooloo' from George Studdy's comic strips of the 1920s, who is perhaps better known to collectors as 'Lucky' from the miniature K series. Other miniature cats, less than one inch tall, were included in the HN collection but these are very hard to find today. At the other end of the scale, Alan Maslankowski modelled a large stylised cat, 11 ½ inches tall, for the flambé range in 1977 and he has produced models for the DA series, the haughty 'Cat (Walking)' DA 148 and has also including the stealthy 'Cat (Stalking)' DA 149. 'The Cat with Bandaged Paw' DA 195, which was introduced by Martyn Alcock in 1992, takes a new sentimental approach and tugs at the heartstrings of all cat lovers. The detailed, realistic approach in the DA series contrasts greatly with the modern streamlined sculptures 'Shadowplay' HN 3526 and 'Playtime' HN 3544 in the Images range and ensures that Royal Doulton's interpretations of cats are as varied as the animals themselves.

Collecting Horses

Royal Doulton was the name of the first horse portrayed in the HN collection. Owned by the Roulston Brothers of New Zealand, this successful racehorse was modelled in action by a French freelance artist G. D'Illiers and launched as 'The Winner' HN 1407 in 1930. Sadly, it is now virtually impossible to find. More accessible is the portrait of another famous racehorse 'Merely a Minor' HN 2530, which was modelled by Frederick Daws, who is better known for his championship dogs.

Most of the early horse models were the work of the distinguished sculptor William Chance, who was responsible for the exceptional model of the royal steeplechaser 'Monaveen.' He also paid tribute to the gentle giants of the horse world in 'Pride of the Shires' HN 2563 and 'Chestnut Mare' HN 2565, portraying them with and without their foals. Some of his first studies also included riders who were later removed to produce independent horses, for example the mount in 'Farmer's Boy' HN 2520 became 'Dapple Grey' HN 2578.

Occasionally stylised horse models have been included in the HN collection, for example Raoh Schorr's 'Prancing Horse' HN 1167 and 'The Gift of Life' HN 3524 from the Images series. There have also been legendary horses such as 'Pegasus' HN 3547 and The 'Unicorn' HN 3549 modelled by Alan Maslankowski.

The range of Royal Doulton horses was expanded when models were transferred from the Beswick range in 1989. Horses had long been the speciality of the John Beswick factory and modellers such as Arthur Gredington and Albert Hallam were renowned in the industry for their portraits of famous racehorses. 'Arkle' DA15 and 'Nijinski' DA16 are just two examples of their work now in the DA series. When Albert Hallam retired, Graham Tongue became head modeller at the Beswick Studio and continued the tradition with portraits of 'Red Rum' DA18 and 'Troy' DA37 amongst others. In more recent years he has modelled Britain's favourite racehorse 'Desert Orchid' DA134.

As well as all his famous models, Graham endeavoured to capture the essential qualities of horses in general with his evocative 'Spirit' range, contrasting subjects such as the powerful 'Spirit of the Earth' DA61 with the playful 'Young Spirit' DA70. His young successors are now contributing to all these established collections, for example Warren Platt has portrayed 'Mr. Frisk' DA190 and Amanda Hughes-Lubeck has modelled several Spirit horses as well as 'My First Horse' DA193B, an ideal purchase to start a collection.

Collecting Birds and Butterflies

Birds have always formed an important part of the Royal Doulton collection, beginning with Charles Noke's models of fledglings for the flambé glaze in 1908. A flock of feathered friends followed in the first few years of the HN collection and by 1920 the list included cockerels, pigeons, pelicans, guinea fowl, eagles, kingfishers, budgies, ducks and penguins, not forgetting all the miscellaneous chicks. Some are realistically rendered like the 'Cockatoo' HN 185, which was modelled by Leslie Harradine, whilst in Noke's hands others assume human characteristics, like 'Granny Owl' HN 187 and the 'Toucan in Tails' HN 208. The comic approach continued during the 1920s with a series of tiny character toucans and penguins but generally a naturalistic style of modelling prevailed over the years.

During the war years two series of birds (HN 2540-2556 and HN 2611-2619) were made specially for export to the USA but these were short lived and are hard to find today. The same applies to the miniature models of birds which, for some reason, were added to both the HN and the K series in the early 1940s. Some of the K birds are so rare that they have eluded discovery in time for this publication.

In 1952 several large bird models were added to the Prestige range and in the 1970s Robert Jefferson produced some magnificent limited edition sculptures of birds specifically for the US market. A few years later, in 1979, the Lem Ward series of decoy ducks was also produced with

American collectors in mind. Ward's carvings of wildfowl counterfeits are very sought after in the USA and Design Manager Harry Sales was asked to interpret the wooden originals in a matt glazed ceramic body.

For a brief period, between 1979 and 1982, the birds produced at the Royal Adderley factory, now one of the companies in the Royal Doulton group, were given Royal Doulton backstamps. There are 50 models in this range and they are quite different in style, body and texture from the earlier Royal Doulton birds.

Birds have regularly provided inspiration for the stylised Images of Nature collection and some have been produced in both white bone china and fiery flambé. In contrast, the team at the John Beswick studio, aim to recreate the feel of the bird's feathers and they are regular visitors to aviaries and falconry displays as well as avid bird watchers. Since 1989 they have introduced a variety of familiar garden birds to the DA range as well as endangered species such as kestrels and owls.

Bird collectors can also find lots of different derivatives from the 1930s. Ashtrays and bowls often have birds perched on top and flower holders were frequently adorned with birds. Some of these were designed to be placed in the floating flower bowls which were fashionable at the time. Models of butterflies on rocks were made for the same purpose and there are also clip-on varieties for attaching to the side of the bowls. During the Second World War a collection of six different species of butterflies alighting in foliage was introduced but, like the birds of the period, they came and went and are consequently very hard to find today.

Collecting Prestige, Limited Editions and Special Commissions

Art Director Charles Noke specialised in large, ambitious sculptures of wild animals. Massive fighting elephants are depicted with their trunks aggressively outstretched, as in HN 1120, whilst others are shown in repose, HN 1121. Big cats, including lions, tigers and leopards, stalk their prey or crouch ready to pounce from rocks. Most of these impressive studies were first introduced to the HN collection during the 1920s and 1930s but, in 1952, a few of them were given new HN numbers and a new prestige status. 'Tiger on Rock' HN 2639, 'Leopard on Rock' HN 2638, 'Lion on Rock' HN 2641 and 'Fighter Elephant' HN 2640 could also be purchased on a special order basis until 1989 and were the most expensive models in the range.

Raoh Schorr's large fox model HN 2634 was also re-classified as a prestige piece in 1952, together with the large 'Peruvian Penguin' HN 2633 and the 'Drake' HN 2635. Peggy Davies modelled 'Indian Runner Drake' HN 2636 especially for the new prestige range and a large study of a polar bear and cub was offered in naturalistic colouring as HN 2637 instead of its earlier flambé finish. With the exception of the fox, these prestige pieces had all been discontinued by the early 1970s.

In 1974 freelance artist Robert Jefferson was commissioned to model Royal Doulton's first limited edition animal sculptures. His studies of animals and birds in their habitats were observed in minute detail and finely executed in matt porcelain to enhance the different textures of fur and feathers. The artistic and technical virtuosity of Jefferson's work is much appreciated by collectors today but examples are hard to find as most were only made in editions of 75-250, exclusively for the US market.

In recent years Graham Tongue has been responsible for most of the prestige and limited edition models in the Royal Doulton range. Many of his studies of prize bulls and famous race horses were originally produced for the Beswick Connoisseur range but since 1989 they have had Royal Doulton backstamps and DA numbers. Connoisseur sculptures are generally mounted on polished wooden bases with metal name plaques to reinforce their prestige status.

In 1989 several prestige sculptures of wild animals and birds were launched to raise funds for the World Wide Fund for Nature and a percentage of sales from 'The Majestic Stag' DA32 and 'The Watering Hole' DA39, amongst others, went to help save endangered species and stop environmental destruction. Lawleys by Post, the mail order division of Royal Doulton, continued this gesture with the limited edition 'Kestrel' DA144, which was commissioned exclusively for their customers in 1991. Since that date they have added several limited editions and prestige pieces to their catalogue.

On occasion, Royal Doulton have been approached by independent companies to produce an animal model for promotional or commemorative purposes, for example a turkey has been made for the well-known poultry company Bernard Matthews and a limited edition paperweight, in the form of a partridge, was produced for the 'Financial Times.' Because of the limited distribution of these pieces to staff and customers of the organisations concerned, they are often difficult to find in the market-place. This is also the case with the older advertising pieces such as the liqueur containers made for Ervan Bols in the 1930s and National Distillers in the 1950s.

Collecting Miniatures

Tiny collectables have always had a special appeal and animals are no exception. They have the advantage of not taking up too much space and a wide range of animal species can be accommodated in a single cabinet. Lots of little models, including frogs, mice and fledglings, were produced in the early 1900s for the flambé glaze and some were later coloured naturalistically for the HN collection. These models are generally less than 2 ½ inches tall but even small pieces, around one inch in height, were introduced during the 1920s. Collectors can have fun looking for all the tiny character birds, which are comic interpretations of owls, puffins, penguins and toucans. There are 11 different models to find in the first series, some in alternative colour schemes (HN 256-66 and 290-93) but unfortunately only a few were located in time for this publication. Also very rare are the six character toucans in the second series (HN 913-918), the character pigs (HN 892-7) and the young elephants (HN 949-952).

Some of the designs resemble Japanese netsuke, in particular the tiny curled up kittens (HN 820-825) and puppies (HN 834-839) which nestle comfortably in the palm of your hand. Some slightly larger seated and standing puppies followed and the star of this group is undoubtedly Bonzo. The creation of George Studdy, this popular cartoon dog, appeared in comic strips, films, advertisements and postcards during the 1920s. Bonzo collectables became all the rage and in 1923 Doulton offered five different models of the famous character in several different colourways plus a very rare Chinese Jade version (HN 804, 808-15, 826). His feline friend Ooloo was sold in five different colours (HN 818, 819, 827-29) and later joined the K series as 'Lucky,' K12, continuing in production until 1977.

The new K numbering system for miniatures was launched in 1931 and applied to 12 little dogs, less than three inches tall, and 'Lucky' the cat. Six more dogs joined the series in 1940 along with three hares, six penguins and 11 other types of birds. These birds are the hardest of all to find as they were withdrawn within a few years of issue. Three of the K dogs are more elusive than the others as they were withdrawn in 1959 compared to 1977 for the rest. K dogs were frequently mounted on calendars, ashtrays and pen trays and they were sometimes offered in conjunction with figures, for example the 'Old Balloon Seller' with the K1 bulldog on a wooden stand was sold as HN 1791

More miniature birds were introduced in 1941 but for some reason they were given HN numbers rather than K ones. To add to the confusion the 'Drake Mallard' is numbered HN 2572 whilst his mate the 'Duck' is K26. Subsequent miniatures were also numbered in the HN series. In the late 1940s and 50s, Peggy Davies modelled some collections of baby animals, including kittens, piglets and lambs. The kittens, in particular, proved very popular and stayed in the range until 1985 together with a collection of little puppies. Sadly there have been no new miniature animals in recent years but, given Royal Doulton's successful revival of tiny character jugs and figures, there would surely be an enthusiastic reception for tiny animals too.

Collecting Animals in Flambé and other Experimental Glazes

The fiery red flambé glaze was inspired by Oriental ceramics and was perfected by Royal Doulton, after many years of experimentation, in 1904. The precise recipe has always been a closely guarded secret but essentially the glaze consists of copper and iron oxides which fire to a glorious red colour when the kiln is deprived of oxygen.

Within a few years of the launch, Charles Noke was applying this lustrous glaze to little animal models and it continued to be used for new designs until 1997. Some of the earliest models, including the cat, the foxes, the ducks and the penguin, were in continuous production for more than 80 years.

The flambé models that were illustrated in the early catalogues and publicity photographs turn up most frequently in the market place and must have been produced in some quantities, for example the 'Cuddling Apes' (52) the 'Guinea Fowl' (69) and the 'Leaping Salmon' (666). Many other animals were decorated with the flambé glaze purely as an experiment and there may be only one or two in existence. Charles Noke was constantly trying out new ideas and some designs turned out to be more suitable for the effect than others.

As well as the monochrome flambé glaze, Noke also developed lots of mottled and veined variations, including Sung and Chang. In most cases, these effects were too capricious to be used on a regular basis but spectacular Sung and Chang animals do come on to the market from time to time. Many of these special pieces bear the monograms of Charles Noke and his assistants Harry Nixon and Fred Moore. Chinese

Jade was another of Noke's special effects, perfected in 1920, and he modelled a range of stylised animals especially for this tactile, soft green glaze, including some fish (625 and 632), an elephant (633) and a pair of cockatoos (630). Production of this unpredictable glaze was very short lived so examples are hard to find. Also for a brief period between the wars, animals were decorated with Noke's Titanian glaze, which ranges from a pale, smoky blue to a deep midnight hue but again only a few examples of each would ever have been produced. Occasionally models appear with a dark blue veining on a white ground, which is the second stage in the flambé decoration so, although interesting, these are actually unfinished pieces.

In the course of his glaze experimentation, Noke produced various bright yellow, orange, and red glazes and a greenish brown which was intended to simulate bronze. These effects turn up on animal models from time to time but they will be isolated examples. During the late 1950s and 60s, the new Art Director, Jo Ledger, also produced some interesting flambé glaze effects, including a mottled blue and green colour which he called Mandarin. Some of the animals in his Chatcull range can be found with this finish but they did not go into commercial production.

After a gap of many years, three large models went into the general flambé range in 1973, the 'Owl' (2249), the 'Rhinoceros' (615), and the 'Dragon' (2085). The 'Cat' (2269) which joined them a few years later, continued in production until 1997. The Royal Doulton International Collectors Club helped promote interest in flambé again when they launched their exclusive 'Dog of Fo' in 1982 and their exotic flambé 'Dragon.' New subjects in 1993 have periodically joined the dramatic Images of Fire collection until 1997 when all the models in this unique glaze effect were discontinued.

MAKING ROYAL DOULTON ANIMALS

Many different creative processes are involved in the production of Royal Doulton animals but essentially they all start the same way with an image in the designer's mind. If the model is to represent a specific breed then the artist will visit the stable, kennel or farm to study the animal in detail. Many photographs will be taken for reference and sometimes sketches will be made of important details. Having decided on the most appropriate pose, the modeller will set to work in clay, recreating the personality of his subject, as well as the precise details of its bone structure, muscles and finally the texture of its skin, fur or feathers. Even if the sculpture is destined for the stylised Images of Nature collection, the artist must study the animal in action to capture the essence of its character and abstract the leading lines of the design.

When the original clay sculpture has been completed and approved, the block maker will divide the model into appropriate sections in order to make the master mould. A few prototype pieces will be cast from this mould to produce colour trials and, once these have been approved by the marketing, design and production teams, together with the animal's owner, working moulds will be made of plaster of Paris.

Over the years both earthenware and bone china have been used to make animals at Royal Doulton's factories in Stoke-on-Trent. Bone china is a traditionally British body, with a high proportion of bone ash, which creates the much admired translucency when the body is fired to a high temperature. Earthenware is fired at a lower temperature than china and remains porous. Earthenware is usually painted under the glaze and bone china on top, creating different decorative effects. In the early 1900s, the same models were often offered in both bodies. Since the early 1970s earthenware models have been made at the John Beswick factory, which has a long tradition in animal production, and bone china models are made at the Royal Doulton factory in Burslem.

Different ingredients and firing techniques are used to produce the two ceramic bodies but the casting process is the same. Liquid clay, known as slip, is poured into the plaster of Paris moulds and, once the body has set to the required thickness, the excess slip is poured out. The pieces are carefully removed from the mould as the clay is still very fragile at this stage and the various parts are jointed together using slip as an adhesive. The seams are then gently sponged away by a process known as fettling and the piece is ready for its first firing, during which the water is driven off and it shrinks to its 'biscuit' state.

Earthenware animal models are decorated at this stage by a combination of spraying and hand painting. For instance, a horse model will have its coat sprayed to the required colour and then all the details, such as head, mane, tail, hooves, etc. will be painted by hand. The Connoisseur collection obviously has a high proportion of hand painting to recreate the animal's distinctive markings, for example the leopard's spots in 'The Watering Hole' DA39 and the variegated plumage on the 'Barn Owl' DA1. Once the painted decoration has dried, some animals are finished with a matt glaze to best capture their natural appearance. Others are coated with a high gloss glaze, creating a typical ceramic look when fired. In some cases the same models are offered with a choice of glaze effects.

Bone china animals are dipped or sprayed with liquid glaze and then fired again before decoration. In the past these would then have been hand painted by specialists in on-glaze colours. However, most of the bone china figures produced today are for the Images of Nature collection and they are left undecorated in their pure white bone china or finished with flambé glazes.

A complex process is used to create the flambé effect and the precise recipe is still a closely guarded secret. The unglazed pieces are taken to the flambé studios in their biscuit state and the features are painted in touches of blue, which will eventually shine through the flambé glaze. The flame effect on larger pieces is achieved by arranging thin strands of hemp over the piece to act as a template and then spraying on various colours. The hemp is removed leaving a unique veined effect and the piece then undergoes the various flambé glaze and firing procedures. In the final stage the kiln is deprived of oxygen which results in the fiery red finish.

CARE AND REPAIR

Careful handling and cleaning of Royal Doulton animal models will ensure that a collection can be enjoyed for many years to come. Tails, ears and other protruding features are particularly prone to damage when transporting, displaying and cleaning the collection. The Championship Dogs, in particular, have very vulnerable tails as they were modelled to portray the show stance as accurately as possible. When purchasing dogs like the 'Dalmatian' HN 1111, always check for restoration to the tail and seek the dealer's opinion. A reputable dealer will stand by any guarantees he gives regarding restorations.

Take care not to damage the animal models during cleaning by following these basic procedures. When dusting 'in situ,' a soft cosmetic brush or photographic lens brush is useful for getting into tight corners. Make sure the animals do not knock against each other causing chips or imperceptible cracks in the glaze which could open up at a later date. When necessary, models should be sponged with lukewarm water, using a mild liquid detergent, and then sponged again with clean water to rinse. It is important that water does not get inside the animal so block up the holes in the bottom before washing. Allow the piece to dry naturally and then, if the piece is glazed, buff gently with a soft cloth.

If the worst happens and a piece gets broken, seek the help and advice of a professional restorer. A skilled practitioner can repair chipped, cracked and shattered models so that the original damage is invisible to all but the most experienced eye.

With the right approach, Royal Doulton animals are much easier to take care of than real pets as they do not need to be walked, fed or house-trained so make the most of them.

CURRENT AND DISCONTINUED ANIMALS

Animals which are produced at the Royal Doulton factories today are referred to as 'current' and most of the range can be purchased in specialist china shops or from mail order companies. Royal Doulton publishes catalogues of their general range and these are obtainable from their Headquarters in England or their distribution companies around the world. Occasionally models have been commissioned exclusively for independent organisations and distribution of these varies. Doulton-Direct, the direct mail division of Royal Doulton, publishes an annual catalogue for their customers which often features animal offers. The Royal Doulton International Collectors Club usually publishes details of these private commissions in their quarterly magazine 'Gallery' and they may have, on occasion, offered animal models exclusively to their members. They also provide information on new introductions to the general range and the pieces being withdrawn to make way for the new models.

Once a piece has been withdrawn from production, it is referred to as 'discontinued' or 'retired' and it enters the secondary market. Many dealers around the world carry discontinued Royal Doulton animals as part of their general stock but some specialise in the field more than others. They regularly exhibit at antique fairs, some of which are exclusively for Royal Doulton products, and many run mail order services. Specialist animal dealers will often help collectors find specific models but it is still fun to scour general antique fairs and flea markets in case there are animals to be found. Auction rooms and estate sales sometimes feature Royal Doulton animals and successful purchases can be made if there is the time to view the lots, armed with techniques for spotting restorations and a good knowledge of prices.

A GUIDE TO DATING AND BACKSTAMPS

The Royal Doulton archive has very little information about the introduction and withdrawal dates of the animals in the HN collection so dating has been based on the study of model numbers, HN numbers and dated examples. Many animals have an impressed model number on the base which tallies with a photographic record book of shapes held at the Sir Henry Doulton Gallery in Stoke-on-Trent. Often the number is indistinct but by close examination of the shape book, it has been possible to match most model numbers with HN numbers. Occasionally photographs are missing from the shape books hence the gaps which still exist - hopefully they can be filled by keen collectors.

The model numbers are entered chronologically and animals are interspersed with figures. Existing information on figure introduction dates has therefore helped in establishing dates when the animals were first modelled. In 1936, many master moulds were destroyed and these are recorded in the shape book thus giving a number of withdrawal dates. Catalogues and price lists have provided further information but there are still several grey areas which have been filled with educated guesses. It is known, for instance, that most early models had been withdrawn by 1946. Collectors are invited to send details of dated pieces in their possession for further editions of this book.

The HN pattern numbers refer to the decorative treatment and many models were offered in a variety of colourways, some over a long period of time. Sequences of HN numbers were reserved for the animals: HN 100 - 300 were all allocated by 1922; HN 800 - 1200 allocated by 1937; HN 2500 - 2670 allocated by 1976 and HN 3500 - 4441 to the present.

The DA numbering system has been in use since 1989 although DA numbers are not found on the base of the piece unless it is a limited edition or prestige piece. There are no separate model numbers for new introductions. Animals transferred from the Beswick range have model numbers relating to the shape book held at the John Beswick Studio. Some of these models can be found with both Royal Doulton and John Beswick backstamps, which has led to some confusion in the market place. Similarly birds transferred from the Royal Adderley range can be found with both company trademarks.

Sometimes early Royal Doulton animals have a date code on the base which enables the piece to be dated to a specific year. Until around 1927, an impressed date was sometimes used to denote the day, month and year of production. Between 1928 and 1957 a date code was printed adjacent to the lion and crown symbol. To calculate the date, add the number beside the backstamp to 1927, for example the 14 numeral found on the Union Jack bulldogs denotes 1941.

Decorator's initials are often found adjacent to the backstamps. E.W. stands for Eric Webster, who was the leading animal painter for many years. He painted the first Championship Dogs and he also worked on special commissions, such as the royal steeplechaser 'Monaveen.'

F.C. is Fred Clark, who painted a variety of animals from prestige penguins to the K series. He remembers that the painters were paid 2 ½ pence for each K dog that they painted in the early years. T. stands for Stan Jones, K. for Ken Taylor and X for Roy Booth - all prolific animal painters. There are many other painter's marks to be found but those mentioned are the most notable.

Many different types of Royal Doulton backstamps have been used on animals over the years and these can also help with the dating process. Some of the most commonly found examples are illustrated below.

With Crown   Without Crown

The earliest mark found on animals is the basic lion and crown trademark which was in use from the launch of the collection until the early 1930s.

Between 1923 and 1927 the lion is sometimes found without the crown.

The words 'Made in England' were first added to the Royal Doulton trademark in the 1920s and this new style of backstamp has been used on animals since the early 1930s.

At the same time, details of the body were incorporated underneath e.g. 'Bone China, Flambé.' If there is no reference then the model is made of earthenware.

Often the complete lion and crown trademark would not fit on to the base of the animals and so only the bottom part of the mark, incorporating the interlacing D device, was used. In many cases this small circular mark was printed on one of the animal's feet, and the HN number written on another. In the early years of the Championship series, the dog's name was also printed on one of the feet if there was sufficient space.

DA 1 Barn Owl (Tyto Alba)

Some early miniature pieces just say 'DOULTON' or 'DOULTON ENGLAND' or 'DOULTON MADE IN ENGLAND.'

A half moon shaped backstamp with the words 'ROYAL DOULTON MADE IN ENGLAND' was sometimes used on the dogs of character.

ROYAL DOULTON YEAR CYPHERS

1998 Umbrella

1999 Top Hat

2000 Fob Watch

2001 Waistcoat

2002 Boot

Not Available at press time

2003 Gloves

Advertising leaflet for Roah Schorr animals (1937)

ROYAL DOULTON

INTERNATIONAL COLLECTORS CLUB

Founded in 1980, the Royal Doulton International Collectors Club provides an information service on all aspects of the company's products, past and present. A club magazine, "Gallery," is published four times a year with information on new products and current events that will keep the collector up-to-date on the happenings in the world of Royal Doulton. Upon joining the club, each new member will recieve a free gift and invitations to special events, and exclusive offers throughout the year. To join the Royal Doulton Collectors Club, please contact your local stockist, or contact the club directly by writing to the address opposite or calling the appropriate number.

International Collectors Club
Sir Henry Doulton House
Forge Lane, Etruria
Stoke-on-Trent, Staffordshire
ST1 5NN, England
Telephone:
   U.K.: 8702 412696
   Overseas: +44 1782 404045
   On-line at www.doulton-direct.co.uk
   E-mail: icc@royal-doulton.com

VISITOR CENTRE

Opened in the Summer of 1996, the Royal Doulton Visitor Centre houses the largest collection of Royal Doulton figurines in the world. Demonstration areas offer the collector a first hand insight on how figurines are assembled and decorated. Also at the Visitor Centre is a restaurant and a retail shop offering both best quality ware and slight seconds. Factory tours may be booked, Monday to Friday

Royal Doulton Visitor Centre
Nile Street, Burslem
Stoke-on-Trent, ST6 2AJ, England
Visitor Centre: Tel.: +44 (0) 1782 292434
               Fax: +44 (0) 1782 292424
Factory Store: Tel.: +44 (0) 1782 292451

WEBSITE AND E-MAIL ADDRESSES

Websites:
   www.royal-doulton.com
   www.doulton-direct.com.au
   www.royal-doulton-brides.com

E-mail:
   Visitor Centre: visitor@royal-doulton.com
   Consumer Enquiries: enquiries@royal-doulton.com
   Museum Curator: heritage@royal-doulton.com
   Doulton-Direct: direct@royal-doulton.com

ROYAL DOULTON FACTORY SHOPS

Royal Doulton Group Factory Shop
Lawley Street, Longton
Stoke-on-Trent, ST3 2PH, England
   Tel.: +44 (0) 1782 291237

Royal Doulton Factory Shop
Forge Lane, Etruria
Stoke-on-Trent, ST1 5NN, England
   Tel.: +44 (0) 1782 284056

Royal Doulton Factory Shop
Victoria Road, Fenton
Stoke-on-Trent, ST4 2PJ, England
   Tel.: +44 (0) 1782 291869

COLLECTOR CLUB CHAPTERS

Detroit Chapter
Ronald Griffin, President
629 Lynne AVenue
Ypsilanti, MI., 48198-3829

Edmonton Chapter
Mildred's Collectibles
6813 104 Street, Edmonton, AB

New England Chapter
Lee Piper, President
Meredith Nelson, Vice President
Michael Lynch, Secretary
Scott Reichenberg, Treasurer
E-mail doingantiq@aol.com

Northern California Chapter
Edward L. Khachadourian, President
P. O. Box 214, Moraga, Ca. 94556-0214
Tel.: (905) 376-2221 Fax: (925) 376-3581
E-mail: khack@pacbell.net

Northwest, Bob Haynes, Chapter
Alan Matthew, President
15202 93rd Place N.E., Bothell
WA., 98011 Tel.: (425) 488-9604

Rochester Chapter
Judith L. Trost, President
103 Garfield Street, Rochester
NY., 14611. Tel.: (716) 436-3321

Ohio Chapter
Reg Morris, President
5556 Whitehaven Avenue
North Olmstead, OH., 44070
Tel.: (216) 779-5554

Western Pennsylvania Chapter
John Re, President
9589 Parkedge Drive, Allison Park, PA., 15101
Tel.: (412) 366-0201
Fax: (412) 366-2558

LAND AUCTIONS

AUSTRALIA

Goodman's
7 Anderson Street
Double Bay, Sydney, 2028, N.S.W. Australia
Tel.: +61 (0) 2 9327 7311; Fax: +61 (0) 2 9327 2917
Enquiries: Suzanne Brett
www.goodmans.com.au
E-mail: info@goodmans.com.au

Sotheby's
1180122 Queen Street, Woollahra
Sydney, 2025, N.S.W., Australia
Tel.: +61 (0) 2 9362 1000; Fax: +61 (0) 2 9362 1100
www.sothebys.com

CANADA

Empire Auctions
Montreal
5500 Paré Street, Montreal, Quebec H4P 2M1
Tel.: (514) 737-6586; Fax: (514) 342-1352
Enquiries: Isadoe Rubinfeld
E-mail: montreal@empireauctions.com

Ottawa
1380 Cyrville Road, Gloucester, On
Tel.: (613) 748-5343; Fax: (613) 748-0354
Enquiries: Elliot Melamed
E-mail: ottawa@empireauctions.com

Toronto
165 Tycos Drive
Toronto, On., M6B 1W6
Tel.: (416) 784-4261; Fax: (416) 784-4262
Enquiries: Michael Rogozinsky
www.empireauctions.com
E-mail: toronto@empireauctions.com

Maynard's Industries Ltd.
Arts / Antiques
415 West 2nd Avenue, Vancouver, BC, V5Y 1E3
Tel.: (604) 876-1311; Fax: (604) 876-1323
www.maynards.com
E-mail: antiques@maynards.com

Richie's
288 King Street East, Toronto, On. M5A 1K4
Tel.: (416) 364-1864; Fax: (416) 364-0704
Enquiries: Caroline Kaiser
www.ritchies.com
E-mail: auction@ritchies.com

Waddington's
111 Bathurst Street, Toronto, On., M5V 2R1
Tel.: (416) 504-9100; Fax: (416) 504-0033
Enquiries: Bill Kime
www.waddingtonsauctions.com
E-mail: info@waddingtonsauctions.com

UNITED KINGDOM

BBR Auctions
Elsecar Heritage Centre, Nr. Barnsley,
South Yorkshire, S74 8HJ, England
Tel.: +44 (0) 1226 745156; Fax: +44 (0) 1226 351561
Enquiries: Alan Blakeman
www.bbrauctions.co.uk
E-mail: sales@bbrauctions.com

Bonhams
Bond Street:
101 New Bond Street, London, W15 1Sr, England
Chelsea:
65-69 Lots Road, Chelsea, London, SW10 0RN
England
Knightsbridge:
Montpelier Street, Knightsbridge, London, SW7 1HH
Tel.: +44 (0) 20 7393 3900; Fax: +44 (0) 20 7393 3905
Enquiries:
    Decorative Arts: Joy McCall
    Tel.: +44 (0) 20 7393 3942
    Comtemporary Ceramics: Gareth Williams
    Tel.: +44 (0) 20 7393 3941
    Doulton Beswick Wares: Marl Oliver
    Tel.: +44 (0) 20 7468 8233
www.bonhams.com
E-mail: info@bonhams.com

Christies:
London
8 King Street, London, SW1 England
Tel.: +44 (0) 207-839-9060; Fax: +44 (0) 207-839-1611
South Kensington
85 Old Brompton Road, London, SW7 3LD, England
Tel.: +44 (0) 20 7581 7611; Fax: +44 (0) 20 7321 3321
Enquiries:
    Decorative Arts: Michael Jeffrey
    Tel.: +44 (0) 20 7321 3237
www.christies.com; E-mail: info@christies.com

Potteries Specialist Auctions
271 Waterloo Road, Cobridge, Stoke-on-Trent
Staffordshire, ST6 3HR, England
Tel.: +44 (0) 1782 286622
Fax: +44 (0) 1782 213777
Enquiries: Stella Ashbrooke
www.potteriesauctions.com
E-mail: enquiries@potteriesauctions.com

Sotheby's
London
34-35 New Bond Street, London, W1A 2AA, England
Tel.: +44 (0) 20 7293 5000; Fax: +44 (0) 20 7293 5989
Olympia
Hammersmith Road, London W14 8UX, England
Tel.: +44 (0) 20 7293 5555; Fax: +44 (0) 20 7293 6939

Sotheby's

Sussex

Summers Place, Billinghurst, Sussex,
RH14 9AF, England
Tel.: +44 (0) 1403 833500; Fax: +44 (0) 1403 833699
www.sothebys.com
E-mail: info@sothebys.com

Louis Taylor

Britannia House,
10 Town Road, Hanley
Stoke-on-Trent, Staffordshire, England
Tel.: +44 (0) 1782 214111; Fax: +44 (0) 1782 215283
Enquires: Clive Hillier

Thomsom Roddick & Mecalf

60 Whitesands
Dumfries, DG1 2RS
Scotland
Tel.: +44 (0) 1387 279879; Fax: +44 (0) 1387 266236
Enquiries: C. R. Graham-Campbell

Peter Wilson Auctioneers

Victoria Gallery, Market Street
Nantwich, Cheshire, CW5 5DG, England
Tel.: +44 (0) 1270 610508; Fax: +44 (0) 1270 610508
Enquiries: Peter Wilson

UNITED STATES

Christie's East

219 East 67th Street, New York, NY 10012
Tel.: +1 212 606 0400
Enquires: Timothy Luke
www.christies.com

William Doyle Galleries

175 East 87th Street, New York, NY 10128
Tel.: +1 212 427 2730
Fax: +1 212 369 0892

Sotheby's Arcade Auctions

1334 York Avenue, New York, NY 10021
Tel.: +1 212 606 7000 I
Enquiries: Andrew Cheney
www.sothebys.com

VIRTUAL AUCTIONS

Amazon.com   Auctions
Main site: www.amazon.com
Plus 4 International sites.

AOL.com Auctions
Main site: www.aol.com
Links to - E-bay.com
ubid.com

E-BAY   The World's On-Line Market Place
Main site: www.ebay.com
Plus 20 International sites.

YAHOO! Auctions
Main site: www.yahoo.com
Plus 15 International auction sites.

FAIRS, MARKETS AND SHOWS

AUSTRALIA

Royal Doulton and Antique Collectable Fair
Marina Hall, Civic Centre,
Hurstville, Sydney

CANADA

Canadian Art & Collectables Show and Sale
Kitchener Memorial Auditorium, Kitchener, Ontario
Usually early May
For information on times and location contact:
Trajan Publishing Corp.
103 Lakeshore Road, Suite 202,
St. Catherines, Ontario L2N 2T6
Tel.: (905) 646-7744; Fax: (905) 646-0995

UNITED KINGDOM

20th Century Fairs
266 Glossop Road, Sheffield S10 2HS, England
Usually in May or June.
For information on times adn dates:
Tel.: +44 (0) 114 275 0333; Fax: +44 (0) 114 275 4443

Doulton and Beswick Collectors Fair
National Motorcycle Museum, Meriden,
Birmingham,
Usually March and August.
For information on times and dates:
Doulton and Beswick Dealers Association
Tel.: +44 (0) 181 303 3316

DMG Antiques Fairs Ltd.
Newark, the largest in the UK with usually six fairs
annually. For information on times adn dates for
this and many other fairs contact:
DMG
Newark, P. O. Box 100, Newark,
Nottinghamshire, NG2 1DJ
Tel.: +44 (0) 1636 702326; Fax: +44 (0) 1636 707923
www.antiquesdirectory.co.uk

U.K. Fairs
Doulton and Beswick Fair for Collectors
River Park Leisure Centre, Winchester
Usually held in October for information on times
and dates contact:
Enquiries U.K. Fairs; Tel.: +44 (0) 20 8500 3505
www.portia.co.uk
E-mail: ukfairs@portia.co.uk

LONDON MARKETS

Alfies Antique Market
13-25 Church Street, London; Tuesday - Saturday
Camden Passage Market
London, Wednesday and Saturday
New Caledonia Market
Bermondsey Square, London; Friday morning
Portobello Road Market
Portobello Road, London, Saturday

UNITED STATES
Atlantique City
Atlantic City Convention Centre
Atlantic City, NJ
International Gift and Collectible Expo
Donald E. Stephens Convention Centre
Rosemont, Illinois

For information on the above two shows contact:
Krause Publications
700 East State Street, Iola, WI 54990-9990
Tel.: (877) 746-9757; Fax: (715) 445-4389
www.collectibleshow.com
E-mail: iceshow@krause.com

Doulton Convention and Sale International
Fort Lauderdale, Florida, U.S.A.
Usually February. For information on times and dates:
Pascoe & Company,
575 S.W. 22nd Ave., Miami, Florida 33135
Tel.: (305) 643-2550; Fax: (305) 643*2123
www.pascoeandcompany.com
E-mail: sales@pascoeandcompany.com

Royal Doulton Convention & Sale
John S. Knight Convention Centre
77 E. Mill Street, Akron, Ohio 44308
Usually August. For information on times and dates:
Colonial House Productions
182 Front Street, Berea, Ohio 44017
Tel.: (866) 885-9024; Fax: (905) 854-3117
www.Colonial-House-Collectibles.com
E-mail: yworry@aol.com

Rabbit Vase with Lettuce by Mark Marshall

FURTHER READING

Storybook Figures

Beatrix Potter Figures and Giftware, edited by Louise Irvine
Beswick Price Guide, by Harvey May
Bunnykins Collectors Book, by Louise Irvine
Cartoon Classics and other Character Figures, by Louise Irvine
Charlton Standard Catalogue of Royal Doulton Beswick Storybook Figurines, by Jean Dale
Charlton Standard Catalogue of Royal Doulton Bunnykins, by Jean Dale and Louise Irvine
Royal Doulton Bunnykins Figures, by Louise Irvine

Animal, Figures and Character Jugs

Character Jug Collectors Handbook, by Kevin Pearson
Charlton Standard Catalogue of Beswick Animals by Callows and Sweets
Charlton Standard Catalogue of Royal Doulton Figurines, by Jean Dale
Charlton Standard Catalogue of Royal Doulton Jugs, by Jean Dale
Collecting Character and Toby Jugs by Jocelyn Lukins
Collecting Doulton Animals by Jocelyn Lukins
Doulton Figure Collectors Handbook, by Kevin Pearson
Doulton Flambé Animals by Jocelyn Lukins
Royal Doulton Figures by Desmond Eyles, Louise Irvine and Valerie Baynton

General

Charlton Standard Catalogue of Beswick Pottery, by Diane and John Callow
Discovering Royal Doulton, by Michael Doulton
Doulton Burslem Advertising Wares, by Jocelyn Lukins
Doulton Burslem Wares, by Desmond Eyles
Doulton for the Collector, by Jocelyn Lukins
Doulton Kingsware Flasks, by Jocelyn Lukins
Doulton Lambeth Advertising Wares, by Jocelyn Lukins
Doulton Lambeth Wares, by Desmond Eyles
Doulton Story, by Paul Atterbury and Louise Irvine
George Tinworth, by Peter Rose
Hannah Barlow, by Peter Rose
John Beswick: A World of Imagination. Catalogue reprint (1950-1996)
Limited Edition Loving Cups and Jugs, by Louise Irvine and Richard Dennis
Phillips Collectors Guide, by Catherine Braithwaite
Royal Doulton by Julie McKeown
Royal Doulton, by Jennifer Queree
Royal Doulton Series Wares, by Louise Irvine (Vols. 1-5)
Sir Henry Doulton Biography, by Edmund Gosse

Magazines and Newsletters

Beswick Quarterly (Beswick Newsletter) Contact Laura J. Rock-Smith: 10 Holmes Court, Sayville, N.Y. 11782-2408, U.S.A. Tel./Fax)631) 589-9027
Collecting Doulton Magazine, Contact Barry Hill, Collecting Doulton, P. O. Box 310, Richmond Surrey TW10 7FU, England
Cottontails (Newsletter of Bunnykins Collectors' Club), Contact Claire Green: 6 Beckett Way, Lewes, East Sussex, BN7 2EB, U.K. E-mail: claireg@2btinternet.com
Rabbitting On (Bunnykins Newsletter) Contact Leah Selig: 2 Harper Street, Merrylands 2160, New South Wales, Australia. Tel/Fax: 61 2 9637 2410 (International), 02 637 2410 (Australia)

JOHN BROAD

STONEWARE

Cockerel

Model No.:	Unknown
Designer:	John Broad
Height:	10 ¼", 26.0 cm
Colour:	Coloured Doultonware
Issued:	c.1900

Description	U.S. $	Can. $	U.K. £
Cockerel			Very Rare

Kangaroo

Model No.:	X7621
Designer:	John Broad
Height:	6 ½", 16.5 cm
Colour:	Brown and green
Issued:	1912

Description	U.S. $	Can. $	U.K. £
Kangaroo			Very Rare

Photograph not
available
at press time

Kangaroo Matchholder

Model No.:	X7056
Designer:	John Broad
Height:	Unknown
Colour:	Unknown
Issued:	1912

Description	U.S. $	Can. $	U.K. £
Kangaroo matchholder			Very Rare

LESLIE HARRADINE

STONEWARE

Cockatoos (pair)
Model No.: H35
Designer: Leslie Harradine
Height: 6", 15.0 cm
Colour: Blue and grey Doultonware
Issued: 1912

Description	U.S. $	Can. $	U.K. £
Cockatoos (pair)	600.00	900.00	375.00

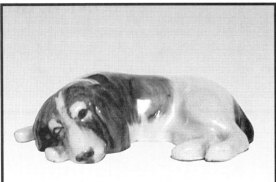

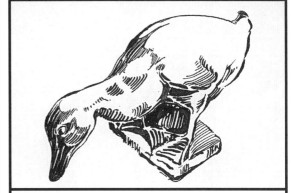

Dog Asleep
Model No.: X7732
Designer: Leslie Harradine
Length: 2 ¾", 7.0 cm
Colour: White and brown
Issued: 1912

Description	U.S. $	Can. $	U.K. £
Dog asleep		Rare	

Duck Doorstop
Model No.: H33
Designer: Leslie Harradine
Height: Unknown
Colour: Unknown
Issued: c.1912

Description	U.S. $	Can. $	U.K. £
Duck doorstop		Very Rare	

Ducklings (pair)

Model No.: X7731, H5
Designer: Leslie Harradine
Height: 4 ½", 11.9 cm
Colour: White and black
Issued: 1912

Description	U.S. $	Can. $	U.K. £
Ducklings (pair)	400.00	600.00	275.00

Monkey with Arms Folded

Model No.: Unknown
Designer: Leslie Harradine
Height: 8", 20.3 cm
Colour: Brown
Issued: c.1912

Description	U.S. $	Can. $	U.K. £
Monkey, arms folded	1,000.00	1,500.00	650.00

Note: A larger version of this design has also been recorded.

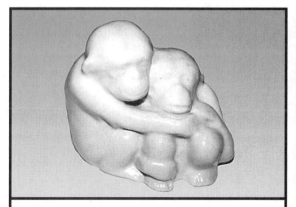

Monkeys Cuddling

Model No.: Unknown
Designer: Leslie Harradine
Height: 3", 7.6 cm
Colour: Cream (slip cast)
Issued: 1912

Description	U.S. $	Can. $	U.K. £
Monkeys cuddling	400.00	600.00	250.00

Note: This model is similar to the Burslem monkey group HN254.

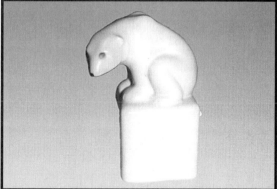

Polar Bear on Block of Ice

Model No.: X7731
Designer: Leslie Harradine
Height: 4", 10.1 cm
Colour: White
Issued: 1912

Description	U.S. $	Can. $	U.K. £
Polar bear on block of ice	400.00	600.00	250.00

Note: See HN119, model 67 for a continuation of this model.

Polar Bears on Ice Floe (pair)

Model No.:	H58
Designer:	Leslie Harradine
Height:	8", 20.1 cm
Colour:	White
Issued:	c.1912

Description	U.S. $	Can. $	U.K. £
Polar Bears on ice floe	1,000.00	1,500.00	650.00

Rhinoceros

Model No.:	Unknown
Designer:	Leslie Harradine
Height:	6 ½", 16.5 cm
Colour:	Brown and blue
Issued:	c.1912

Description	U.S. $	Can. $	U.K. £
Rhinoceros		Extremely Rare	

MARK MARSHALL

STONEWARE

Bear Family

Model No.:   Unknown
Designer: Mark Marshall
Height: 3", 7.5 cm
Colour: Brown
Issued: c.1905

Description	U.S. $	Can. $	U.K. £
Bear family	2,250.00	3,500.00	1,500.00

Chicken Bowl

Model No.:   896
Designer: Mark Marshall
Height: 11 ½", 29.0 cm
Colour: Light and dark green/white/
    reddish-brown/black
Issued: Unknown

Description	U.S. $	Can. $	U.K. £
Chicken bowl	3,000.00	4,500.00	2,000.00

Creature Smiling

Model No.:   Unknown
Designer: Mark Marshall
Height: 3 ½", 8.9 cm
Colour: Blue and brown
Issued: c.1902

Description	U.S. $	Can. $	U.K. £
Creature smiling	900.00	1,350.00	600.00

Fabulous Fish (Jug)

Model No.:   125
Designer: Mark Marshall
Height: 9", 23.0 cm
Colour: Browns/pinks/white/cream
Issued: c.1885

Description	U.S. $	Can. $	U.K. £
Fabulous fish	4,000.00	6,000.00	2,500.00

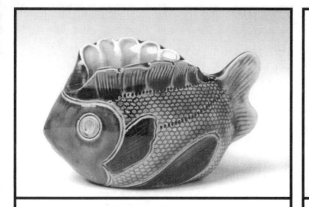

Fish Bowl

Model No.:	Unknown	
Designer:	Mark Marshall	
Height:	2 ½", 5.5 cm	
Colour:	1. Blue/white/green/brown	
	2. Browns and pale blue	
Issued:	Unknown	

Description	U.S. $	Can. $	U.K. £
1. Blue	1,500.00	2,250.00	1,000.00
2. Brown	1,500.00	2,250.00	1,000.00

Grotesque

Model No.:	Unknown
Designer:	Mark Marshall
Height:	3 ½", 8.9 cm
Colour:	Unknown
Issued:	c.1902

Description	U.S. $	Can. $	U.K. £
Grotesque	450.00	675.00	300.00

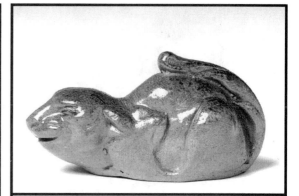

Grotesque - Bird

Model No.:	Unknown
Designer:	Mark Marshall
Height:	3", 7.6 cm
Colour:	Blue or brown
Issued:	c.1902

Colourways	U.S. $	Can. $	U.K. £
1. Blue	850.00	1,250.00	500.00
2. Brown	850.00	1,250.00	500.00

Grotesque - Cheshire Cat
(from *Alice in Wonderland*)

Model No.:	X6986
Designer:	Mark Marshall
Height:	1 ¾", 4.4 cm
Colour:	Blue, brown or green
Issued:	c.1902

Colourways	U.S. $	Can. $	U.K. £
1. Blue	450.00	675.00	300.00
2. Brown	450.00	675.00	300.00
3. Green	450.00	675.00	300.00

Grotesque - Duck

Model No.:	Unknown
Designer:	Mark Marshall
Height:	2 ¾", 7.0 cm
Colour:	Blue or green
Issued:	c.1902

Colourways	U.S. $	Can. $	U.K. £
1. Blue	450.00	675.00	300.00
2. Green	450.00	675.00	300.00

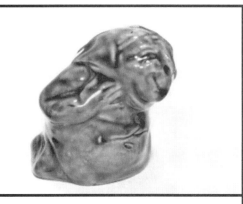

**Grotesque - Mock Turtle
(from *Alice in Wonderland*)**

Model No.:	X6987
Designer:	Mark Marshall
Height:	2 ½", 5.7 cm
Colour:	Blue or green
Issued:	c.1902

Colourways	U.S. $	Can. $	U.K. £
1. Blue	450.00	675.00	300.00
2. Green	450.00	675.00	300.00

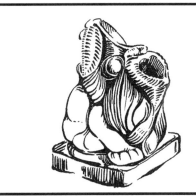

Grotesque - Rabbit

Model No.:	Unknown
Designer:	Mark Marshall
Height:	2", 5.0 cm
Colour:	Green rabbit on brown base
Issued:	c.1922

Description	U.S. $	Can. $	U.K. £
Rabbit	450.00	675.00	300.00

Grotesque - Snake

Model No.:	Unknown
Designer:	Mark Marshall
Height:	Unknown
Colour:	Green and brown
Issued:	c.1902

Description	U.S. $	Can. $	U.K. £
Snake	450.00	675.00	300.00

Grotesque - Toad

Model No.:	Unknown
Designer:	Mark Marshall
Height:	Unknown
Colour:	Unknown
Issued:	c.1902

Description	U.S. $	Can. $	U.K. £
Toad	450.00	675.00	300.00

Lizard

Model No.:	X6988
Designer:	Mark Marshall
Length:	4 ½", 27.9 cm
Colour:	Brown
Issued:	1904

Description	U.S. $	Can. $	U.K. £
Lizard	1,000.00	1,350.00	500.00

Lizard on Rock

Model No.:	Unknown
Designer:	Mark Marshall
Height:	5", 12.7 cm
Colour:	Brown
Issued:	c.1905

Description	U.S. $	Can. $	U.K. £
Lizard on rock	1,500.00	2,000.00	750.00

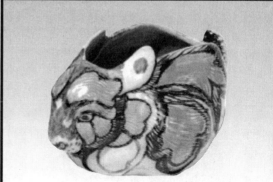

Rabbit Vase

Model No.:	381
Designer:	Mark Marshall
Length:	8", 20.5 cm
Colour:	Blue/green/cream/purple/black
Issued:	c.1880

Description	U.S. $	Can. $	U.K. £
Rabbit vase	3,000.00	4,500.00	2,000.00

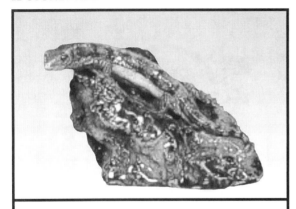

Salamander on Rock

Model No.:	Unknown
Designer:	Mark Marshall
Height:	3 ½", 8.5 cm
Colour:	Browns, purple and black
Issued:	Unknown

Description	U.S. $	Can. $	U.K. £
Salamander	2,500.00	3,750.00	1,750.00

Seahorse

Model No.:	Unknown
Designer:	Mark Marshall
Height:	6", 15.0 cm
Colour:	Green or white glazed Carraraware
Issued:	c.1910

Colourways	U.S. $	Can. $	U.K. £
1. Green	800.00	1,250.00	500.00
2. White	1,200.00	1,800.00	750.00

'The Waning of the Honeymoon' Rabbit Vase

Model No.:	Unknown
Designer:	Mark Marshall
Height:	4 ¾", 12.1 cm
Colour:	1. Blue stoneware
	2. Brown Siliconware
	3. Coloured Doultonware
Issued:	1880

Description	U.S. $	Can. $	U.K. £
1. Blue stoneware	3,000.00	5,000.00	1,250.00
2. Brown Siliconware	3,000.00	5,000.00	1,250.00
3. Coloured Doultonware	3,000.00	5,000.00	1,250.00

'The Yawn Rabbit'

Model No.:	Unknown
Designer:	Mark Marshall
Height:	Unknown
Colour:	Brown
Issued:	c.1880

Description	U.S. $	Can. $	U.K. £
The Yawn rabbit		Very Rare	

HARRY SIMEON

STONEWARE

Character Bird

Model No.:	X8598
Designer:	Harry Simeon
Height:	3 ¾", 9.5 cm
Colour:	Blue, green, purple and yellow
Issued:	1926

Description	U.S. $	Can. $	U.K. £
Character bird	375.00	575.00	250.00

Character Bird Looking Down

Model No.:	X8597
Designer:	Harry Simeon
Height:	3 ¾", 9.5 cm
Colour:	Brown, white and blue
Issued:	1926

Description	U.S. $	Can. $	U.K. £
Bird looking down	375.00	575.00	250.00

Photograph not
available
at press time

Cormorant

Model No.:	X7622
Designer:	Harry Simeon
Height:	Unknown
Colour:	Unknown
Issued:	1912

Description	U.S. $	Can. $	U.K. £
Cormorant		Extremely Rare	

Duck

Model No.:	X8604
Designer:	Harry Simeon
Height:	5", 12.7 cm
Colour:	Beige, brown and blue
Issued:	1926

Description	U.S. $	Can. $	U.K. £
Duck	2,000.00	3,000.00	1,000.00

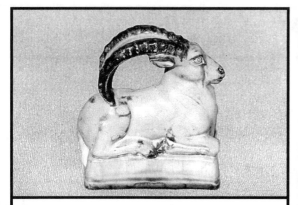

Ibex

Model No.:	X8605
Designer:	Harry Simeon
Height:	5", 12.7 cm
Colour:	Green and brown
Issued:	1926

Description	U.S. $	Can. $	U.K. £
Ibex	1,000.00	1,350.00	500.00

Monkey and Young Bookend

Model No.:	X8768
Designer:	Harry Simeon
Height:	6 ½", 16.5 cm
Colour:	Brown
Issued:	1928

Description	U.S. $	Can. $	U.K. £
Bookend		Extremely Rare	

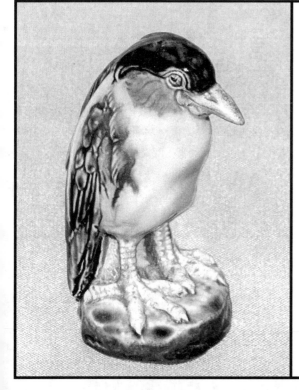

Night Heron

Model No.:	X8606
Designer:	Harry Simeon
Height:	5 ¾", 14.6 cm
Colour:	White, blue and brown
Issued:	1926

Description	U.S. $	Can. $	U.K. £
Night heron	450.00	675.00	300.00

Note: Night Heron used for tray see page 20.

Harry Simeon Stoneware Bibelots

Bird on Stump (Heron)

Model No.:	X8596
Designer:	Harry Simeon
Height:	7", 17.8 cm
Colour:	Gilt enamelled
Issued:	1926

Description	U.S. $	Can. $	U.K. £
Bird on stump (heron)	500.00	750.00	350.00

Photograph not available at press time

Bird Tray

Model No.:	X8617
Designer:	Harry Simeon
Height:	Unknown
Colour:	Unknown
Issued:	1926

Description	U.S. $	Can. $	U.K. £
Bird tray		Very Rare	

Bird (With Beak Open) Tray

Model No.:	X8740
Designer:	Harry Simeon
Height:	3", 7.6 cm
Colour:	Brown, green, white and blue
Issued:	1928

Description	U.S. $	Can. $	U.K. £
Bird/beak open	375.00	575.00	250.00

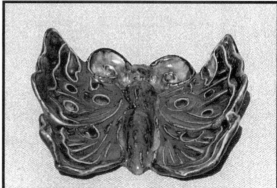

Bird (With Outstretched Wings) Tray

Model No.:	X8728
Designer:	Harry Simeon
Diameter:	5 ¾", 14.6 cm
Colour:	Blue, green and brown
Issued:	1928

Description	U.S. $	Can. $	U.K. £
Bird/outstretched wings	175.00	275.00	100.00

Butterfly Tray

Model No.:	X7107
Designer:	Harry Simeon
Diameter:	5", 12.7 cm
Colour:	Blue, green and brown
Issued:	c.1925

Description	U.S. $	Can. $	U.K. £
Butterfly tray	250.00	350.00	150.00

Character Bird On Boat Tray (Kookaburra On Boat)

Model No.:	X8685
Designer:	Harry Simeon
Height:	4 ¼", 10.8 cm
Colour:	Blue, brown, green and white
Issued:	1927

Description	U.S. $	Can. $	U.K. £
Bird on boat tray	375.00	575.00	250.00

Note: This model is similar to X8598, X8614 and X8686.

Character Bird On Shell Tray

Model No.:	X8686
Designer:	Harry Simeon
Height:	4 ¼", 10.8 cm
Colour:	Blue, brown, green and purple
Issued:	1927

Description	U.S. $	Can. $	U.K. £
Bird on shell tray	375.00	575.00	250.00

Note: This model is similar to X8598, X8614 and X8685.

Photograph not
available
at press time

Character Bird On Tray

Model No.: X8614
Designer: Harry Simeon
Height: 4 ¼", 10.8 cm
Colour: Blue, green and white
Issued: 1926

Description	U.S. $	Can. $	U.K. £
Bird on tray	375.00	575.00	250.00

Note: This model is similar to X8598, X8685 and X8686.

Dragonfly Tray

Model No.: X8713
Designer: Harry Simeon
Diameter: 6", 15.0 cm
Colour: Blue, green and white
Issued: 1928

Description	U.S. $	Can. $	U.K. £
Dragonfly tray	175.00	275.00	100.00

Note: A similar design was made for Wright's Coal
Tar Soap c.1920.

Duck Tray

Model No.: Unknown
Designer: Harry Simeon
Height: 6 ½", 16.5 cm
Colour: Blue, green, pink and brown
Issued: 1928

Description	U.S. $	Can. $	U.K. £
Duck tray	300.00	475.00	200.00

Fish Tray

Model No.: X8906
Designer: Harry Simeon
Height: 6", 15.0 cm
Colour: Blue, green, white and brown
Issued: 1934

Description	U.S. $	Can. $	U.K. £
Fish tray	300.00	475.00	200.00

Photograph not
available
at press time

Fish Tray (Plaice)

Model No.:	X8705
Designer:	Harry Simeon
Height:	Unknown
Colour:	Unknown
Issued:	1928

Description	U.S. $	Can. $	U.K. £
Fish tray		Extremely Rare	

Koala Tray

Model No.:	X8902
Designer:	Harry Simeon
Height:	4", 10.1 cm
Colour:	Blue, brown and green
Issued:	1934

Description	U.S. $	Can. $	U.K. £
Koala tray	275.00	450.00	175.00

Moth Tray

Model No.:	X8730
Designer:	Harry Simeon
Height:	5 ¾", 14.6 cm
Colour:	Blue, green, brown and purple
Issued:	1928

Description	U.S. $	Can. $	U.K. £
Moth tray	175.00	275.00	100.00

Mouse Ring Stand

Model No.:	X8673
Designer:	Harry Simeon
Height:	4", 10.1 cm
Colour:	Blue and brown
Issued:	1927

Description	U.S. $	Can. $	U.K. £
Mouse ring stand	400.00	650.00	250.00

Mouse Tray

Model No.:	X8669
Designer:	Harry Simeon
Height:	1. Large — 3 ½", 8.9 cm
	2. Small — 2 ¾", 7.0 cm
Colour:	Brown
Issued:	1927

Description	U.S. $	Can. $	U.K. £
1. Large	375.00	575.00	250.00
2. Small	300.00	475.00	200.00

Night Heron Tray

Model No.:	X8948
Designer:	Harry Simeon
Height:	1. Large — 7", 15.5 cm
	2. Small — 4", 10.1 cm
Colour:	Blue, brown, green and white
Issued:	1934

Description	U.S. $	Can. $	U.K. £
1. Large	500.00	750.00	350.00
2. Small	375.00	575.00	250.00

Owl Tray

Model No.:	X8667
Designer:	Vera Huggins
Diameter:	1. Large — 3 ½", 8.9 cm
	2. Small — 2 ¾", 7.0 cm
Colour:	Brown and beige
Issued:	1926

Description	U.S. $	Can. $	U.K. £
1. Large	475.00	550.00	300.00
2. Small	300.00	475.00	200.00

Pelican On Octagonal Tray

Model No.:   X8978
Designer: Harry Simeon
Height: 5 ¾", 14.6 cm
Colour: Blue, brown and white
Issued: 1934

Description	U.S. $	Can. $	U.K. £
Pelican /octagonal tray	400.00	650.00	250.00

Pelican On Round Tray

Model No.:   X8900
Designer: Harry Simeon
Height: 3 ¾", 9.5 cm
Colour: Blue, brown, green and white
Issued: 1934

Description	U.S. $	Can. $	U.K. £
Pelican /round tray	400.00	650.00	250.00

Pigeon Tray

Model No.:   X8979
Designer: Harry Simeon
Height: 4 ¼", 10.8 cm
Colour: Blue, brown and white
Issued: 1934

Description	U.S. $	Can. $	U.K. £
Pigeon tray	400.00	650.00	250.00

Polar Bear Tray

Model No.: X8715
Designer: Harry Simeon
Height: 4 ¾", 12.1 cm
Colour: White, blue and green
Issued: 1928

Description	U.S. $	Can. $	U.K. £
Polar bear tray	475.00	750.00	300.00

Rabbit Tray

Model No.: X8756
Designer: Harry Simeon
Height: 3 ¼", 8.3 cm
Colour: Blue, brown, white and green
Issued: 1928

Description	U.S. $	Can. $	U.K. £
1. Brown rabbit	400.00	650.00	250.00
2. White rabbit	400.00	650.00	250.00

Photograph not
available
at press time

Seal tray

Model No.: Not recorded
Designer: Harry Simeon
Height: 3", 7.6 cm
Colour: Silver lustre and blue
Issued: c.1925

Description	U.S. $	Can. $	U.K. £
Seal tray	400.00	650.00	250.00

Note: This ashtray was made for McMullen's Silver Seal Port.

Swan Tray

Model No.: X8668
Designer: Harry Simeon
Height: Unknown
Colour: Unknown
Issued: 1927

Description	U.S. $	Can. $	U.K. £
Swan tray		Extremely Rare	

GEORGE TINWORTH

STONEWARE

Fables
Frog and Monkey Groups
Frog and Mice Groups
Mice Groups
Mouse Musicians

Fables

The Cat And The Sparrow

Model No.: Unknown
Designer: George Tinworth
Height: 3 ½", 8.9 cm
Colour: Brown and green
Issued: c.1882

Description	U.S. $	Can. $	U.K. £
Cat/sparrow	3,000.00	4,000.00	1,500.00

The Eagle And The Fox With Vase

Model No.: Unknown
Designer: George Tinworth
Height: 6", 15.0 cm
Colour: Brown and green
Issued: c.1882

Description	U.S. $	Can. $	U.K. £
Eagle/fox with vase	3,500.00	5,000.00	2,000.00

The Fox Inviting The Stork To Dinner

Model No.: Unknown
Designer: George Tinworth
Height: 4", 10.1 cm
Colour: Blue, brown and green
Issued: c.1882

Description	U.S. $	Can. $	U.K. £
Fox/stork	3,500.00	5,000.00	2,000.00

The Monkey That Would Be King

Model No.: Unknown
Designer: George Tinworth
Height: 4", 10.1 cm
Colour: Brown and blue
Issued: c.1882

Description	U.S. $	Can. $	U.K. £
Monkey	3,000.00	4,000.00	1,500.00

Monkey, Cats And Cheese

Model No.:	Unknown
Designer:	George Tinworth
Height:	6", 15.0 cm
Colour:	Brown and blue
Issued:	1882

Description	U.S. $	Can. $	U.K. £
Monkey/cats/cheese	1,500.00	2,000.00	750.00

The Ox And The Frogs

Model No.:	Unknown
Designer:	George Tinworth
Height:	3", 7.6 cm
Length:	7 ¼", 18.4 cm
Colour:	Brown and green
Issued:	1881

Description	U.S. $	Can. $	U.K. £
Ox/frogs	1,500.00	2,000.00	700.00

The Vain Jackdaw With Vase

Model No.:	Unknown
Designer:	George Tinworth
Height:	6", 15.0 cm
Colour:	Blue, green and brown
Issued:	c.1882

Description	U.S. $	Can. $	U.K. £
Vain jackdaw	1,200.00	1,800.00	750.00

Frog and Monkey Groups

Bicyclist
Model No.:	X929
Designer:	George Tinworth
Height:	4 ½", 11.9 cm
Colour:	Green, brown and yellow
Issued:	c.1885

Description	U.S. $	Can. $	U.K. £
Bicyclist	3,500.00	5,500.00	2,250.00

Canoeist
Model No.:	Unknown
Designer:	George Tinworth
Height:	4, 10.1 cm
Colour:	Blue and brown
Issued:	c.1885

Description	U.S. $	Can. $	U.K. £
1. Blue boat	2,500.00	3,750.00	1,750.00
2. Brown boat	2,500,00	3,750.00	1,750.00

Cricketer
Model No.:	Unknown
Designer:	George Tinworth
Height:	4 ¾", 12.1 cm
Colour:	Blue and brown
Issued:	c.1885

Description	U.S. $	Can. $	U.K. £
Cricketer	3,000.00	4,500.00	2,000.00

Football

Model No.:	Unknown
Designer:	George Tinworth
Height:	5", 12.7 cm
Colour:	Blue and brown
Issued:	c.1885
Varieties:	Also called 'Football Scrimmage'

Description	U.S. $	Can. $	U.K. £
Football	6,000.00	9,000.00	4,000.00

Frogs With Vase

Model No.:	Unknown
Designer:	George Tinworth
Height:	4 ½", 11.9 cm
Colour:	Blue and brown
Issued:	c.1890

Description	U.S. $	Can. $	U.K. £
Frogs with vase	2,250.00	3,500.00	1,500.00

Jack In The Green

Model No.:	Unknown
Designer:	George Tinworth
Height:	5 ¼", 13.3 cm
Colour:	Brown and green
Issued:	c.1885

Description	U.S. $	Can. $	U.K. £
Jack in the green	4,000.00	6,000.00	2,500.00

The Public Library's Act

Model No.:	Unknown
Designer:	George Tinworth
Height:	5 ¼", 13.3 cm
Colour:	Brown and blue
Issued:	1888

Description	U.S. $	Can. $	U.K. £
Public library's act	2,500.00	3,750.00	1,750.00

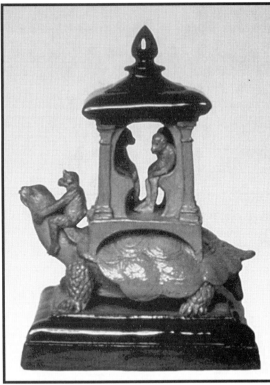

**Safe Travelling
(Monkeys Riding A Tortoise)**

Model No.:   Unknown
Designer: George Tinworth
Height: 6 ¾", 17.2 cm
Colour: Brown and blue
Issued: c.1885
Varieties: Also called 'Slow but Sure'

Description	U.S. $	Can. $	U.K. £
Safe travelling	7,500.00	12,000.00	5,000.00

Note: This piece is also known with front monkey wearing a hat.

**United Family
(Monkeys Grooming Each Other)**

Model No.:   Unknown
Designer: George Tinworth
Height: 5", 12.7 cm
Colour: 1. Carraraware
            2. Green
Issued: c.1892
Varieties: Also called 'Busy,' 'Contentment'

Description	U.S. $	Can. $	U.K. £
1. Carraraware	1,800.00	2,750.00	1,200.00
2. Green stoneware	3,500.00	5,500.00	2,250.00

Frog And Mice Groups

Art and Agriculture

Model No.:	Unknown
Designer:	George Tinworth
Length:	7", 17.8 cm
Colour:	Brown
Issued:	c.1885

Description	U.S. $	Can. $	U.K. £
Art/agriculture	6,000.00	9,000.00	2,500.00

The Combat

Model No.:	Unknown
Designer:	George Tinworth
Height:	3 ¾", 9.5 cm
Colour:	Blue and brown
Issued:	c.1885

Description	U.S. $	Can. $	U.K. £
Combat	4,000.00	5,500.00	2,000.00

Crossing The Channel

Model No.:	Unknown
Designer:	George Tinworth
Height:	5", 12.7 cm
Colour:	Blue and brown
Issued:	c.1885

Description	U.S. $	Can. $	U.K. £
Crossing the channel	5,000.00	7,500.00	3,000.00

The Frog Is Trying To Persuade The Mouse Across The Stream

Model No.:	Unknown
Designer:	George Tinworth
Height:	3", 7.6 cm
Colour:	Blue, green and brown
Issued:	c.1888

Description	U.S. $	Can. $	U.K. £
Across the stream	2,750.00	3,500.00	1,350.00

Photograph not
available
at press time

Photograph not
available
at press time

Frogs Carrying Mouse in Sedan Chair

Model No.:	Unknown
Designer:	George Tinworth
Height:	Unknown
Colour:	Unknown
Issued:	1888

Description	U.S. $	Can. $	U.K. £
Carrying sedan chair		Extremely Rare	

Note: Companion piece to 'Frogs Returning Drunk with Sedan Chair.'

Frogs Returning Drunk with Sedan Chair

Model No.:	Unknown
Designer:	George Tinworth
Height:	Unknown
Colour:	Unknown
Issued:	1888

Description	U.S. $	Can. $	U.K. £
Drunk with sedan chair		Extremely Rare	

Note: Companion piece to 'Frogs Carrying Mouse in Sedan Chair.'

Going to the Derby

Model No.:	Unknown
Designer:	George Tinworth
Height:	4", 10.1 cm
Colour:	Brown and blue
Issued:	1886

Colourways	U.S. $	Can. $	U.K. £
1. White frogs/mouse	4,000.00	6,000.00	2,750.00
2. Blue frogs/brown mouse	4,000.00	6,000.00	2,750.00

Note: Companion piece to 'Lost and Serves them Right.'

Lost and Serves them Right

Model No.:	Unknown
Designer:	George Tinworth
Height:	4", 10.1 cm
Colour:	Brown and blue
Issued:	1886

Colourways	U.S. $	Can. $	U.K. £
1. White frogs/mouse	4,000.00	6,000.00	2,750.00
2. Blue frogs/brown mouse	4,000.00	6,000.00	2,750.00

Note: Companion piece to 'Going to the Derby.'

Music and Literature

Model No.:	Unknown
Designer:	George Tinworth
Height:	5 ¼", 13.3 cm
Colour:	Brown
Issued:	c.1885
Varieties:	Also called 'The Albert Embankment'

Description	U.S. $	Can. $	U.K. £
Music and literature	6,000.00	9,000.00	2,500.00

The Race

Model No.:	Unknown
Designer:	George Tinworth
Height:	5 ¼", 13.3 cm
Colour:	White, brown and green
Issued:	c.1885

Description	U.S. $	Can. $	U.K. £
The Race	7,500.00	10,000.00	3,000.00

Steeplechase

Model No.:	Unknown
Designer:	George Tinworth
Height:	4 ½", 11.9 cm
Colour:	White, brown and green
Issued:	c.1888
Varieties:	Also called 'Hunting'

Description	U.S. $	Can. $	U.K. £
Steeplechase	6,000.00	9,000.00	2,750.00

Tug of War

Model No.:	Unknown
Designer:	George Tinworth
Height:	3 ¾" 9.5 cm
Colour:	White, blue and brown
Issued:	c.1885

Description	U.S. $	Can. $	U.K. £
Tug of war	5,000.00	8,000.00	3,500.00

Mice Groups

Apple Stall Menu Holder

Model No.:	Unknown
Designer:	George Tinworth
Height:	3 ¾", 9.5 cm
Colour:	Green and brown
Issued:	c.1885

Description	U.S. $	Can. $	U.K. £
Apple stall	1,500.00	2,000.00	750.00

Barber

Model No.:	X1212 - Unknown
	X1108 - Menu holder
Designer:	George Tinworth
Height:	3 ¼", 8.3 cm
Colour:	White, brown and blue
Issued:	1886

Description	U.S. $	Can. $	U.K. £
Barber	1,500.00	2,000.00	750.00

Chess Set

This set originally consisted of 32 pieces but now the pieces are usually found individually. For illustration of complete chess set see page 46.

Model No.:	Unknown
Designer:	George Tinworth
Height:	2 ½" - 3", 6.4 cm - 7.6 cm
Colour:	1. White with red or black details
	2. Brown
Issued:	c.1900

Description	U.S. $	Can. $	U.K. £
1. Major chessmen	800.00	1,200.00	550.00
2. Pawns	400.00	600.00	300.00

Note: A Chess Set (32 pieces) plus a Jacques carved wooden box sold by Sotheby's for $12,000.00 USF. Harriman Judd Collection, Part One, January 2001.

Cockneys at Brighton

Model No.:	Unknown
Designer:	George Tinworth
Height:	4", 10.1 cm
Colour:	White or brown, green and blue
Issued:	1886

Colourways	U.S. $	Can. $	U.K. £
1. White mice	5,000.00	8,000.00	3,500.00
2. Brown mice	5,000.00	8,000.00	3,500.00

Conjurers

Model No.:	X944
Designer:	George Tinworth
Height:	3 ¼", 8.3 cm
Colour:	White, blue and brown
Issued:	1885

Description	U.S. $	Can. $	U.K. £
Conjurers	1,250.00	1,500.00	650.00

Note: This model was also made in bone china.

Currant Bun

Model No.:	X64
Designer:	George Tinworth
Height:	2 ¾", 7.0 cm
Colour:	White or brown mouse on brown current bun
Issued:	1884

Colourways	U.S. $	Can. $	U.K. £
1. Brown mouse	1,250.00	2,000.00	850.00
2. White mouse	1,250.00	2,000.00	850.00

Drunkards

Model No.:	Unknown
Designer:	George Tinworth
Height:	3 ¼", 8.3 cm
Colour:	White and brown
Issued:	1888

Description	U.S. $	Can. $	U.K. £
Drunkards	4,000.00	6,500.00	2,700.00

Electricity

Model No.:	X1111 - Menu holder		
	X1208 - Vase		
Designer:	George Tinworth		
Height:	5 ¼", 13.3 cm		
Colour:	Brown and blue		
Issued:	c.1885		

Description	U.S. $	Can. $	U.K. £
1. Menu holder	3,000.00	4,500.00	2,000.00
2. Vase	3,000.00	4,500.00	2,000.00

Note: Vase variety illustrated.

Gunpowder Treason

Model No.:	Unknown - Menu holder		
Designer:	George Tinworth		
Height:	4 ¼", 10.8 cm		
Colour:	Brown and blue		
Issued:	c.1885		

Description	U.S. $	Can. $	U.K. £
Gunpowder	3,000.00	4,500.00	2,000.00

Hide and Seek Napkin Holder (Mouse and Frog)

Model No.:	Unknown		
Designer:	George Tinworth		
Height:	5 ½", 14.0 cm		
Colour:	Blue and brown		
Issued:	1881		

Description	U.S. $	Can. $	U.K. £
Hide/seek (mouse/frog)	5,500.00	8,500.00	3,500.00

Hide and Seek Napkin Holder (Two Mice)

Model No.:	Unknown		
Designer:	George Tinworth		
Height:	5 ½", 14.0 cm		
Colour:	Blue and brown		
Issued:	1881		

Description	U.S. $	Can. $	U.K. £
Hide/seek (two mice)	5,500.00	8,500.00	3,500.00

Note: Also known with the two mice on the base of the model.

Home Comforts With Vase

Model No.:	Unknown		
Designer:	George Tinworth		
Height:	4 ½", 11.9 cm		
Colour:	Blue and green		
Issued:	c.1885		

Description	U.S. $	Can. $	U.K. £
Home comforts	1,200.00	1,800.00	750.00

Note: Companion piece to 'Homeless with Vase.'

Homeless With Vase

Model No.:	Unknown		
Designer:	George Tinworth		
Height:	4", 10.1 cm		
Colour:	Blue and green		
Issued:	c.1885		

Description	U.S. $	Can. $	U.K. £
Homeless with vase	1,200.00	1,800.00	750.00

Note: Companion piece to 'Home Comforts with Vase.'

Photograph not
available
at press time

Mice Eating Plum Pudding

Model No.:	Unknown		
Designer:	George Tinworth		
Height:	Unknown		
Colour:	Unknown		
Issued:	1888		

Description	U.S. $	Can. $	U.K. £
Mice/plum pudding		Extremely Rare	

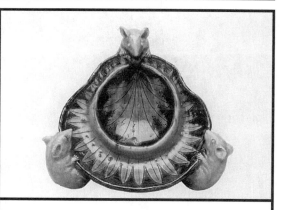

Mice Pocket Watch Holder

Model No.:	Unknown		
Designer:	George Tinworth		
Height:	4 ½", 11.9 cm		
Colour:	White, brown and green		
Issued:	c.1885		

Description	U.S. $	Can. $	U.K. £
Pocket watch holder	2,500.00	3,750.00	1,750.00

The Modeller

Model No.:	Unknown - Menu holder
Designer:	George Tinworth
Height:	4 ½", 11.9 cm
Colour:	White, brown and blue
Issued:	c.1885
Varieties:	Also called 'Sculptor'

Description	U.S. $	Can. $	U.K. £
The Modeller	3,000.00	4,750.00	2,000.00

Mouse Asleep Vase

Model No.:	Unknown
Designer:	George Tinworth
Height:	3 ¾", 9.5 cm
Colour:	Blue, green and brown
Issued:	c.1885

Description	U.S. $	Can. $	U.K. £
Mouse asleep vase	950.00	1,400.00	600.00

Mouse Smoking Tobacco Jar

Model No.:	Unknown
Designer:	George Tinworth
Height:	7 ¼", 18.4 cm
Colour:	Green, blue and brown
Issued:	c.1885

Description	U.S. $	Can. $	U.K. £
Tobacco jar	1,200.00	1,800.00	750.00

Painting

Model No.:	X1213
	X1113 - Menu holder
Designer:	George Tinworth
Height:	3 ½", 8.9 cm
Colour:	Blue; white or brown mice
Issued:	1886

Colourways	U.S. $	Can. $	U.K. £
1. White mice	3,000.00	4,750.00	2,000.00
2. Brown mice	3,000.00	4,750.00	2,000.00

Photography

Model No.:	Unknown
Designer:	George Tinworth
Height:	4 ½", 11.9 cm
Colour:	Blue; white or brown mice
Issued:	c.1885

Colourways	U.S. $	Can. $	U.K. £
1. White mice	3,000.00	4,750.00	2,000.00
2. Brown mice	3,000.00	4,750.00	2,000.00

The Pillars of Wealth and Poverty Between

Model No.:	Unknown
Designer:	George Tinworth
Height:	4 ½", 11.9 cm
Colour:	Brown and blue
Issued:	c.1885

Description	U.S. $	Can. $	U.K. £
Wealth and poverty	1,200.00	1,800.00	750.00

Playgoers

Model No.:	Unknown
Designer:	George Tinworth
Height:	5 ¼", 13.3 cm
Colour:	Blue, green; white or brown mice
Issued:	1886

Colourways	U.S. $	Can. $	U.K. £
1. White mice	6,000.00	9,000.00	4,000.00
2. Brown mice	6,000.00	9,000.00	4,000.00

Photograph not
available
at press time

Potter

Model No.:	X1210
	X1110 - Menu holder
Designer:	George Tinworth
Height:	3 ¾", 9.5 cm
Colour:	Blue and brown
Issued:	c.1885

Description	U.S. $	Can. $	U.K. £
Potter	3,000.00	4,750.00	2,000.00

Quack Doctor

Model No.:	Unknown - Menu holder
Designer:	George Tinworth
Height:	4", 10.1 cm
Colour:	Brown; white or brown mice
Issued:	c.1885

Colourways	U.S. $	Can. $	U.K. £
1. White mice	3,500.00	5,500.00	2,250.00
2. Brown mice	3,000.00	4,750.00	2,000.00

School Board

Model No.:	Unknown - Menu holder
Designer:	George Tinworth
Height:	3 ½", 8.9
Colour:	Blue, green; white or brown mice
Issued:	c.1885

Colourways	U.S. $	Can. $	U.K. £
1. White mice	3,000.00	4,750.00	2,000.00
2. Brown mice	3,000.00	4,750.00	2,000.00

Tea Time Scandal

Model No.:	Unknown
Designer:	George Tinworth
Height:	3 ½", 8.9 cm
Colour:	Green and brown
Issued:	1888

Description	U.S. $	Can. $	U.K. £
Tea time scandal	4,000.00	6,500.00	2,750.00

Waits

Model No.:	Unknown
Designer:	George Tinworth
Height:	5 ¼", 13.3 cm
Colour:	Green and blue; white or brown mice
Issued:	c.1885
Varieties:	Also called Christmas Waits

Colourways	U.S. $	Can. $	U.K. £
1. White mice	4,000.00	6,000.00	2,750.00
2. Brown mice	4,000.00	6,000.00	2,750.00

Note: Companion piece to 'Waits Water.'

Waits Water

Model No.:	Unknown
Designer:	George Tinworth
Height:	5 ¼", 13.3 cm
Colour:	Blue; white or brown mice
Issued:	c.1885

Colourways	U.S. $	Can. $	U.K. £
1. White mice	5,000.00	8,000.00	3,500.00
2. Brown mice	5,000.00	8,000.00	3,500.00

Note: Companion piece to 'Waits.'

Wheelbarrow With Vase

Model No.:	Unknown		
Designer:	George Tinworth		
Height:	3 ¾", 9.5 cm		
Colour:	Blue and green; white or brown mouse		
Issued:	c.1885		

Colourways	U.S. $	Can. $	U.K. £
1. White mouse	3,000.00	4,750.00	2,000.00
2. Brown mouse	3,000.00	4,750.00	2,000.00
3. Brown mouse with silver rim vase	3,500.00	5,500.00	2,250.00

The Wheelwright

Model No.:	X1107 - Menu Holder		
Designer:	George Tinworth		
Height:	3 ½", 8.9 cm		
Colour:	Brown and green		
Issued:	1886		

Description	U.S. $	Can. $	U.K. £
Wheelwright	3,000.00	4,750.00	2,000.00

Mouse Musicians

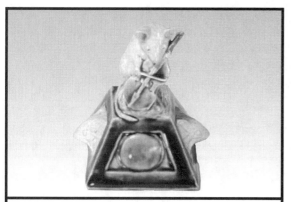

Bass Viol

Model No.:	X1207
Designer:	George Tinworth
Height:	Unknown
Colour:	White, blue and brown
Issued:	c.1884

Description	U.S. $	Can. $	U.K. £
Bass Viol	1,200.00	1,800.00	800.00

Cornet and Double Bass

Model No.:	Unknown - Menu holder
Designer:	George Tinworth
Height:	3 ½", 8.9 cm
Colour:	Brown and green
Issued:	c.1885

Description	U.S. $	Can. $	U.K. £
Cornet/double bass	3,000.00	4,750.00	2,000.00

Cornet Player

Model No.:	X1214 - Unknown
	X947 - Menu holder
Designer:	George Tinworth
Height:	3 ¼", 8.3 cm
Colour:	Brown and blue
Issued:	1886

Description	U.S. $	Can. $	U.K. £
1. Round base	1,500.00	2,250.00	1,000.00
2. Square base	1,500.00	2,250.00	1,000.00
3. Menu holder	1,500.00	2,250.00	1,000.00

Double Bass and Fiddle

Model No.:	X948 - Menu holder
	Unknown - Vase
Designer:	George Tinworth
Height:	5 ¼", 13.3 cm
Colour:	Green
Issued:	c.1884
Varieties:	Also made with a vase

Description	U.S. $	Can. $	U.K. £
Double bass/fiddle	3,000.00	4,750.00	2,000.00

Note: This piece was also made in bone china.

Flute Player

Model No.:	Unknown - see below
Designer:	George Tinworth
Height:	4 ¼", 10.8 cm
Colour:	Brown
Issued:	1884

Description	U.S. $	Can. $	U.K. £
1. Round base	1,500.00	2,250.00	1,000.00
2. Square base	1,500.00	2,250.00	1,000.00

Guitar and Tambourine

Model No.:	Unknown - Vase
Designer:	George Tinworth
Height:	5 ¼", 13.3 cm
Colour:	Green, brown and white
Issued:	c.1884

Description	U.S. $	Can. $	U.K. £
Guitar/tambourine	3,000.00	4,750.00	2,000.00

Harp and Concertina

Model No.:	Unknown - Menu holder
Designer:	George Tinworth
Height:	4", 10.1 cm
Colour:	Blue, green and brown
Issued:	c.1884

Description	U.S. $	Can. $	U.K. £
Harp/concertina	3,000.00	4,750.00	2,000.00

Harp and Cornet

Model No.:	X1112 - Menu holder
	Unknown - Vase
Designer:	George Tinworth
Height:	5 ¼", 13.3 cm
Colour:	Green and brown
Issued:	c.1884

Description	U.S. $	Can. $	U.K. £
Harp/cornet	3,000.00	4,750.00	2,000.00

Harp and Piano

Model No.:	Unknown - Menu holder
Designer:	George Tinworth
Height:	3 ½", 8.9 cm
Colour:	White and brown
Issued:	1886

Description	U.S. $	Can. $	U.K. £
Harp/piano	2,750.00	4,000.00	1,850.00

Harp and Violoncello

Model No.:	X1211 - Unknown
	X1109 - Menu holder
Designer:	George Tinworth
Height:	3 ¾", 9.5 cm
Colour:	White, blue and green
Issued:	1885

Description	U.S. $	Can. $	U.K. £
Harp/violoncello	3,000.00	4,750.00	2,000.00

Photograph not
available
at press time

Italian Music

Model No.:	X946
Designer:	George Tinworth
Height:	Unknown
Colour:	Unknown
Issued:	Unknown

Description	U.S. $	Can. $	U.K. £
Italian music		Extremely Rare	

Mouse Musician Tobacco Jar

Model No.:	Unknown
Designer:	George Tinworth
Height:	6 ½", 16.5 cm
Colour:	White and brown
Issued:	c.1885

Description	U.S. $	Can. $	U.K. £
Tobacco Jar	2,750.00	4,000.00	1,750.00

Niggers

Model No.:	Unknown
Designer:	George Tinworth
Height:	3 ¾", 9.5 cm
Colour:	Brown and blue
Issued:	c.1885

Description	U.S. $	Can. $	U.K. £
Niggers	3,750.00	6,000.00	2,500.00

Organ Grinder and Triangle

Model No.:	X945 - Menu holder
	X1209 - Vase
Designer:	George Tinworth
Height:	3 ¼", 8.3 cm
Colour:	Grey, blue and brown
Issued:	1885

Description	U.S. $	Can. $	U.K. £
1. Menu holder	2,500.00	3,750.00	1,650.00
2. Vase	2,500.00	3,750.00	1,650.00

Pianist, Horn Player and Singer

Model No.:	Unknown
Designer:	George Tinworth
Height:	3 ¼", 8.3 cm
Colour:	White, brown and green
Issued:	c.1884
Varieties:	Also called 'A Little Of It Is All Very Well'

Description	U.S. $	Can. $	U.K. £
Pianist/horn/singer	3,750.00	6,000.00	2,500.00

Photograph not
available
at press time

The Piano Player

Model No.:	Unknown
Designer:	George Tinworth
Height:	4", 10.1 cm
Colour:	Unknown
Issued:	c.1884

Description	U.S. $	Can. $	U.K. £
Piano player	3,000.00	4,750.00	2,000.00

Sousaphone

Model No.:	Unknown
Designer:	George Tinworth
Height:	3 ½", 8.9 cm
Colour:	White, blue and brown
Issued:	1884
Varieties:	Also called 'French Horn'

Description	U.S. $	Can. $	U.K. £
1. Round base	1,500.00	2,250.00	1,000.00
2. Square base	1,500.00	2,250.00	1,000.00

Tuba Player

Model No.:	Unknown
Designer:	George Tinworth
Height:	3 ½", 8.9 cm
Colour:	White, brown and blue
Issued:	1886

Description	U.S. $	Can. $	U.K. £
Round base	1,500.00	2,250.00	1,000.00

Tuba and Trumpet

Model No.:	X1214 - Menu holder
Designer:	George Tinworth
Height:	3 ¾", 9.5 cm
Colour:	1. White and brown
	2. Brown
Issued:	c.1884
Varieties:	Also called 'The Cornet Blowers'

Description	U.S. $	Can. $	U.K. £
1. White mice	3,000.00	4,750.00	2,000.00
2. Brown mice	3,000.00	4,750.00	2,000.00

Note: This model was also made in bone china.

Violin

Model No.:	Unknown
Designer:	George Tinworth
Height:	3 ½", 8.9 cm
Colour:	Brown and blue, white mouse
Issued:	c.1884

Description	U.S. $	Can. $	U.K. £
1. Round base	1,500.00	2,250.00	1,000.00
2. Square base	1,500.00	2,250.00	1,000.00

Mice — 32-piece chess set
16-red and white pieces plus
16-black and white pieces.
circa 1900.

GARDEN ORNAMENTS

Beast

Model No.:	Unknown
Designer:	Mark Marshall
Height:	16 ½", 42.0 cm
Colour:	Brown
Issued:	c.1900

Description	U.S. $	Can. $	U.K. £
Beast	750.00	1,200.00	500.00

Cat

Model No.:	R21
Designer:	Unknown
Height:	16", 40.6 cm
Colour:	Terracotta
Issued:	c.1930

Description	U.S. $	Can. $	U.K. £
Cat	1,200.00	1,800.00	750.00

Drake

Model No.:	Unknown
Designer:	Richard Garbe
Height:	7", 17.8 cm
Length:	10 ½", 26.7 cm
Colour:	Green or white glaze
Issued:	c.1935

Colourways	U.S. $	Can. $	U.K. £
1. Green	1,500.00	2,250.00	1,000.00
2. White	1,500.00	2,250.00	1,000.00

Duck

Model No.:	R24
Designer:	Unknown
Height:	15", 38.1 cm
Colour:	Terracotta
Issued:	c.1930

Description	U.S. $	Can. $	U.K. £
Duck	1,500.00	2,250.00	1,000.00

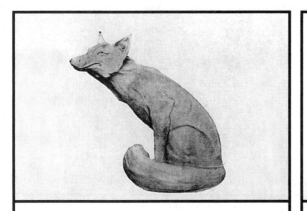

Fox

Model No.:	R16
Designer:	Harry Simeon
Height:	16", 40.6 cm
Colour:	Terracotta
Issued:	c.1930

Description	U.S. $	Can. $	U.K. £
Fox	1,200.00	1,800.00	750.00

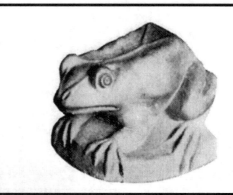

Frog

Model No.:	R37
Designer:	Unknown
Length:	8", 20.3 cm
Colour:	Terracotta
Issued:	c.1920

Description	U.S. $	Can. $	U.K. £
Frog	750.00	1,200.00	500.00

Goat

Model No.:	R20
Designer:	Francis Pope
Height:	21", 53.3 cm
Colour:	Terracotta
Issued:	c.1930

Description	U.S. $	Can. $	U.K. £
Goat	1,200.00	1,800.00	750.00

Hare

Model No.:	R25
Designer:	Unknown
Height:	11" x 24", 27.9 x 61.0 cm
Colour:	Terracotta
Issued:	c.1930

Description	U.S. $	Can. $	U.K. £
Hare	1,200.00	1,800.00	750.00

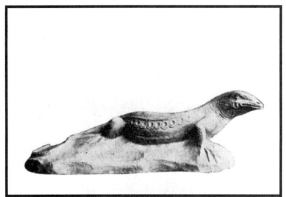

Lizard (Style One)

Model No.:	R31
Designer:	Unknown
Length:	16", 40.6 cm
Colour:	Terracotta
Issued:	c.1930

Description	U.S. $	Can. $	U.K. £
Lizard, style one	750.00	1,200.00	500.00

Lizard (Style Two)

Model No.:	Unknown
Designer:	Harry Simeon
Height:	Unknown
Colour:	Terracotta
Issued:	c.1930

Description	U.S. $	Can. $	U.K. £
Lizard, style two	750.00	1,200.00	500.00

Owl (Style One)

Model No.:	R29
Designer:	Unknown
Height:	14", 35.6 cm
Colour:	Terracotta
Issued:	c.1930

Description	U.S. $	Can. $	U.K. £
Owl, style one	1,350.00	2,000.00	850.00

Owl (Style Two)

Model No.:	Unknown
Designer:	Francis Pope
Height:	17 ½", 44.5 cm
Colour:	Terracotta
Issued:	c.1930

Description	U.S. $	Can. $	U.K. £
Owl, style two	1,350.00	2,000.00	850.00

Pelican

Model No.:	R19
Designer:	Mark Marshall
Height:	14", 35.6 cm
Colour:	1. Brown
	2. Terracotta
Issued:	c.1930

Colourways	U.S. $	Can. $	U.K. £
1. Brown stoneware	750.00	1,200.00	500.00
2. Terracotta	750.00	1,200.00	500.00

Penguin

Model No.:	R23
Designer:	Unknown
Height:	17", 43.1 cm
Colour:	Terracotta
Issued:	c.1930

Description	U.S. $	Can. $	U.K. £
Penguin	1,350.00	2,000.00	850.00

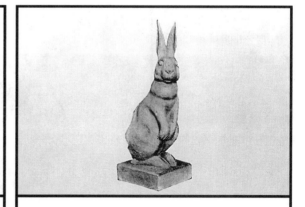

Rabbit

Model No.:	R17
Designer:	Harry Simeon
Height:	18", 45.8 cm
Colour:	Terracotta
Issued:	c.1930

Description	U.S. $	Can. $	U.K. £
Rabbit	1,350.00	2,000.00	850.00

Rabbit and Young

Model No.:	R22
Designer:	Harry Simeon
Height:	7 ½" x 14", 19.0 x 35.6 cm
Colour:	Terracotta
Issued:	c.1930

Description	U.S. $	Can. $	U.K. £
Rabbit and young	750.00	1,200.00	500.00

Sealion Statue

Model No.:	Unknown
Designer:	Richard Garbe
Height:	Unknown
Colour:	Dark brown
Issued:	c.1935

Description	U.S. $	Can. $	U.K. £
Sealion statue	1,500.00	2,250.00	1,000.00

Squirrel

Model No.:	R36
Designer:	Harry Simeon
Height:	13", 33.0 cm
Colour:	Terracotta
Issued:	c.1930

Description	U.S. $	Can. $	U.K. £
Squirrel	1,350.00	2,000.00	850.00

PRACTICAL ANIMALS

Baboon Cruet Set

Model No.: Unknown
Designer: Harry Simeon
Height: Unknown
Colour: Siliconware, silver rim
Issued: c.1900

Description	U.S. $	Can. $	U.K. £
Mustard	600.00	900.00	400.00
Pepper	525.00	800.00	350.00
Open salt	600.00	900.00	400.00
Complete Set	1,800.00	2,750.00	1,200.00

Note: Open salt illustrated.

Bears Cruet Set

Model No.: Unknown
Designer: Harry Simeon
Height: 3", 7.6 cm
Colour: Brown Siliconware, silver rim
Issued: c.1900

Description	U.S. $	Can. $	U.K. £
Mustard	450.00	675.00	300.00
Pepper	450.00	675.00	300.00
Open salt	450.00	675.00	300.00
Complete Set	1,350.00	2,000.00	900.00

Bear with Honey Pot

Model No.: Unknown
Designer: Unknown
Height: 4 ¼", 10.8 cm
Colour: Brown and beige
Issued: c.1910

Description	U.S. $	Can. $	U.K. £
Bear/honey pot	450.00	675.00	300.00

Cat Collecting Box for RSPCA

Model No.: Unknown
Designer: Unknown
Height: 8 ½", 21.6 cm
Colour: Light blue and dark blue
Issued: c.1900

Description	U.S. $	Can. $	U.K. £
Cat box	1,200.00	1,800.00	750.00

Dog Collecting Box for RSPCA

Model No.:	Unknown
Designer:	Unknown
Height:	7 ½", 19.1 cm
Colour:	Blue; brown or white dog
Issued:	c.1900

Description	U.S. $	Can. $	U.K. £
1. White	1,200.00	1,800.00	750.00
2. Brown	1,200.00	1,800.00	750.00

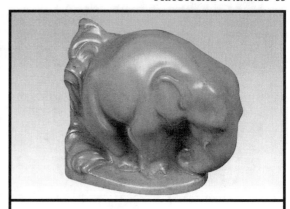

Elephant Bookends (Pair)

Model No.:	Unknown
Designer:	Gilbert Bayes
Height:	6 ¼", 13.5 cm
Colour:	Green glaze
Issued:	c.1935

Description	U.S. $	Can. $	U.K. £
Bookends (pair)	1,250.00	2,000.00	850.00

Photograph not
available
at press time

Frog Flowerstand

Model No.:	X8716
Designer:	Unknown
Height:	Unknown
Colour:	Unknown
Issued:	1933

Description	U.S. $	Can. $	U.K. £
Frog flowerstand		Extremely Rare	

Frog with Open Mouth

Model No.:	X8901
Designer:	Vera Huggins
Height:	3 ¾", 9.5 cm
Colour:	Blue
Issued:	1933

Description	U.S. $	Can. $	U.K. £
Frog with open mouth		Rare	

Marmoset Cruet Set

Model No.:	Unknown
Designer:	Unknown
Height:	2 ¾", 7.0 cm
Colour:	Siliconware
Issued:	c.1900

Description	U.S. $	Can. $	U.K. £
Mustard	525.00	800.00	350.00
Pepper	525.00	800.00	350.00
Open salt	525.00	800.00	350.00
Complete Set	1,500.00	2,250.00	1,000.00

Note: Mustard pot illustrated.

Owls (pair) Bookend

Model No.:	X8767
Designer:	Vera Huggins
Height:	6", 15.0 cm
Colour:	Brown, beige and green
Issued:	c.1925

Description	U.S. $	Can. $	U.K. £
Bookend		Rare	

Note: An example in a crystalline brown glaze sold at Phillips, London, May 2000 for £230.

Owl Matchholder

Model No.:	Unknown
Designer:	Unknown
Height:	3 ¼", 8.3 cm
Colour:	Black Siliconware with silver beak
Issued:	c.1895

Description	U.S. $	Can. $	U.K. £
Matchholder	750.00	1,200.00	500.00

Note: Other sizes are known.

Owl Sugar Dredger

Model No.:	X8692
Designer:	Unknown
Height:	4 ¾", 12.1 cm
Colour:	Blue
Issued:	c.1910

Description	U.S. $	Can. $	U.K. £
Sugar dredger	600.00	900.00	400.00

Owl Tobacco Jar

Model No.:   Unknown
Designer: Possibly John Broad
Height: 7 ½", 19.1 cm
Colour: 1. Brown and blue Siliconware
              2. Coloured Doultonware
Issued: c.1910

Colourways	U.S. $	Can. $	U.K. £
1. Brown/blue	1,500.00	2,250.00	1,000.00
2. Coloured	1,500.00	2,250.00	1,000.00

Polar Bear Sitting

Model No.:   Unknown
Designer: Leslie Harradine
Height: 6 ¾", 17.2 cm
Colour: White Carraraware
Issued: c.1910

Description	U.S. $	Can. $	U.K. £
Polar bear	400.00	600.00	250.00

Note: This model was used to promote Doulton's
Carraraware, a white glazed building material.

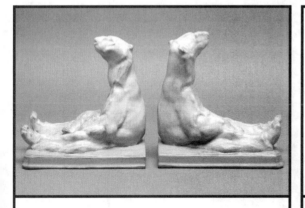

Photograph not
available
at press time

Polar Bear Bookends

Model No.:   Unknown
Designer: F. G. R. Roth
Height: 8 ¾" x 8 ¼", 22.2 x 21.0 cm
Colour: White, light brown shading,
              green base
Issued: c.1930

Description	U.S. $	Can. $	U.K. £
Bookends (Pair)	3,000.00	4,500.00	2,000.00

Polar Bears on Bowl

Model No.:   Unknown
Designer: Vera Huggins
Height: 5", 12.7 cm
Colour: Cream stoneware
Issued: c.1930

Description	U.S. $	Can. $	U.K. £
Polar bears on bowl		Rare	

Brown and blue Siliconeware Owl Tobacco Jar
c.1910

MISCELLANEOUS

Cat

Designer:	Unknown
Height:	6 ½", 16.5 cm
Colour:	White Carraraware
Issued:	c.1910

Description	U.S. $	Can. $	U.K. £
Cat	525.00	800.00	350.00

Note: This model was made to promote Doulton's Carraraware, a white glazed building material.

Cat

Designer:	Agnete Hoy
Height:	10 ½", 26.7 cm
Colour:	See below
Issued:	1955

Colourways	U.S. $	Can. $	U.K. £
1. Black/blue	7,000.00	10,000.00	4,500.00
2. Black/white	7,000.00	10,000.00	4,500.00
3. Blue stripes	7,000.00	10,000.00	4,500.00
4. Brown stripes	7,000.00	10,000.00	4,500.00

Note: It is believed only 12 of these models, each in a different colurways were made.

Rabbit

Model No.:	Unknown
Designer:	Unknown
Height:	2 ¾", 7.0 cm
Colour:	1. Green
	2. Light brown
Issued:	c.1922

Colourways	U.S. $	Can. $	U.K. £
1. Green	300.00	400.00	150.00
2. Light brown	300.00	400.00	150.00

Squirrel

Model No.:	X8802
Designer:	Unknown
Height:	6 ½", 16.5 cm
Colour:	1. Brown
	2. Green
Issued:	c.1930

Colourways	U.S. $	Can. $	U.K. £
1. Brown	750.00	1,200.00	500.00
2. Green	750.00	1,200.00	500.00

HN SERIES

H.N. 197. H.N. 163. H.N. 133. H.N. 205. H.N. 158.

H.N. 116. 12. H.N. 147. H.N. 125. H.N. 176. H.N. 151.

H.N. 117. 231. H.N. 168. 61. H.N. 802.

H.N. 181. H.N. 27. H.N. 128. H.N. 134. H.N. 132.

H.N. 276. H.N. 161. H.N. 118. H.N. 280. H.N. 137. H.N. 145.

ROYAL DOULTON BIRDS AND ANIMALS.

HN 7
Pedlar Wolf

Model No.:	76
Designer:	Charles Noke
Height:	5 ½", 14.0 cm
Colour:	See below
Issued:	1. 1913-1938
	2. c.1913-1938

Description	U.S. $	Can. $	U.K. £
1. Black wolf/blue cloak		Extremely Rare	
2. Flambé		Extremely Rare	

HN 100
Fox In Hunting Dress

Model No.:	151
Designer:	Charles Noke
Height:	6", 15.2 cm
Colour:	Brown fox wearing hunting pink riding coat, white shirt and cravat, gold stud
Issued:	1913-1942

Description	U.S. $	Can. $	U.K. £
Fox in hunting dress	1,250.00	1,875.00	750.00

Note: Also known with a green jacket.

HN 101
Rabbit In Morning Dress

Model No.:	152
Designer:	Charles Noke
Height:	6 ½", 16.5 cm
Colour:	Red coat, white trousers, black and white checkered cravat
Issued:	1913-by 1938
Varieties:	Also called "Hare In White Coat" HN 102

Description	U.S. $	Can. $	U.K. £
Rabbit in morning dress		Extremely Rare	

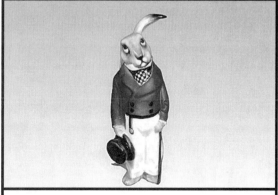

HN 102
Hare In White Coat

Model No.:	152
Designer:	Charles Noke
Height:	6 ½", 16.5 cm
Colour:	White coat
Issued:	1913-by 1938
Varieties:	Also called "Rabbit In Morning Dress" HN 101

Description	U.S. $	Can. $	U.K. £
Hare in white coat		Extremely Rare	

HN 103
Penguins

Model No.:	103
Height:	6", 15.2 cm
Colour:	See below
Issued:	1913-by 1946
Varieties:	HN 133

Colourways	U.S. $	Can. $	U.K. £
1. Grey/white/black	675.00	1,000.00	450.00
2. Flambé	1,000.00	1,500.00	650.00
3. Blue	1,200.00	1,800.00	800.00

HN 104
Penguin
Style One

Model No.:	85
Height:	4 ½", 11.4 cm
Colour:	See below
Issued:	1913-by 1946
Varieties:	HN 134

Colourways	U.S. $	Can. $	U.K. £
1. Black/white (earthenware)	300.00	450.00	200.00
2. Flambé	525.00	775.00	350.00

HN 105
Collie, Seated - brown

Model No.:	47
Height:	7 ½", 19.1 cm
Colour:	See below
Issued:	1. 1912-by 1946; 2. and 3. c.1912
Varieties:	HN 106, 112

Colourways	U.S. $	Can. $	U.K. £
1. Brown/black/white	450.00	675.00	300.00
2. Black (gloss)	1,000.00	1,500.00	500.00
3. Red (matt)	1,000.00	1,500.00	500.00
4. Flambé	1,000.00	1,500.00	750.00
5. Sung	1,500.00	2,250.00	1,000.00

HN 106
Collie, Seated - blue (earthenware)

Model No.:	47
Height:	7 ½", 19.1 cm
Colour:	See below
Issued:	1. 1912-by 1946; 2. and 3. c.1912
Varieties:	HN 105, 112

Colourways	U.S. $	Can. $	U.K. £
1. Blue-grey (earthenware)	450.00	675.00	300.00
2. Black (gloss)	1,000.00	1,500.00	500.00
3. Red (matt)	1,000.00	1,500.00	500.00
4. Flambé	1,000.00	1,500.00	750.00
5. Sung	1,500.00	2,250.00	1,000.00

HN 107
Hare
Crouching - Style One

Model No.:	119		
Height:	2" x 4 ½", 5.1 x 11.4 cm		
Colour:	See below		
Issued:	1913-by 1946		
Varieties:	HN 126, 142, 273, 803		

Colourways	U.S. $	Can. $	U.K. £
1. Brown (earthenware)	375.00	550.00	250.00
2. Flambé	375.00	550.00	250.00
3. Sung	900.00	1,350.00	600.00

HN 108
Lop-eared Rabbit

Model No.:	113	
Height:	4", 10.1 cm	
Colour:	See below	
Issued:	1. 1913-by 1946	
	2. Unknown	
Varieties:	HN 151, 276	

Colourways	U.S. $	Can. $	U.K. £
1. White	750.00	1,100.00	500.00
2. Flambé (illustrated)		Rare	

HN 109
Cat
Seated - Style One

Model No.:	9	
Designer:	Charles Noke	
Height:	4 ½", 11.4 cm	
Colour:	See below	
Issued:	1. 1912-by 1946 2. 1920-1996	
Varieties:	HN 120, 967	

Colourways	U.S. $	Can. $	U.K. £
1. White/black (earthenware)	750.00	1,100.00	500.00
2. Flambé	175.00	250.00	100.00
3. Sung		Extremely Rare	

HN 110
Titanian Bowl Decorated with a Butterfly

Model No.:	Unknown
Height:	3", 7.6 cm
Colour:	Lid of bowl decorated in turquoise with brown and orange butterfly (china)
Issued:	1912

Description	U.S. $	Can. $	U.K. £
Titanian bowl		Extremely Rare	

HN 111
Cockerel
Crowing

Model No.:	25
Height:	3 ¼", 8.3 cm
Colour:	See below
Issued:	1. 1912-1936
	2. c.1912-1936

Colourways	U.S. $	Can. $	U.K. £
1. White/black/red	375.00	550.00	250.00
2. Flambé		Rare	

HN 112
Collie, Seated - Blue (china)

Model No.:	47
Height:	7 ½", 19.1 cm
Colour:	See below
Issued:	1. 1912-by 1946; 2. and 3. c.1912
Varieties:	HN 105, 106

Colourways	U.S. $	Can. $	U.K. £
1. Blue-grey (china)	600.00	900.00	400.00
2. Black (gloss)	1,000.00	1,500.00	500.00
3. Red (matt)	1,000.00	1,500.00	500.00
4. Flambé	1,000.00	1,700.00	750.00
5. Sung	1,500.00	2,250.00	1,000.00

HN 113
Emperor Penguin

Model No.:	84
Designer:	Unknown
Height:	6", 15.2 cm
Colour:	See below
Issued:	1. 1913-by 1946
	2. 1913-1996
Varieties:	HN 296

Colourways	U.S. $	Can. $	U.K. £
1. Black/white/grey	900.00	1,350.00	600.00
2. Flambé (illustrated)	200.00	300.00	125.00

HN 114
Mallard Drake
Standing - Malachite head

Model No.:	137
Height:	5 ½", 14.0 cm
Size:	Medium
Colour:	See below
Issued:	1. 1913-by 1946
	2. 1913-1996
Varieties:	HN 115, 116, 956, 1191, 2555, 2647

Colourways	U.S. $	Can. $	U.K. £
1. Malachite/green/white	400.00	600.00	250.00
2. Flambé	200.00	300.00	125.00

HN 115
Mallard Drake
Standing - Blue head

Model No.:	137
Height:	5 ½", 14.0 cm
Size:	Medium
Colour:	See below
Issued:	1. 1913-by 1946
	2. 1913-1996
Varieties:	HN 114, 116, 956, 1191, 2555, 2647

Colourways	U.S. $	Can. $	U.K. £
1. Blue/green/white	400.00	600.00	250.00
2. Flambé	200.00	300.00	125.00

HN 116
Mallard Duck
Standing - Green head

Model No.:	137
Height:	5 ½", 14.0 cm
Size:	Medium
Colour:	See below
Issued:	1. 1913-by 1946
	2. 1913-1996
Varieties:	HN 114, 115, 956, 1191, 2555, 2647

Colourways	U.S. $	Can. $	U.K. £
1. Green/white	400.00	600.00	250.00
2. Flambé	200.00	300.00	125.00

HN 117
Foxes, Curled - Style One

Model No.:	6
Height:	3 ½", 8.9 cm
Colour:	See below
Issued:	1. 1912-by 1946
	2, 3, and 4. c.1912
Varieties:	HN 179

Colourways	U.S. $	Can. $	U.K. £
1. Grey/light brown	1,200.00	1,800.00	750.00
2. Flambé	750.00	1,100.00	500.00
3. Holbien	450.00	700.00	300.00
4. Sung	1,275.00	2,000.00	850.00

HN 118
Monkey
Seated, arms folded

Model No.:	53
Height:	3", 7.6 cm
Colour:	See below
Issued:	1912-by 1946
Varieties:	HN 253
Derivative:	On alabaster base

Colourways	U.S. $	Can. $	U.K. £
1. Grey (china)	450.00	700.00	300.00
2. Flambé	525.00	800.00	350.00
3. Titanian		Rare	

HN 119
Polar Bear on Cube

Model No.:	67
Designer:	Leslie Harradine
Height:	4", 10.1 cm
Colour:	See below
Issued:	1. 1912-1936
	2. c.1936

Colourways	U.S. $	Can. $	U.K. £
1. Grey/yellow/green	450.00	675.00	300.00
2. Flambé	1,200.00	1,800.00	800.00

HN 120
Cat, Seated - Style One

Model No.:	9
Designer:	Charles Noke
Height:	4 ½", 11.4 cm
Colour:	See below
Issued:	1. 1912-by 1946
	2. and 3. 1920-1996
Varieties:	HN 109, 967

Colourways	U.S. $	Can. $	U.K. £
1. White/black (china)	1,000.00	1,500.00	650.00
2. Flambé	175.00	250.00	100.00
3. Sung		Extremely Rare	

HN 121
Polar Bear, Seated

Model No.:	39
Height:	3 ¾", 9.5 cm
Colour:	See below
Issued:	1. 1912-1936
	2. 3 and 4. c.1912-1936
Derivative:	Polar bear on dish, Model 40 (flambé)

Colourways	U.S. $	Can. $	U.K. £
1. White (china)	750.00	1,100.00	500.00
2. Flambé	950.00	1,425.00	650.00
3. Sung	1,400.00	1,750.00	950.00
4. Titanian	1,125.00	1,650.00	750.00

HN 122
Fantail Pigeons

Model No.:	46
Height:	4", 10.1 cm
Colour:	See below
Issued:	1. 1912-1936
	2. c.1912-by 1946

Colourways	U.S. $	Can. $	U.K. £
1. Grey-blue/black	400.00	600.00	275.00
2. Flambé	1,000.00	1,500.00	675.00

HN 123
Pelican
Beak Up

Model No.:	109
Height:	4", 10.1 cm
Colour:	See below
Issued:	1. 1913-1936
	2. c.1913-1936

Colourways	U.S. $	Can. $	U.K. £
1. White/black/orange	750.00	1,100.00	500.00
2. Flambé	850.00	1,250.00	750.00
3. Kingsware	750.00	1,100.00	500.00

HN 124
Cockerel, Crouching - cream

Model No.:	30
Height:	3 ¼", 8.3 cm
Colour:	See below
Issued:	1. 1912-1936
	2. c.1912
Varieties:	HN 178, 180, 267
Derivative:	Cockerel bowl with hollow centre and sterling silver rim (flambé)

Colourways	U.S. $	Can. $	U.K. £
1. Cream/black/red	250.00	375.00	175.00
2. Flambé	450.00	675.00	300.00

HN 125
Guinea Fowl

Model No.:	69
Height:	3 ¼" x 5 ¼", 8.3 x13.3 cm
Colour:	See below
Issued:	1. 1912-by 1946
	2. 1912-1967

Colourways	U.S. $	Can. $	U.K. £
1. Grey-pink/red-brown	450.00	675.00	300.00
2. Flambé	525.00	775.00	350.00

HN 126
Hare
Crouching - Style One

Model No.:	119
Height:	2" x 4 ½", 5.1 x 11.4 cm
Colour:	See below
Issued:	1913-by 1946
Varieties:	HN 107, 142, 273, 803

Colourways	U.S. $	Can. $	U.K. £
1. Brown (china)	450.00	675.00	300.00
2. Flambé	375.00	550.00	250.00
3. Sung	900.00	1,350.00	600.00

HN 127
Cavalier King Charles Spaniel
Style One

Model No.:	82
Designer:	Charles Noke
Height:	3 ½", 8.9 cm
Colour:	See below
Issued:	1. 1912-1936
	2. and 3. 1920-1936

Colourways	U.S. $	Can. $	U.K. £
1. Natural colours	700.00	1,100.00	475.00
2. Chinese Jade	1,900.00	2,850.00	1,250.00
3. Flambé	750.00	1,100.00	500.00

HN 128
Puppy
Seated

Model No.:	116
Height:	4", 10.1 cm
Colour:	See below
Issued:	1. 1913-by 1946
	2 and 3. c.1913
Derivative:	Flambé puppy on onyx pin tray

Colourways	U.S. $	Can. $	U.K. £
1. Natural colours (china)	675.00	1,000.00	450.00
2. Flambé	675.00	1,000.00	450.00
3. Sung	1,275.00	1,900.00	850.00

HN 129
Bulldog, Seated - Style Four

Model No.:	1.	Natural 135
	2.	Flambé 135A
Height:	6", 15.2 cm	
Colour:	See below	
Issued:	1.	1913-by 1946
	2.	c.1913
Varieties:	HN 948	

Colourways	U.S. $	Can. $	U.K. £
1. White/black	4,500.00	6,750.00	3,000.00
2. Flambé	2,500.00	3,750.00	1,750.00
3. Sung	3,750.00	5,500.00	2,500.00

HN 130
Fox, Seated - Style Three

Model No.:	102	
Designer:	Charles Noke	
Height:	1.	8 ½", 21.6 cm
	2.	9 ¼", 23.5 cm
Size:	Large	
Colour:	See below	
Issued:	1.	1913-by 1946
	2.	1913-1962

Colourways	U.S. $	Can. $	U.K. £
1. Brown	975.00	1,500.00	650.00
2. Flambé	750.00	1,100.00	500.00

HN 131
Kingfisher on Rock
Style One

Model No.:	44
Height:	4″, 10.1 cm
Colour:	See below
Issued:	1. 1913-1936
	2. c.1913-by 1946
Varieties:	HN 152

Colourways	U.S. $	Can. $	U.K. £
1. Malachite/blue/green	150.00	225.00	100.00
2. Flambe	450.00	675.00	300.00

HN 132
Drake on Rock

Model No.:	138
Height:	3 ½″, 8.9 cm
Colour:	See below
Issued:	1. 1913-1936
	2. c.1913-1936
Derivative:	Chinese Jade pin tray

Colourways	U.S. $	Can. $	U.K. £
1. Turquoise/white/ brown/pearl rock	200.00	300.00	125.00
2. Flambé	550.00	825.00	350.00

Note: Also known with a brown rock.

HN 133
Penguins

Model No.:	103
Height:	6″, 15.2 cm
Colour:	See below
Issued:	1913-by 1946
Varieties:	HN 103

Colourways	U.S. $	Can. $	U.K. £
1. Black/white/brown	675.00	1,000.00	450.00
2. Blue	1,200.00	1,800.00	800.00
3. Flambé	1,000.00	1,500.00	650.00

HN 134
Penguin
Style One

Model No.:	85
Designer:	Unknown
Height:	4 ½″, 11.4 cm
Colour:	See below
Issued:	1913-by 1946
Varieties:	HN 104

Colourways	U.S. $	Can. $	U.K. £
1. Black/white (china)	300.00	450.00	200.00
2. Flambé	525.00	775.00	350.00

HN 135
Raven

Model No.:	43
Height:	3" x 5 ¼", 7.6 x 13.3 cm
Colour:	See below
Issued:	1. 1913-1936
	2. c.1912

Colourways	U.S. $	Can. $	U.K. £
1. Blue/green/purple		Extremely Rare	
2. Flambé (illustrated)	1,100.00	1,650.00	700.00

HN 136
Swallow on Rock

Model No.:	196
Height:	4 ½", 11.4 cm
Colour:	Blue feathers, brown head, red, grey and white breast, beige rock
Issued:	1917-1936
Varieties:	HN 149; Also called 'Blue Bird on Rock' HN 269

Description	U.S. $	Can. $	U.K. £
Blue swallow	275.00	400.00	175.00

HN 137A
Fledgling
Style Four

Model No.:	99
Height:	2", 5.1 cm
Colour:	See below
Issued:	1. and 2. 1917-1936
	3. c.1912-by 1946

Colourways	U.S. $	Can. $	U.K. £
1. Blue/black	135.00	200.00	90.00
2. Yellow/black	135.00	200.00	90.00
3. Flambé	300.00	450.00	200.00

HN 137B
Fledgling
Style Two

Model No.:	1238
Height:	Natural 1 ¼", 3.2 cm
	Flambé 2", 5.1 cm
Colour:	See below
Issued:	1. and 2. 1917-1936
	3. c.1908

Colourways	U.S. $	Can. $	U.K. £
1. Blue/black	135.00	200.00	90.00
2. Yellow/black	135.00	200.00	90.00
3. Flambé	300.00	450.00	200.00

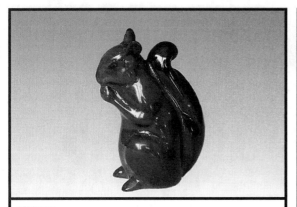

HN 138
Squirrel

Model No.:	115
Height:	2 ¼", 5.7 cm
Colour:	See below
Issued:	1. 1917-by 1946
	2. c.1912-by 1946
Varieties:	HN 1093A on fluted ashtray
	HN 1093B on plain ashtray

Colourways	U.S. $	Can. $	U.K. £
1. Brown	375.00	550.00	250.00
2. Flambé	1,150.00	1,750.00	750.00

HN 139
Eagle on Rock

Model No.:	145
Height:	9", 22.9 cm
Colour:	See below
Issued:	1. 1917-1936
	2. c.1913-1936

Colourways	U.S. $	Can. $	U.K. £
1. Brown/orange/yellow/ blue	Extremely Rare		
2. Pale brown (illustrated)	975.00	1,450.00	600.00
3. Titanian	975.00	1,450.00	600.00

HN 140
Ape

Model No.:	147
Height:	6", 15.2 cm
Colour:	Brown with orange highlights
Issued:	1917-1936

Description	U.S. $	Can. $	U.K. £
Ape	1,150.00	1,750.00	750.00

HN 141
Rhinoceros
Standing

Model No.:	107
Height:	3" x 6 ½", 7.6 x 16.5 cm
Colour:	See below
Issued:	1. 1917-by 1946
	2. c.1912

Colourways	U.S. $	Can. $	U.K. £
1. Grey/black/white	1,500.00	2,250.00	1,000.00
2. Flambé	1,150.00	1,750.00	750.00

HN 142
Hare, Crouching - Style One
Model No.: 119
Height: 2", 5.1 cm
Colour: See below
Issued: 1. 1917-by 1946
 2. and 3. 1913-by 1946
Varieties: HN 107, 126, 273, 803

Colourways	U.S. $	Can. $	U.K. £
1. Brown (china)	450.00	675.00	300.00
2. Flambé	375.00	550.00	250.00
3. Sung	900.00	1,350.00	600.00

HN 143
Fledgling
Style Three
Model No.: 98
Height: 2", 5.1 cm
Colour: See below
Issued: 1. and 2. 1917-by 1946
 3. c.1912

Colourways	U.S. $	Can. $	U.K. £
1. Blue/yellow	135.00	200.00	90.00
2. Yellow	135.00	200.00	90.00
3. Flambé	300.00	450.00	200.00

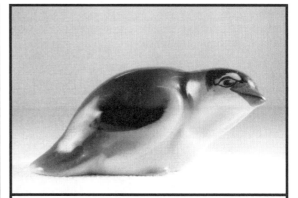

HN 144
Robin , Style One
Model No.: 104
Height: 2", 5.1 cm
Colour: See below
Issued: 1. 1917-by 1946
 2. c.1913-by 1946
Varieties: Also called 'Wren' Style One, HN 277;
 HN 1089A on fluted ashtray,
 HN 1089B on plain ashtray

Colourways	U.S. $	Can. $	U.K. £
1. Dark brown/red	225.00	300.00	150.00
2. Flambé	450.00	675.00	300.00

HN 145A
Fledgling
Style One
Model No.: 1236
Height: Natural 1 ½", 3.8 cm
 Flambé 2 ½", 5.1 cm
Colour: See below
Issued: 1. and 2. 1917-1936
 3. c.1908-by 1946

Colourways	U..S. $	Can. $	U.K. £
1. Blue/yellow/black	135.00	200.00	90.00
2. Yellow/black	135.00	200.00	90.00
3. Flambé	300.00	450.00	200.00

HN 145B
Fledgling on Rock
Style One

Model No.:	139
Height:	3 ¾", 9.5 cm
Colour:	1. Dark blue feathers, yellow breast, dark blue rock
	2. Green-turquoise feathers, yellow breast, beige rock
	3. White feathers, cream rock, overall pearl glaze
	4. Yellow feathers, black wing tips, yellow rock
	5. Flambé
Issued:	1. to 4. 1917-1936
	5. c.1913
Derivative:	Flambé on onyx base

Colourways	U.S. $	Can. $	U.K. £
1. Dark blue	200.00	300.00	125.00
2. Green-turquoise	200.00	300.00	125.00
3. White	200.00	300.00	125.00
4. Yellow	200.00	300.00	125.00
5. Flambé	550.00	825.00	350.00

HN 145C
Fledgling
Style Five

Model No.:	1237
Height:	2", 5.1 cm
Colour:	1. Blue and yellow, black wing tips
	2. Yellow, black wing tips
	3. Yellow, brown wing tips
Issued:	1917-by 1946

Colourways	U.S. $	Can. $	U.K. £
1. Blue/yellow	135.00	200.00	90.00
2. Yellow/black	135.00	200.00	90.00
3. Yellow/brown	135.00	200.00	90.00

HN 146
Bulldog with Helmet and Haversack (Old Bill)

Model No.:	Unknown
Height:	6 ½", 16.5 cm
Size:	Large
Colour:	See below
Issued:	1. 1918-c.1925
	2. Unknown

Colourways	U.S. $	Can. $	U.K. £
1. Brown/bronze helmet	750.00	1,100.00	500.00
2. Titanian	Sold at Auction for £3,500.00		

HN 147A
Fox, Stalking - large

Model No.:	29A
Height:	2 ½″ x 12 ½″, 6.4 x 31.7 cm
Size:	Large
Colour:	See below
Issued:	1. 1918-by 1946
	2. c.1912-1962

Colourways	U.S. $	Can. $	U.K. £
1. Light and dark brown	900.00	1,350.00	600.00
2. Flambé	600.00	900.00	400.00

HN 147A-1
Fox, Stalking - small

Model No.:	29B
Height:	1″ x 5 ¼″, 2.5 x 13.3 cm
Colour:	See below
Issued:	1. 1918-by 1946
	2. and 4. Unknown
	3. c.1912-1996

Colourways	U.S. $	Can. $	U.K. £
1. Natural colours	375.00	550.00	250.00
2. Chinese Jade	1,100.00	1,650.00	700.00
3. Flambé	125.00	175.00	75.00
4. Sung	450.00	675.00	300.00

HN 147B
Fox, Seated - Style Two - small

Model No.:	14
Height:	4 ½″, 12.1 cm
Colour:	See below
Issued:	1. 1918-by 1946
	2. 1912-1996
	3. c.1920

Colourways	U.S. $	Can. $	U.K. £
1. Brown/cream/black	225.00	300.00	150.00
2. Flambé	125.00	175.00	75.00
3. Sung	400.00	600.00	275.00

HN 147C
Fox, Seated - Style One - medium

Model No.:	12
Height:	4 ¾″, 12.1 cm
Colour:	See below
Issued:	1. 1918-by 1946
	2. and 3. c.1912-1946
Varieties:	Also decorated with transfer prints of grapes and vines

Colourways	U.S. $	Can. $	U.K. £
1. Brown/white/black	450.00	675.00	300.00
2. Flambé (illustrated)	450.00	675.00	300.00
3. Sung	750.00	1,100.00	500.00

HN 147C-1
Fox
Seated - Style One - small
Model No.: 12A
Height: 3", 7.6 cm
Colour: See below
Issued: 1. 1918-by 1946
2. 1912-1938
Derivative: Fox seated on sterling silver tray

Colourways	U.S. $	Can. $	U.K. £
1. Browns/black	450.00	675.00	300.00
2. Flambé	450.00	675.00	300.00

HN 147D
Fox
Curled - Style One
Model No.: 15
Height: 4 ¾", 12.1 cm
Colour: See below
Issued: 1. 1918-by 1946
2. and 3. c.1912

Colourways	U.S. $	Can. $	U.K. £
1. Brown/black	525.00	800.00	350.00
2. Flambé	450.00	675.00	300.00
3. Holbien	375.00	550.00	250.00

HN 147E
Fox
Stalking - medium
Model No.: 29
Height: 1 ½" x 8 ¼", 5.1 x 21.0 cm
Size: Medium
Colour: See below
Issued: 1. 1918-by 1946
2. c.1912-1962

Colourways	U.S. $	Can. $	U.K. £
1. Browns	600.00	900.00	400.00
2. Flambé	450.00	675.00	300.00

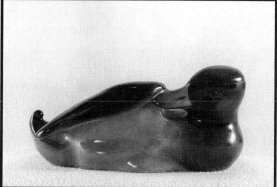

HN 148A
Duck
Preening - Style Two
Model No.: 4
Height: 1 ½" x 3 ½", 3.8 x 8.9 cm
Colour: See below
Issued: 1. 1913-1936
2. c.1912
Varieties: HN 271, 299

Colourways	U.S. $	Can. $	U.K. £
1. Blue/green/brown (china)	300.00	450.00	200.00
2. Flambé	400.00	600.00	250.00

HN 148B
Duck
Resting

Model No.:	112
Height:	2″, 5.1 cm
Size:	Small
Colour:	See below
Issued:	1. 1918-by 1946
	2. 1912-1996

Colourways	U.S. $	Can. $	U.K. £
1. Blue/green/brown	450.00	675.00	300.00
2. Flambé (illustrated)	100.00	150.00	65.00

HN 149
Swallow on Rock

Model No.:	196
Height:	4 ¾″, 12.1 cm
Colour:	Dark blue-black feathers, red markings on head, white breast, beige rock
Issued:	1918-by 1946
Varieties:	HN 136; Also called 'Blue Bird on Rock' HN 269

Description	U.S. $	Can. $	U.K. £
Dark blue swallow	275.00	400.00	175.00

HN 150
Duck
Head stretched forward

Model No.:	207
Height:	4″, 10.1 cm
Size:	Large
Colour:	See below
Issued:	1. 1918-by 1946
	2. c.1917
Varieties:	HN 229, 2556

Colourways	U.S. $	Can. $	U.K. £
1. Browns/cream/blue	375.00	550.00	250.00
2. Flambé	525.00	800.00	350.00

HN 151
Lop-eared Rabbit

Model No.:	113
Height:	4″, 10.1 cm
Colour:	See below
Issued:	1. 1918-by 1946
	2. Unknown
Varieties:	HN 108, 276

Colourways	U.S. $	Can. $	U.K. £
1. White/black patches	750.00	1,100.00	500.00
2. Flambé		Rare	

HN 152
Kingfisher on Rock
Style One

Model No.:	44	
Height:	4", 10.1 cm	
Colour:	See below	
Issued:	1. 1918-1936	
	2. c.1913-by 1946	
Varieties:	HN 131, Flambé	

Colourways	U.S. $	Can. $	U.K. £
1. Turquoise/yellow/beige	150.00	225.00	100.00
2. Flambé	450.00	675.00	300.00

HN 153
Bulldog With Tam O'Shanter and Haversack

Model No.:	Unknown	
Height:	7", 17.8 cm	
Colour:	See below	
Issued:	1. 1918-c.1925	
	2. Unknown	

Colourways	U.S. $	Can. $	U.K. £
1. Brown/bronze tam	1,150.00	1,700.00	750.00
2. Titanian		Extremely Rare	

HN 154
'Kateroo' Character Cat

Model No.:	214
Designer:	Charles Noke
Height:	12 ¾", 32.0 cm
Colour:	1. Black and white (china)
	2. Green
	3. Yellow
Issued:	1918-c.1925

Colourways	U.S. $	Can. $	U.K. £
1. Black and white		Extremely Rare	
2. Green		In all	
3. Yellow		Colourways	

HN 155
Owl
Style One

Model No.:	153
Designer:	Charles Noke
Height:	5", 12.7 cm
Colour:	Light and dark brown
Issued:	1918-by 1946

Description	U.S. $	Can. $	U.K. £
Owl		Very Rare	

HN 156
Monkey
Hand raised to ear

Model No.:	156
Height:	3 ½", 8.9 cm
Colour:	See below
Issued:	1. 1918-by 1946
	2. c.1912

Colourways	U.S. $	Can. $	U.K. £
1. Natural colours	675.00	1,000.00	450.00
2. Flambé	900.00	1,350.00	600.00

Note: A model is known in an experimental Sung-like glaze.

HN 157
Cockerel
Seated - Style One

Model No.:	50
Height:	Unknown
Colour:	Blue and purple
Issued:	1918-1936

Description	U.S. $	Can. $	U.K. £
Cockerel		Extremely Rare	

HN 158
Toucan on Perch - green

Model No.:	212
Height:	7 ½", 19.1 cm
Colour:	Green, blue and black plumage, orange and black beak, black perch
Issued:	1918-1936
Varieties:	HN 159, 196, 294

Colourways	U.S. $	Can. $	U.K. £
Green/blue/black	525.00	900.00	350.00

HN 159
Toucan on Perch - black

Model No.:	212
Height:	7 ½", 19.1 cm
Colour:	Black, green, yellow and orange
Issued:	1918-1936
Varieties:	HN 158, 196, 294

Colourways	U.S. $	Can. $	U.K. £
Black/green/yellow	525.00	900.00	350.00

HN 160
Owl With Owlet Under Wing

Model No.:	71
Designer:	Charles Noke
Height:	4 ¾", 12.1 cm
Colour:	See below
Issued:	1. 1918-1936
	2. c.1912-1936
Derivative:	Flambé, on onyx base

Colourways	U.S. $	Can. $	U.K. £
1. Browns		Extremely Rare	
2. Flambé (illustrated)		Extremely Rare	

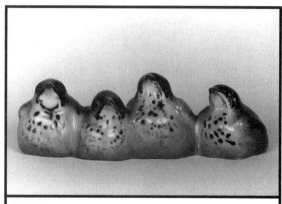

HN 161
Thrush Chicks (four)

Model No.:	208
Height:	2" x 5 ½", 5.1 x 14.0 cm
Colour:	See below
Issued:	1. 1918-by 1946
	2. c.1912
Varieties:	Also called 'Four Fledglings' HN 171

Colourways	U.S. $	Can. $	U.K. £
1. Yellow/black/brown	300.00	450.00	200.00
2. Flambé		Very Rare	

HN 162
Butterfly on Stump

Model No.:	141
Height:	3", 7.6 cm
Colour:	Light blue wings, dark blue markings, gold body, beige rock
Issued:	1918-1936

Description	U.S. $	Can. $	U.K. £
Blue butterfly	450.00	675.00	300.00

HN 163
Budgerigar on Tree Stump

Model No.:	221
Height:	7", 17.8 cm
Colour:	See below
Issued:	1. and 2. 1918-1936; 3. and 4. c.1918-1936
Varieties:	HN 199
Derivative:	Onyx pin tray

Colourways	U.S. $	Can. $	U.K. £
1. Green/yellow/black	375.00	550.00	250.00
2. White/green/pearl	375.00	550.00	250.00
3. Flambé	600.00	900.00	400.00
4. Sung	900.00	1,350.00	600.00

HN 164
Rooster
Style One

Model No.:	225
Height:	9", 22.9 cm
Colour:	Orange back, brown breast, red head
Issued:	1918-by 1946
Varieties:	HN 184

Description	U.S. $	Can. $	U.K. £
Orange rooster		Extremely Rare	

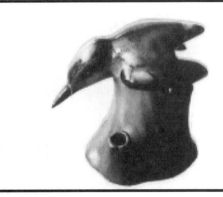

HN 165
Kingfisher on Tree Stump (flower holder)
Style One

Model No.:	227
Height:	3", 7.6 cm
Colour:	See below
Issued:	1. 1918-1936
	2. c.1918-1936
Varieties:	HN 858

Colourways	U.S. $	Can. $	U.K. £
1. Blue/turquoise/orange	525.00	800.00	350.00
2. Flambé	750.00	1,100.00	500.00

HN 166
Foxhound, Seated - Style One

Model No.:	209
Height:	1 4", 10.1 cm
	2. 3", 7.6 cm
Colour:	See below
Issued:	1. 1918-by 1946
	2. c.1917

Colourways	U.S. $	Can. $	U.K. £
1. White/brown	600.00	900.00	400.00
2. Flambé	900.00	1,350.00	600.00

Note: A Foxhound on a plinth is model 40A.

HN 167
Tern (female)

Model No.:	231
Height:	2 ½" x 8 ½", 6.4 x 21.6 cm
Colour:	See below
Issued:	1. 1918-by 1946
	2. c.1912
Varieties:	HN 1194; Also called 'Tern (male)'
	HN 168, 1193

Colourways	U.S. $	Can. $	U.K. £
1. Grey/white/red	300.00	450.00	200.00
2. Flambé	750.00	1,100.00	500.00

HN 168
Tern (male)

Model No.:	231
Height:	2 ½" x 8 ½", 6.4 x 21.6 cm
Colour:	See below
Issued:	1. 1918-by 1946
	2. c.1912
Varieties:	HN 1193; Also called 'Tern (female)'
	HN 167, 1194

Colourways	U.S. $	Can. $	U.K. £
1. Blue-grey/white/black	300.00	450.00	200.00
2. Flambé	750.00	1,100.00	500.00

HN 169
Barn Owl
Style One

Model No.:	148
Designer:	Harry Tittensor
Height:	3", 7.6 cm
Colour:	See below)
Issued:	1. 1918-by 1946
	2. c.1913

Colourways	U.S. $	Can. $	U.K. £
1. Cream/brown (china)	750.00	1,100.00	500.00
2. Flambé	975.00	1,500.00	650.00

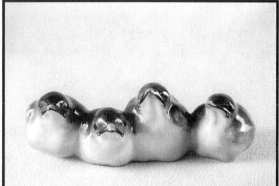

HN 170
Comic Brown Bear

Model No.:	58
Designer:	Charles Noke
Height:	5", 12.7 cm
Colour:	See below
Issued:	1. 1918-1936
	2. and 3. c.1918-1936
Varieties:	HN 270

Colourways	U.S. $	Can. $	U.K. £
1. Brown	600.00	900.00	400.00
2. Blue	750.00	1,100.00	500.00
3. Flambé	750.00	1,100.00	500.00

HN 171
Four Fledglings

Model No.:	208
Height:	2" x 5 ½", 5.1 x 14.0 cm
Colour:	See below
Issued:	1. 1918-by 1946
	2. c.1912
Varieties:	Also called 'Thrush Chicks (four)' HN 161

Colourways	U.S. $	Can. $	U.K. £
1. Browns/cream	300.00	450.00	200.00
2. Flambé		Very Rare	

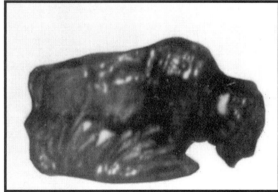

HN 172
Bison
Style One

Model No.:	136
Height:	5", 12.7 cm
Colour:	Light and dark brown
Issued:	1918-1936

Description	U.S. $	Can. $	U.K. £
Bison		Very Rare	

HN 173
Granny Owl

Model No.:	228
Designer:	Charles Noke
Height:	7 ½", 19.1 cm
Colour:	Red cloak and ermine collar
Issued:	1918-1936
Varieties:	HN 187; Also called 'Wise Old Owl'

Description	U.S. $	Can. $	U.K. £
Granny owl	3,000.00	4,500.00	2,000.00

*

HN 175
Great-Crested Grebe

Model No.:	233
Height:	12", 30.5 cm
Colour:	Green back and beak, pale breast
Issued:	1918-by 1946

Description	U.S. $	Can. $	U.K. £
Great-crested grebe		Extremely Rare	

HN 176
Bloodhound

Model No.:	48
Height:	5 ¾", 14.6 cm
Colour:	See below
Issued:	1. 1919-by 1946
	2. c.1926

Colourways	U.S. $	Can. $	U.K. £
1. Brown	900.00	1,350.00	600.00
2. Flambé	1,200.00	1,750.00	800.00

*

HN 178
Cockerel, Crouching - green

Model No.:	30
Height:	3 ¼", 8.3 cm
Colour:	Green
Issued:	1. 1919-1936; 2. c.1912
Varieties:	HN 124, 180, 267
Derivative:	Cockerel bowl with hollow centre and sterling silver rim (flambé)

Colourways	U.S. $	Can. $	U.K. £
1. Green	350.00	525.00	225.00
2. Flambé	450.00	675.00	300.00

HN 179
Foxes, Curled - Style One

Model No.:	6
Height:	4", 10.1 cm
Colour:	See below
Issued:	1. 1919-by 1946
	2. 3. and 4. c.1912
Varieties:	HN 117

Colourways	U.S. $	Can. $	U.K. £
1. Brown/orange	1,200.00	1,800.00	750.00
2. Flambé	750.00	1,100.00	500.00
3. Holbien	450.00	700.00	300.00
4. Sung	1,275.00	2,000.00	850.00

HN 180
Cockerel, Crouching - red

Model No.:	30
Height:	3 ¼", 8.3 cm
Colour:	See below
Issued:	1. 1919-1936 2. c.1912
Varieties:	HN 124, 178, 267
Derivative:	Cockerel bowl with hollow centre and sterling silver rim (flambé)

Colourways	U.S. $	Can. $	U.K. £
1. Red/orange	350.00	525.00	225.00
2. Flambé	450.00	675.00	300.00

HN 181
Elephant, Trunk down, curled

Model No.:	65
Designer:	Charles Noke
Height:	4", 10.1 cm (small)
Colour:	See below
Issued:	1. 1920-by 1946
	2. and 3. c.1913-by 1946
Varieties:	HN 186

Colourways	U.S. $	Can. $	U.K. £
1. Grey/black (china)	375.00	550.00	250.00
2. Flambé	525.00	800.00	350.00
3. Sung	750.00	1,100.00	500.00

HN 182
Character Monkey - green

Model No.:	213
Designer:	Charles Noke
Height:	7", 17.8 cm
Colour:	See below
Issued:	1. 1920-1936
	2. c.1920
Varieties:	HN 183

Colourways	U.S. $	Can. $	U.K. £
1. Green jacket/hat		Very Rare	
2. Flambé		Very Rare	

HN 183
Character Monkey - blue

Model No.:	213
Designer:	Charles Noke
Height:	7", 17.8 cm
Colour:	See below
Issued:	1. 1920-1936
	2. c.1920
Varieties:	HN 182

Colourways	U.S. $	Can. $	U.K. £
1. Blue jacket/hat		Very Rare	
2. Flambé		Very Rare	

HN 184
Rooster
Style One

Model No.:	225
Height:	9", 22.9 cm
Colour:	White and grey body, black tail feathers, red comb
Issued:	1920-by 1946
Varieties:	HN 164

Description	U.S. $	Can. $	U.K. £
White/grey rooster		Extremely Rare	

HN 185
Cockatoo on a Rock - yellow

Model No.:	68
Designer:	Leslie Harradine
Height:	6", 15.2 cm
Colour:	See below
Issued:	1. 1920-1936
	2. c.1912-1936
Varieties:	HN 191, 192, 200, 877
Derivative:	Onyx pin tray

Colourways	U.S. $	Can. $	U.K. £
1. Yellow/white	375.00	550.00	250.00
2. Flambé	750.00	1,100.00	500.00

HN 186
Elephant, Trunk down, curled

Model No.:	65
Designer:	Charles Noke
Height:	4", 10.1 cm (small)
Colour:	See below
Issued:	1. 1920-by 1946
	2. and 3. c.1913-by 1946
Varieties:	HN 181

Colourways	U.S. $	Can. $	U.K. £
1. Brown	375.00	550.00	250.00
2. Flambé	525.00	800.00	350.00
3. Sung	750.00	1,100.00	500.00

HN 187
Granny Owl

Model No.:	228
Designer:	Charles Noke
Height:	7 ½", 19.1 cm
Colour:	Blue-grey check shawl with white mob cap
Issued:	1920-by 1946
Varieties:	HN 173; Also called 'Wise Old Owl'

Description	U.S. $	Can. $	U.K. £
Granny owl	3,000.00	4,500.00	2,000.00

HN 188
Duckling
New born - yellow/brown

Model No.:	3
Height:	3", 7.6 cm
Colour:	See below
Issued:	1. 1920-1936
	2. c.1912
Varieties:	HN 189, 190

Colourways	U.S. $	Can. $	U.K. £
1. Yellow/brown		Rare	
2. Flambé		Rare	

HN 189
Duckling
New born - yellow/black

Model No.:	3
Height:	3", 7.6 cm
Colour:	See below
Issued:	1. 1920-1936
	2. c.1912
Varieties:	HN 188, 190

Colourways	U.S. $	Can. $	U.K. £
1. Black/yellow		Rare	
2. Flambé		Rare	

HN 190
Duckling
New born - green

Model No.:	3
Height:	3", 7.6 cm
Colour:	See below
Issued:	1. 1920-1936
	2. c.1912
Varieties:	HN 188, 189

Colourways	U.S. $	Can. $	U.K. £
1. Green/blue		Rare	
2. Flambé (illustrated)		Rare	

HN 191
Cockatoo on a Rock - blue

Model No.:	68
Designer:	Leslie Harradine
Height:	6", 15.2 cm
Colour:	See below
Issued:	1. 1920-1936
	2. c.1912-1936
Varieties:	HN 185, 192, 200, 877
Derivative:	Onyx pin tray

Colourways	U.S. $	Can. $	U.K. £
1. Blue/purple	375.00	550.00	250.00
2. Flambé	750.00	1,100.00	500.00

HN 192
Cockatoo on a Rock - red

Model No.:	68
Designer:	Leslie Harradine
Height:	6", 15.2 cm
Colour:	See below
Issued:	1. 1920-1936
	2. c.1912-1936
Varieties:	HN 185, 191, 200, 877
Derivative:	Onyx pin tray

Colourways	U.S. $	Can. $	U.K. £
1. Red/orange	375.00	550.00	250.00
2. Flambé	750.00	1,100.00	500.00

HN 193
Tortoise

Model No.:	101
Height:	2" x 4 ¾", 5.1 x 12.1 cm
Size:	Large
Colour:	See below
Issued:	1. 1920-by 1946
	2. c.1912

Colourways	U.S. $	Can. $	U.K. £
1. Grey/red head	375.00	550.00	250.00
2. Flambé	1,100.00	1,650.00	750.00
3. Sung	1,500.00	2,250.00	1,000.00

HN 194
Terrier Puppy
Lying

Model No.:	121
Height:	3″ x 7 ¾″, 7.6 x 19.7 cm
Colour:	See below
Issued:	1. 1920-by 1946
	2. c.1913

Colourways	U.S. $	Can. $	U.K. £
1. White/black	900.00	1,350.00	600.00
2. Flambé		Very Rare	

HN 195
Gannet

Model No.:	243
Height:	6 ½″, 16.5 cm
Colour:	See below
Issued:	1. 1920-by 1946
	2. c.1919
Varieties:	HN 1197

Colourways	U.S. $	Can. $	U.K. £
1. Blue-grey/white	675.00	1,000.00	450.00
2. Flambé		Very Rare	

HN 196
Toucan on Perch

Model No.:	212
Height:	7 ½″, 19.1 cm
Colour:	Blue and purple toucan on brown perch
Issued:	1920-1936
Varieties:	HN 158, 159, 294

Description	U.S. $	Can. $	U.K. £
Blue toucan	525.00	800.00	350.00

HN 197
Weaver Bird on Rock

Model No.:	251
Height:	5″ 12.7 cm
Colour:	Black with orange breast
Issued:	1920-by 1946
Varieties:	HN 220

Description	U.S. $	Can. $	U.K. £
Black/orange weaver bird	750.00	1,200.00	500.00

HN 198
King Penguin and Chick

Model No.:	239
Height:	5 ½", 14.0 cm
Colour:	See below
Issued:	1. 1920-by 1946
	2. c.1918-1961
Varieties:	HN 297, 998

Colourways	U.S. $	Can. $	U.K. £
1. Black/white	900.00	1,350.00	600.00
2. Flambé (illustrated)	825.00	1,250.00	550.00

HN 199
Budgerigar on Tree Stump

Model No.:	221
Height:	6 ¾", 17.2 cm
Colour:	See below
Issued:	1. 1920-1936
	2. and 3. c.1918-1936
Varieties:	HN 163
Derivative:	Onyx pin tray

Colourways	U.S. $	Can. $	U.K. £
1. Light blue/yellow	375.00	550.00	250.00
2. Flambé (illustrated)	600.00	900.00	400.00
3. Sung	900.00	1,350.00	600.00

HN 200
Cockatoo on a Rock

Model No.:	68
Designer:	Leslie Harradine
Height:	6", 15.2 cm
Colour:	See below
Issued:	1. 1920-1936
	2. c.1912-1936
Varieties:	HN 185, 191, 192, 877
Derivative:	Onyx pin tray

Colourways	U.S. $	Can. $	U.K. £
1. Blue/green	375.00	550.00	250.00
2. Flambé	750.00	1,100.00	500.00

HN 201
Cat with Mouse on Tail
Tabby

Model No.:	216
Height:	4 ¼", 10.8 cm
Colour:	See below
Issued:	1. 1920-by 1946
	2 and 3. c.1920
Varieties:	HN 202

Colourways	U.S. $	Can. $	U.K. £
1. Tabby	1,500.00	2,250.00	1,000.00
2. Flambé (illustrated)	1,100.00	1,650.00	750.00
3. Sung	1,500.00	2,250.00	1,000.00

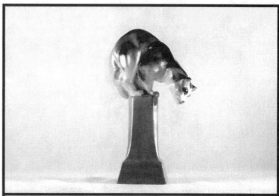

HN 202
Cat with Mouse on Tail
Black

Model No.:	216
Height:	4 ¼", 10.8 cm
Colour:	See below
Issued:	1. 1920-by 1946
	2 and 3. c.1920
Varieties:	HN 201

Colourways	U.S. $	Can. $	U.K. £
1. Black/white/grey	1,500.00	2,250.00	1,000.00
2. Flambé	1,100.00	1,650.00	750.00
3. Sung	1,500.00	2,250.00	1,000.00

HN 203
Cat on a Column/or Plinth

Model No.:	240
Height:	1. On column - 7", 17.8 cm
	2. On plinth - 4", 10.1 cm
Colour:	Tabby cat on brown pillar
Issued:	1920-by 1946
Varieties:	HN 244, 245

Description	U.S. $	Can. $	U.K. £
1. On column (illustrated)	2,000.00	3,000.00	1,250.00
2. On plinth	2,000.00	3,000.00	1,250.00

HN 204
Persian Kitten
Style One

Model No.:	242
Height:	5", 12.7 cm
Colour:	See below
Issued:	1. 1920-by 1946
	2. c.1920
Varieties:	HN 221

Colurways	U.S. $	Can. $	U.K. £
1. Tabby		Extremely rare	
2. Sung		Extremely rare	

HN 205
Ducklings
Standing - black

Model No.:	247
Height:	2 ¾", 7.0 cm
Colour:	See below
Issued:	1. 1920-by 1946
	2. c.1919
Varieties:	HN 206, 275

Colourways	U.S. $	Can. $	U.K. £
1. Black/light yellow	600.00	900.00	375.00
2. Flambé		Very Rare	

HN 206
Ducklings
Standing - brown

Model No.:	247
Height:	2 ¾", 7.0 cm
Colour:	See below
Issued:	1. 1920-by 1946
	2. c.1919
Varieties:	HN 205, 275

Colourways	U.S. $	Can. $	U.K. £
1. Browns/white	600.00	900.00	300.00
2. Flambé		Very Rare	

HN 207
Country Mouse

Model No.:	250
Designer:	Charles Noke
Height:	Unknown
Colour:	Cream coat, brown head and tail
Issued:	1920-1936

Description	U.S. $	Can. $	U.K. £
Country mouse		Extremely rare	

HN 208
Toucan in Tail Coat and Bow Tie

Model No.:	234
Designer:	Charles Noke
Height:	4 ½", 11.4 cm
Colour:	Black and white
Issued:	1920-by 1946
Derivative:	Place name holder

Description	U.S. $	Can. $	U.K. £
Toucan	1,500.00	2,250.00	1,000.00

HN 209
Rabbits
Brown, one with Dark Head

Model No.:	249
Height:	3 ½", 8.9 cm
Colour:	See below
Issued:	1. 1920-by 1946
	2. c.1919
Varieties:	HN 217, 218, 219, 969

Colourways	U.S. $	Can. $	U.K. £
1. Brown	900.00	1,350.00	600.00
2. Flambé		Very Rare	

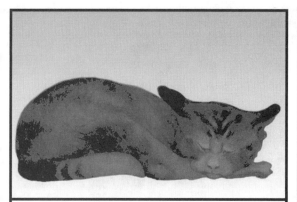

HN 210
Cat Asleep, Head on Paw
Model No.: 23
Height: 1 ½", 3.8 cm
Colour: Black and white
Issued: 1920-1936
Varieties: HN 227

Description	U.S. $	Can. $	U.K. £
Black/white cat		Very Rare	

HN 211
Black-Headed Gull (male)
Model No.: 235
Height: 4", 10.1 cm
Colour: Black-head, grey feathers, white breast
Issued: 1920-by 1946
Varieties: HN 1195; Also called 'Seagull (female)' HN 212, 1196

Description	U.S. $	Can. $	U.K. £
Black-headed gull (male)	375.00	550.00	250.00

HN 212
Seagull (female)
Model No.: 235
Height: 4", 10.1 cm
Colour: White head and breast, grey feathers, red beak
Issued: 1920-by 1946
Varieties: HN 1196; Also called 'Black-headed Gull (male)' HN 211, 1195

Description	U.S. $	Can. $	U.K. £
Seagull (female)	375.00	550.00	250.00

HN 213
Pigs
Snoozing - Both Pigs' Ears Up
Model No.: 61
Height: 4" x 7", 10.1 x 17.8 cm
Colour: See below
Issued: 1. 1920-1936
2. 1912-1936
Varieties: HN 238, 802

Colourways	U.S. $	Can. $	U.K. £
1. Green/mauve		Very Rare	
2. Flambé (illustrated)	1,200.00	1,800.00	750.00

HN 214
Bird with Five Chicks - black

Model No.:	246
Height:	3 ¼", 8.3 cm
Colour:	Black, pink and brown
Issued:	1920-1936
Varieties:	HN 215, 216, 272

Colourways	U.S. $	Can. $	U.K. £
1. Black	300.00	450.00	200.00
2. Flambé	600.00	900.00	400.00

HN 215
Bird with Five Chicks - grey

Model No.:	246
Height:	3 ¼", 8.3 cm
Colour:	Grey, blue and lemon
Issued:	1920-1936
Varieties:	HN 214, 216, 272

Colourways	U.S. $	Can. $	U.K. £
1. Grey	300.00	450.00	200.00
2. Flambé	600.00	900.00	400.00

HN 216
Bird with Five Chicks - green

Model No.:	246
Height:	3 ¼", 8.3 cm
Colour:	Green, blue and lemon
Issued:	1920-1936
Varieties:	HN 214, 215, 272

Colourways	U.S. $	Can. $	U.K. £
1. Green	300.00	450.00	200.00
2. Flambé	600.00	900.00	400.00

HN 217
Rabbits
Brown patches on Faces

Model No.:	249
Height:	3 ½", 8.9 cm
Colour:	See below
Issued:	1. 1920-by 1946
	2. c.1919
Varieties:	HN 209, 218, 219, 969

Colourways	U.S. $	Can. $	U.K. £
1. Brown	900.00	1,350.00	600.00
2. Flambé		Very Rare	

HN 218
Rabbits
Black patches on Face

Model No.:	249
Height:	3 ½", 8.9 cm
Colour:	See below
Issued:	1. 1920-by 1946
	2. c.1919
Varieties:	HN 209, 217, 219, 969

Colourways	U.S. $	Can. $	U.K. £
1. Brown/black patches	900.00	1,350.00	600.00
2. Flambé		Very Rare	

HN 219
Rabbits
Black and Yellow patches on Face

Model No.:	249
Height:	3 ½", 8.9 cm
Colour:	See below
Issued:	1. 1920-by 1946
	2. c.1919
Varieties:	HN 209, 217, 218, 969

Colourways	U.S. $	Can. $	U.K. £
1. Brown/black/yellow	900.00	1,350.00	600.00
2. Flambé		Very Rare	

HN 220
Weaver Bird on Rock

Model No.:	251
Height:	5", 12.7 cm
Colour:	Red and brown
Issued:	1920-by 1946
Varieties:	HN 197

Description	U.S. $	Can. $	U.K. £
Red/brown Weaver bird	750.00	1,200.00	500.00

HN 221
Persian Kitten
Style One

Model No.:	242
Height:	5", 12.7 cm
Colour:	See below
Issued:	1. 1920-by 1946
	2. c.1920
Varieties:	HN 204

Colourways	U.S. $	Can. $	U.K. £
1. Black/white		Extremely Rare	
2. Sung (illustrated)		Extremely Rare	

HN 222
Owl in a Crescent Moon-Shaped Dish

Model No.:	37	
Height:	4", 10.1 cm	
Colour:	See below	
Issued:	1. and 2. 1920-1936	
	3. c.1912	

Colourways	U.S. $	Can. $	U.K. £
1. White/gold highlights	Very Rare		
2. Yellow/green lustre	Very Rare		
3. Flambé	Very Rare		

HN 223
Lion
Seated

Model No.:	59	
Height:	6 ½", 16.5 cm	
Colour:	See below	
Issued:	1. 1920-by 1946	
	2 and 3. c.1912	

Colourways	U.S. $	Can. $	U.K. £
1. Brown		Very Rare	
2. Flambé		Very Rare	
3. Holbien		Very Rare	

HN 224
Kingfisher on Rock
Style Two

Model No.:	258	
Height:	3 ½", 8.9 cm	
Colour:	Blue	
Issued:	1920-by 1946	

Description	U.S. $	Can. $	U.K. £
Kingfisher	900.00	1,350.00	600.00

HN 225
Tiger
Crouching

Model No.:	111	
Designer:	Charles Noke	
Height:	2" x 9 ½", 5.1 x 24.0 cm	
Colour:	See below	
Issued:	1. 1920-1936; 2. c.1912-1968	

Colourways	U.S. $	Can. $	U.K. £
1. Browns	600.00	900.00	400.00
2. Flambé (illustrated)	750.00	1,100.00	500.00

Note: Model No. 111 was also used to produce flambé panther.

HN 226
Town Mouse - blue

Model No.:	256
Designer:	Charles Noke
Height:	2 ½″, 6.4 cm
Colour:	Blue coat, blue hat with yellow and green feather, green and yellow scarf
Issued:	1920-by 1946
Varieties:	HN 228

Description	U.S. $	Can. $	U.K. £
Blue coat and hat	1,150.00	1,700.00	750.00

HN 227
Cat Asleep, Head on Paw

Model No.:	23
Height:	1 ½″, 3.8 cm
Colour:	Tabby
Issued:	1920-1936
Varieties:	HN 210

Description	U.S. $	Can. $	U.K. £
Tabby cat		Very Rare	

HN 228
Town Mouse - yellow

Model No.:	256
Designer:	Charles Noke
Height:	2 ½″, 6.4 cm
Colour:	Yellow coat
Issued:	1920-by 1946
Varieties:	HN 226

Description	U.S. $	Can. $	U.K. £
Yellow coat	1,275.00	1,900.00	850.00

HN 229
Duck
Head stretched forward

Model No.:	207
Height:	4″, 10.1 cm
Colour:	See below
Issued:	1. 1920-by 1946
	2. c.1917
Varieties:	HN 150, 2556

Colourways	U.S. $	Can. $	U.K. £
1. Browns/green	375.00	550.00	250.00
2. Flambé	525.00	800.00	350.00

HN 231
English St. Bernard
Model No.:   262
Height: 1. 7", 17.8 cm
              2. 7 ¾", 19.7 cm
Colour: See below
Issued: 1. 1920-by 1946
              2. c.1919

Colourways	U.S. $	Can. $	U.K. £
1. Natural colours	1,500.00	2,250.00	1,000.00
2. Flambé	1,800.00	2,700.00	1,200.00

HN 232
Puppy with Bone
Model No.:   118
Height: 4", 10.1 cm
Colour: See below
Issued: 1. 1920-by 1946
              2. c.1913

Colourways	U.S. $	Can. $	U.K. £
1. Light/dark brown	Extremely Rare		
2. Flambé	Extremely Rare		

HN 233
Cat
Lying
Model No.:   70
Height: 3 ½", 8.9 cm
Colour: See below
Issued: 1. 1920-1936
              2. c.1920-1936

Colourways	U.S. $	Can. $	U.K. £
1. Yellow/orange/black	1,350.00	2,000.00	900.00
2. Flambé (illustrated)	900.00	1,300.00	600.00

HN 234
Cats
Model No.:   259
Height: 5", 12.7 cm
Colour: Black, brown and white
Issued: 1920-1936

Description	U.S. $	Can. $	U.K. £
Cats	1,350.00	2,000.00	900.00

STONEWARE

GEORGE TINWORTH
"THE OX AND THE FROGS"

POSSIBLY JOHN BROAD
OWL JAR

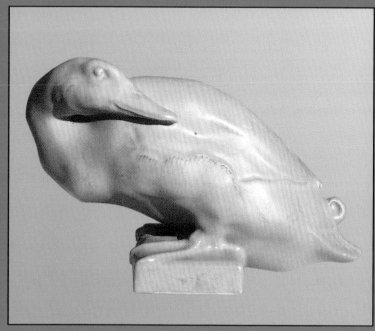

MARK MARSHALL
GROTESQUE BIRD

RICHARD GARBE
DRAKE

GILBERT BAYES
LAMBETH BOOKEND

STONEWARE

GEORGE TINWORTH
"COCKNEYS AT BRIGHTON"

GEORGE TINWORTH
"STEEPLECHASE"

GEORGE TINWORTH
"NIGGERS"

GEORGE TINWORTH
"PLAYGOERS"

CHARACTER ANIMALS

HN101
RABBIT IN MORNING DRESS

D6448
HUNTSMAN FOX

HN187
GRANNY OWL

HN1096
CHARACTER FOX WITH STOLEN GOOSE

HN940
BEARS DRINKING

CATS

HN2655
SIAMESE CAT, SEATED

HN2582
CHARACTER KITTEN ON HIND LEGS

HN2660
SIAMESE CAT, STANDING

HN2583
CHARACTER KITTEN LICKING FRONT PAW

HN999
PERSIAN CAT, SEATED

HN2584
CHARACTER KITTEN LOOKING UP

CHATCULL SERIES

HN2665
LLAMA

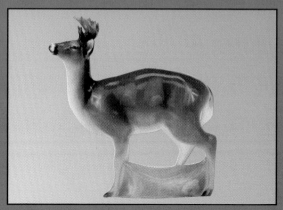

HN2658
WHITE-TAILED DEER

HN2663
RIVER HOG

HN2661
MOUNTAIN SHEEP

HN2656
PINE MARTIN

HN2666
BADGER

WILD ANIMALS

HN254
MONKEYS (MOTHER AND BABY)

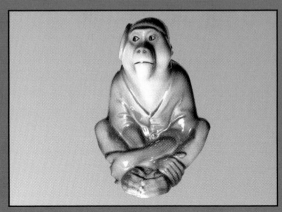

COLOURWAY OF HN182/183
CHARACTER MONKEY

HN2638
LEOPARD ON ROCK

HN1085
LION

HN920
FOXES, CURLED

HN1083
TIGER, STALKING

WILD ANIMALS

K38; HARE (TOP)
K39; HARE (BOTTOM)

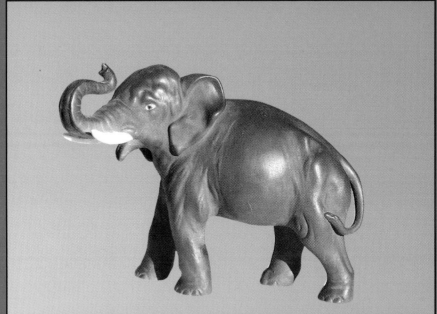

HN966
ELEPHANT, TRUNK IN SALUTE

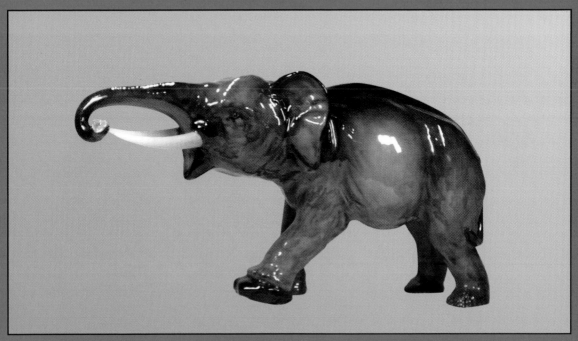

HN2640
FIGHTER ELEPHANT

WILD ANIMALS

HN2644
ELEPHANT, TRUNK IN SALUTE

DA6
HARE, STANDING

HN2634
FOX, SEATED

DA8
BADGER

HN 235
Duck
Preening - Style One

Model No.:	2
Height:	2 ½", 6.4 cm
Colour:	See below
Issued:	1. 1920-1936
	2. c.1912-1936
Varieties:	HN 298

Colourways	U.S. $	Can. $	U.K. £
1. Orange/black	750.00	1,100.00	500.00
2. Flambé	600.00	900.00	400.00

HN 236
Chicks (two)

Model No.:	1163A
Designer:	Charles Noke
Height:	2 ½", 6.4 cm
Colour:	See below
Issued:	1. 1920-by 1946
	2 and 3. c.1908-by 1946

Colourways	U.S. $	Can. $	U.K. £
1. Dark blue/turquoise	450.00	675.00	300.00
2. Black	450.00	675.00	300.00
3. Flambé (illustrated)	300.00	450.00	200.00
4. Sung	600.00	900.00	400.00

HN 237
Mrs Gamp Mouse

Model No.:	257
Designer:	Charles Noke
Height:	Unknown
Colour:	Unknown
Issued:	1920-by 1946

Description	U.S. $	Can. $	U.K. £
Mrs Gamp Mouse		Extremely Rare	

NOTES ON PRICING

- Animal figures are not as plentiful as pretty ladies or character figures and caution in pricing must prevail.

- In the pricing tables N/A (not available) indicates that the animal figure was not available in that particular market.

- Italicized prices are an indication only and form a starting point for discussion on the final price, which may be lower or higher depending on supply and demand.

- Rarity classification provides a range for the collector to work with.

Rarity Class	Rare	Very Rare	Extremely Rare
U.S. $	1,100./1,500.	1,500./2,250.	2,250./3,250.
Can. $	1,650./2,200.	2,250./3,250.	3,250./4,500.
U.K. £	750./1,000.	1,000./1,500.	1,500./2,250.

- Always remember that when dealing with rare animal figures you need two willing parties, a buyer and a seller. One without the other will not work and only when they agree do you have a market price.

HN 238
Pigs
Snoozing - Both Pigs' Ears Up
Model No.: 61
Height: 4" x 7", 10.1 x 17.8 cm
Colour: See below
Issued: 1. 1920-1936
2. 1912-1936
Varieties: HN 213, 802

Colourways	U.S. $	Can. $	U.K. £
1. Unknown		Very Rare	
2. Flambé (illustrated)	1,200.00	1,800.00	750.00

HN 239
Ducklings
Resting
Model No.: 97
Height: 1 ¾" x 5 ½", 4.5 x 14.0 cm
Colour: See below
Issued: 1. 1920-by 1946
2. c.1913

Colourways	U.S. $	Can. $	U.K. £
1. Light brown	375.00	550.00	250.00
2. Red (matt)	450.00	675.00	300.00
3. Flambé	600.00	900.00	400.00

HN 240
Thrush on Rock
Model No.: 253
Height: 5 ½", 14.0 cm
Colour: Blue, red, black and green
Issued: 1920-1936

Description	U.S. $	Can. $	U.K. £
Thrush	750.00	1,100.00	500.00

HN 241
Eagle Crouching on Rock - brown
Model No.: 265
Height: 5", 12.7 cm
Colour: Brown and gold
Issued: 1920-by 1946
Varieties: HN 242

Colourways	U.S. $	Can. $	U.K. £
Brown eagle	1,200.00	1,800.00	800.00

HN 242
Eagle Crouching on Rock - light brown

Model No.:	265
Height:	5", 12.7 cm
Colour:	Light brown and gold, white head and neck
Issued:	1920-by 1946
Varieties:	HN 241

Description	U.S. $	Can. $	U.K. £
Light brown eagle	1,200.00	1,800.00	800.00

HN 243
Pig Bowl, Style One

Model No.:	Unknown
Height:	2 ½" x 5 ½", 6.4 x 14.0 cm
Colour:	See below
Issued:	1. 1920-1936
	2. c.1920
	3. 1934

Colourways	U.S. $	Can. $	U.K. £
1. Brown/cream/silver	450.00	675.00	300.00
2. Flambé	750.00	1,100.00	500.00
3. Titanian	750.00	1,100.00	500.00
4. Kingsware	375.00	550.00	250.00

HN 244
Cat on a Column/or Plinth - black and white

Model No.:	240
Height:	1. On column - 7", 17.8 cm
	2. On plinth - 4", 10.1 cm
Colour:	Black and white cat on brown base
Issued:	1920-by 1946
Varieties:	HN 203, 245

Description	U.S. $	Can. $	U.K. £
1. On column	2,000.00	3,000.00	1,250.00
2. On plinth (illustrated)	2,000.00	3,000.00	1,250.00

HN 245
Cat on a Column/or Plinth - black

Model No.:	240
Height:	1. On column - 7", 17.8 cm
	2. On plinth - 4", 10.1 cm
Colour:	Black and white cat on brown base
Issued:	1920-by 1946
Varieties:	HN 203, 244

Description	U.S. $	Can. $	U.K. £
1. On column (illustrated)	2,000.00	3,000.00	1,250.00
2. On plinth	2,000.00	3,000.00	1,250.00

HN 246
Comic Pig

Model No.:	57		
Designer:	Charles Noke		
Height:	5 ½", 14.0 cm		
Colour:	See below		
Issued:	1. 1920-1936		
	2. Unknown		

Colourways	U.S. $	Can. $	U.K. £
1. Unknown		Very Rare	
2. Titanian		Very Rare	

HN 247
Peahen

Model No.:	270	
Height:	4 ½", 11.4 cm	
Colour:	See below	
Issued:	1. 1921-by 1946	
	2. c.1920	

Colourways	U.S. $	Can. $	U.K. £
1. Grey/pink/black/red	525.00	800.00	350.00
2. Flambé		Very Rare	

HN 248
Duck
Standing - white / blue

Model No.:	307
Height:	13", 33.0 cm
Size:	Large
Colour:	White and blue
Issued:	1921-by 1946
Varieties:	HN 249, 252, 1198, 2635

Description	U.S. $	Can. $	U.K. £
White and blue duck	1,500.00	2,250.00	1,000.00

HN 249
Drake
Standing - blue / white

Model No.:	307
Height:	13", 33.0 cm
Size:	Large
Colour:	Blue and white
Issued:	1921-by 1946
Varieties:	HN 248, 252, 1198, 2635

Description	U.S. $	Can. $	U.K. £
Blue and white duck	1,500.00	2,250.00	1,000.00

HN 250
Heron

Model No.:	314
Height:	5 ½", 14.0 cm
Colour:	See below
Issued:	1. 1921-1936
	2. c.1921
Varieties:	HN 251

Colourways	U.S. $	Can. $	U.K. £
1. Unknown		Very Rare	
2. Flambé		Rare	

HN 251
Heron

Model No.:	314
Height:	5 ½", 14.0 cm
Colour:	See below
Issued:	1. 1921-1936
	2. c.1921
Varieties:	HN 250

Colourways	U.S. $	Can. $	U.K. £
1. Grey/green/white		Very Rare	
2. Flambé		Rare	

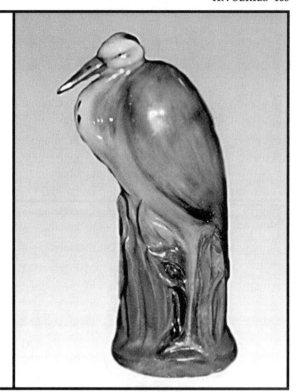

HN 252
Duck
Standing - white

Model No.:	307
Height:	13", 33.0 cm
Size:	Large
Colour:	White
Issued:	1921-by 1946
Varieties:	HN 248, 249, 1198, 2635

Description	U.S. $	Can. $	U.K. £
White duck	1,500.00	2,250.00	1,000.00

HN 253
Monkey, Seated, arms folded

Model No.:	53
Height:	3", 7.6 cm
Colour:	See below
Issued:	1. 1921-by 1946
	2. and 3. c.1912-by 1946
Varieties:	HN 118
Derivative:	On alabaster base

Colourways	U.S. $	Can. $	U.K. £
1. Brown/orange	450.00	700.00	300.00
2. Flambé	525.00	800.00	350.00
3. Titanian		Rare	

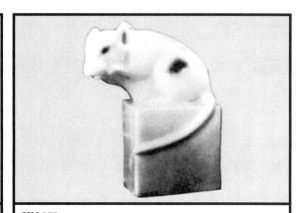

HN 254
Monkeys (Mother and Baby)

Model No.:	52
Designer:	Leslie Harradine
Height:	3", 7.6 cm
Colour:	See below
Issued:	1. 1921-by 1946
	2 and 3. c.1912-1962

Colourways	U.S. $	Can. $	U.K. £
1. Brown/orange	400.00	600.00	275.00
2. Flambé	450.00	675.00	300.00
3. Sung	2,250.00	3,250.00	1,500.00

HN 255
Mouse on a Cube

Model No.:	1164
Designer:	Charles Noke
Height:	2 ½", 6.4 cm
Colour:	See below
Issued:	1. 1921-by 1946
	2. c.1912-by 1946

Colourways	U.S. $	Can. $	U.K. £
1. White/green cube	750.00	1,100.00	500.00
2. Flambé	750.00	1,100.00	500.00

For an illustration of HN 256
see page 106

For an illustration of HN 257
see page 106

HN 256
Character Bird
Style One - green / blue

Model No.:	333
Height:	1", 2.5 cm
Colour:	Green and blue
Issued:	1922-by 1946
Varieties:	HN 283

Colourways	U.S. $	Can. $	U.K. £
Green/blue	600.00	900.00	400.00

HN 257
Character Bird
Style Two - yellow / red

Model No.:	334
Height:	1 ½", 3.8 cm
Colour:	Yellow with red head
Issued:	1922-by 1946
Varieties:	HN 284

Colourways	U.S. $	Can. $	U.K. £
Yellow/red	600.00	900.00	400.00

For an illustration of HN 258
see page 106

For an illustration of HN 259
see page 106

HN 258
Character Bird
Style Three - yellow / black

Model No.:	335		
Height:	1″, 2.5 cm		
Colour:	Yellow with black head		
Issued:	1922-by 1946		
Varieties:	HN 285		

Colourways	*U.S. $*	*Can. $*	*U.K. £*
Yellow/black	600.00	900.00	400.00

HN 259
Character Bird
Style Four - grey / red

Model No.:	336		
Height:	1″, 2.5 cm		
Colour:	Grey with red head and beak and green eyes		
Issued:	1922-by 1946		
Varieties:	HN 286		

Colourways	*U.S. $*	*Can. $*	*U.K. £*
Grey/red	600.00	900.00	400.00

HN 260
Character Bird
Style Five - orange

Model No.:	337		
Height:	1″, 2.5 cm		
Colour:	Orange		
Issued:	1922-by 1946		
Varieties:	HN 287		
Derivative:	Ashtray		

Colourways	*U.S. $*	*Can. $*	*U.K. £*
Orange	600.00	900.00	400.00

HN 261
Character Bird
Style Six - green / red

Model No.:	338		
Height:	1″, 2.5 cm		
Colour:	Green with red beak		
Issued:	1922-by 1946		
Varieties:	HN 288		

Colourways	*U.S. $*	*Can. $*	*U.K. £*
Green/red	600.00	900.00	400.00

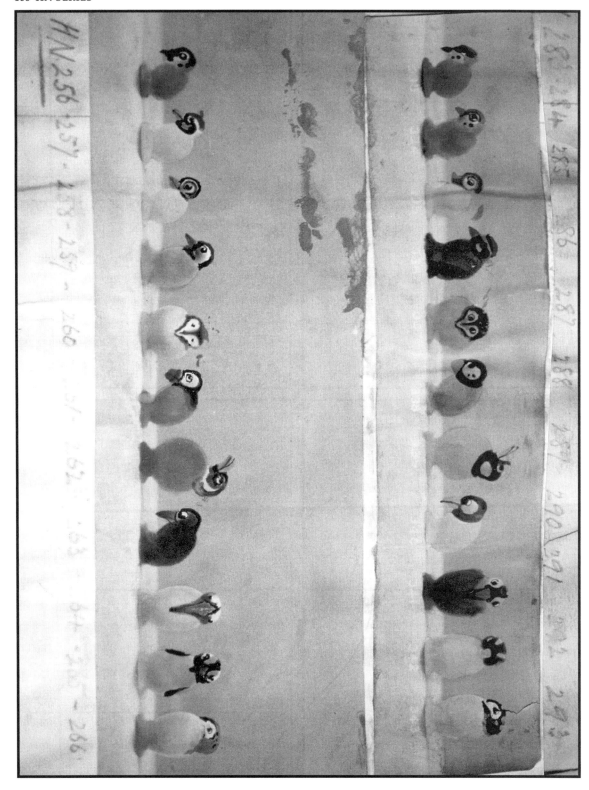

For an illustration of HN 262
see page 106

For an illustration of HN 263
see page 106

HN 262
Character Bird
Style Seven - orange

Model No.:	339
Height:	1", 2.5 cm
Colour:	Orange
Issued:	1922-by 1946
Varieties:	HN 289

Colourways	U.S. $	Can. $	U.K. £
Orange	600.00	900.00	400.00

HN 263
Character Bird
Style Eight - turquoise

Model No.:	340
Height:	1", 2.5 cm
Colour:	Turquoise
Issued:	1922-by 1946
Varieties:	HN 290

Colourways	U.S. $	Can. $	U.K. £
Turquoise	600.00	900.00	400.00

HN 264
Character Bird
Style Nine - orange / black

Model No.:	341
Height:	1 ¾", 4.4 cm
Colour:	Pale orange with black highlights
Issued:	1922-by 1946
Varieties:	HN 291
Derivative:	Onyx pin tray

Colourways	U.S. $	Can. $	U.K. £
Orange/black	600.00	900.00	400.00

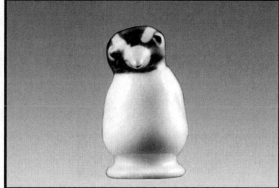

HN 265
Character Bird
Style Ten - grey / black

Model No.:	342
Height:	1 ½", 3.8 cm
Colour:	Grey, black and orange
Issued:	1922-by 1946
Varieties:	HN 292

Colourways	U.S. $	Can. $	U.K. £
Grey/black	600.00	900.00	400.00

For an illustration of HN 266
see page 106

HN 266
Character Bird
Style Eleven - orange / black

Model No.:	343
Height:	1″, 2.5 cm
Colour:	Pale orange with black beak
Issued:	1922-by 1946
Varieties:	HN 293

Colourways	U.S. $	Can. $	U.K. £
Orange/black	600.00	900.00	400.00

HN 267
Cockerel, Crouching

Model No.:	30
Height:	3 ¼″, 8.3 cm
Colour:	See below
Issued:	1. 1922-1936
	2. c.1912
Varieties:	HN 124, 178, 180
Derivative:	Cockerel Bowl with hollow centre and sterling silver rim (Flambé)

Colourways	U.S. $	Can. $	U.K. £
1. Brown/blue/black	350.00	525.00	225.00
2. Flambé	450.00	675.00	300.00

HN 268
Kingfisher
Style One

Model No.:	91
Height:	2 ½″, 6.4 cm
Colour:	See below
Issued:	1. 1922-by 1946
	2. c.1912

Colourways	U.S. $	Can. $	U.K. £
1. Blue/yellow		Very Rare	
2. Flambé (illustrated)	375.00	575.00	250.00

HN 269
Blue Bird on Rock

Model No.:	196
Height:	4 ½″, 11.4 cm
Colour:	Blue and yellow
Issued:	1922-by 1946
Varieties:	Also called 'Swallow on Rock' HN 136, 149

Description	U.S. $	Can. $	U.K. £
Blue bird	450.00	675.00	300.00

HN 270
Comic Brown Bear

Model No.:	58
Designer:	Charles Noke
Height:	5", 12.7 cm
Colour:	See below
Issued:	1. 1922-1936
	2 and 3. c.1918-1936
Varieties:	HN 170

Colourways	U.S. $	Can. $	U.K. £
1. Brown	600.00	900.00	400.00
2. Blue	750.00	1,100.00	500.00
3. Flambé	750.00	1,100.00	500.00

HN 271
Duck
Preening - Style Two

Model No.:	4
Height:	1 ½" x 3 ½", 3.8 x 8.9 cm
Colour:	See below
Issued:	1. 1922-1936
	2. c.1912
Varieties:	HN 148A, 299

Colourways	U.S. $	Can. $	U.K. £
1. Green	450.00	675.00	300.00
2. Flambé	400.00	600.00	250.00

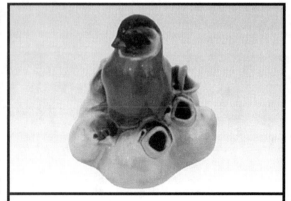

HN 272
Bird with Five Chicks

Model No.:	246
Height:	3 ¼", 8.3 cm
Colour:	Bird: jade green and brown with red head
	Chicks: pale blue with brown heads
Issued:	1922-1936
Varieties:	HN 214, 215, 216

Colourways	U.S. $	Can. $	U.K. £
1. Jade	300.00	450.00	200.00
2. Flambé	600.00	900.00	400.00

HN 273
Hare
Crouching - Style One

Model No.:	119
Height:	2" x 4 ½", 5.1 x 11.4 cm
Colour:	See below
Issued:	1. 1922-by 1946
	2. and 3. 1913-by 1946
Varieties:	HN 107, 126, 142, 803

Colourways	U.S. $	Can. $	U.K. £
1. Yellow/black	450.00	675.00	300.00
2. Flambé	375.00	550.00	250.00
3. Sung	900.00	1,350.00	600.00

HN 274
Chick

Model No.:	1163B
Designer:	Charles Noke
Height:	2 ¼", 5.7 cm
Colour:	See below
Issued:	1. 1922-by 1946
	2. c.1908
Varieties:	HN 282

Colourways	U.S. $	Can. $	U.K. £
1. Green	300.00	450.00	200.00
2. Flambé (illustrated)	225.00	325.00	150.00

HN 275
Ducklings
Standing - orange

Model No.:	247
Height:	2 ¾", 7.0 cm
Colour:	See below
Issued:	1. 1922-by 1946
	2. c.1919
Varieties:	HN 205, 206

Colourways	U.S. $	Can. $	U.K. £
1. Orange	600.00	900.00	375.00
2. Flambé		Very Rare	

HN 276
Lop-eared Rabbit

Model No.:	113
Height:	Large - 4", 10.1 cm
Colour:	See below
Issued:	1. 1922-by 1946
	2. Unknown
Varieties:	HN 108, 151

Colourways	U.S. $	Can. $	U.K. £
1. Yellow/black	750.00	1,100.00	500.00
2. Flambé		Rare	

HN 277
Wren
Style One

Model No.:	104
Height:	2", 5.1 cm
Colour:	See below
Issued:	1. 1922-by 1946
	2. c.1913-by 1946
Varieties:	Also called 'Robin' HN 144

Colourways	U.S. $	Can. $	U.K. £
1. Unknown	225.00	300.00	150.00
2. Flambé	450.00	675.00	300.00

Photograph not
available
at press time

HN 278
Finches (two)

Model No.:	263		
Height:	2 ¾″, 7.0 cm		
Colour:	See below		
Issued:	1. 1922-by 1946		
	2. c.1922		

Colourways	U.S. $	Can. $	U.K. £
1. Green/yellow	525.00	800.00	350.00
2. Flambé		Very Rare	

HN 279
Fledgling on Rock
Style Two - green

Model No.:	140
Designer:	Charles Noke
Height:	4 ½″, 11.4 cm
Colour:	Green
Issued:	1922-1936
Varieties:	HN 281

Description	U.S. $	Can. $	U.K. £
Green fledgling	225.00	350.00	150.00

HN 280
Finches (three)

Model No.:	264
Designer:	Charles Noke
Height:	2″ x 3 ¾″, 5.1 x 9.5 cm
Colour:	See below
Issued:	1. 1922-by 1946
	2. c.1913

Colourways	U.S. $	Can. $	U.K. £
1. Yellow/brown	300.00	450.00	200.00
2. Flambé		Very Rare	

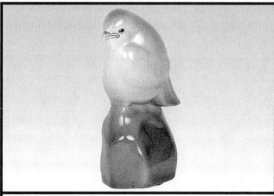

HN 281
Fledgling on Rock
Style Two - yellow

Model No.:	140
Designer:	Charles Noke
Height:	4 ½″, 11.4 cm
Colour:	Yellow
Issued:	1922-1936
Varieties:	HN 279

Description	U.S. $	Can. $	U.K. £
Yellow fledgling	225.00	350.00	150.00

HN 282
Chick

Model No.:	1163B
Designer:	Charles Noke
Height:	2 ¼", 5.7 cm
Colour:	See below
Issued:	1. 1922-by 1946
	2. c.1908
Varieties:	HN 274

Colourways	U.S. $	Can. $	U.K. £
1. Blue	300.00	450.00	200.00
2. Flambé (illustrated)	225.00	325.00	150.00

For an illustration of HN 283
see page 106

HN 283
Character Bird
Style One - green

Model No.:	333
Height:	1", 2.5 cm
Colour:	Green with green beak
Issued:	1922-by 1946
Varieties:	HN 256

Colourways	U.S. $	Can. $	U.K. £
Green	600.00	900.00	400.00

For an illustration of HN 284
see page 106

HN 284
Character Bird
Style Two - mauve / green

Model No.:	334
Height:	1 ½", 3.8 cm
Colour:	Mauve and green head with orange beak
Issued:	1922-by 1946
Varieties:	HN 257

Colourways	U.S. $	Can. $	U.K. £
Mauve/green	600.00	900.00	400.00

For an illustration of HN 285
see page 106

HN 285
Character Bird
Style Three - yellow / green

Model No.:	335
Height:	1", 2.5 cm
Colour:	Yellow with green head
Issued:	1922-by 1946
Varieties:	HN 258

Colourways	U.S. $	Can. $	U.K. £
Yellow/green	600.00	900.00	400.00

For an illustration of HN 286
see page 106

HN 286
Character Bird
Style Four - blue / red

Model No.:	336	
Height:	1″, 2.5 cm	
Colour:	Blue with red head and beak	
Issued:	1922-by 1946	
Varieties:	HN 259	

Colourways	U.S. $	Can. $	U.K. £
Blue/red	600.00	900.00	400.00

HN 287
Character Bird
Style Five - green / black

Model No.:	337	
Height:	1″, 2.5 cm	
Colour:	Green with black head	
Issued:	1922-by 1946	
Varieties:	HN 260	
Derivative:	Ashtray	

Colourways	U.S. $	Can. $	U.K. £
Green/black	600.00	900.00	400.00

HN 288
Character Bird
Style Six - purple / green

Model No.:	338	
Height:	1″, 2.5 cm	
Colour:	Purple with green beak	
Issued:	1922-by 1946	
Varieties:	HN 261	

Colourways	U.S. $	Can. $	U.K. £
Purple/green	600.00	900.00	400.00

For an illustration of HN 289
see page 106

HN 289
Character Bird
Style Seven - orange / green

Model No.:	339	
Height:	1″, 2.5 cm	
Colour:	Orange with green beak	
Issued:	1922-by 1946	
Varieties:	HN 262	

Colourways	U.S. $	Can. $	U.K. £
Orange/green	600.00	900.00	400.00

For an illustration of HN 290
see page 106

HN 290
Character Bird
Style Eight - yellow / green

Model No.:	340
Height:	1", 2.5 cm
Colour:	Yellow with green head and orange beak
Issued:	1922-by 1946
Varieties:	HN 263

Colourways	U.S. $	Can. $	U.K. £
Yellow / green	600.00	900.00	400.00

HN 291
Character Bird
Style Nine - blue / green

Model No.:	341
Height:	1 ¾", 4.5 cm
Colour:	Blue with green head and yellow eyes
Issued:	1922-by 1946
Varieties:	HN 264
Derivative:	Onyx pin tray

Colourways	U.S. $	Can. $	U.K. £
Blue / green	600.00	900.00	400.00

HN 292
Character Bird
Style Ten - yellow / blue

Model No.:	342
Height:	1 ½", 3.8 cm
Colour:	Yellow with blue and yellow striped head
Issued:	1922-by 1946
Varieties:	HN 265

Colourways	U.S. $	Can. $	U.K. £
Yellow / blue	600.00	900.00	400.00

For an illustration of HN 293
see page 106

HN 293
Character Bird
Style Eleven - yellow / orange

Model No.:	343
Height:	1", 2.5 cm
Colour:	Yellow with orange spot on head
Issued:	1922-by 1946
Varieties:	HN 266

Colourways	U.S. $	Can. $	U.K. £
Yellow / orange	600.00	900.00	400.00

HN 294
Toucan on Perch

Model No.:	212
Height:	7 ½", 19.1 cm
Colour:	Black and white, red beak
Issued:	1922-by 1946
Varieties	HN 158, 159, 196

Colourways	U.S. $	Can. $	U.K. £
Black/white/red	525.00	900.00	350.00

HN 295
Pelican
Beak Down

Model No.:	125
Height:	6 ¼", 15.9 cm
Colour:	See below
Issued:	1 and 2. 1922-by 1946
	3. c.1920

Colourways	U.S. $	Can. $	U.K. £
1. Black/green/brown beak	750.00	1,100.00	500.00
2. Black/green/red beak	750.00	1,100.00	500.00
3. Pale brown	525.00	775.00	350.00
4. Flambé		Very Rare	

HN 296
Emperor Penguin

Model No.:	84
Height:	6", 15.2 cm
Colour:	See below
Issued:	1. 1922-by 1946
	2. 1913-1996
Varieties:	HN 113

Colourways	U.S. $	Can. $	U.K. £
1. Black/grey	900.00	1,350.00	600.00
2. Flambé (illustrated)	200.00	300.00	125.00

HN 297
King Penguin and Chick

Model No.:	239
Height:	5 ½", 14.0 cm
Colour:	See below
Issued:	1. 1922-by 1946
	2. c.1918-1961
Varieties:	HN 198, 998

Colourways	U.S. $	Can. $	U.K. £
1. Black/white	900.00	1,350.00	600.00
2. Flambé (illustrated)	825.00	1,250.00	550.00

HN 298
Duck
Preening - Style One

Model No.:	2			
Height:	2 ½", 6.4 cm			
Colour:	See below			
Issued:	1. 1922-1936			
	2. c.1912-1936			
Varieties:	HN 235			

Colourways	U.S. $	Can. $	U.K. £
1. Unknown	750.00	1,100.00	500.00
2. Flambé (illustrated)	600.00	900.00	400.00

HN 299
Drake
Preening - Style Two

Model No.:	4			
Height:	1 ½" x 3 ½", 3.8 x 8.9 cm			
Colour:	See below			
Issued:	1. 1922-by 1946			
	2. c.1912			
Varieties:	HN 148A, 271			

Colourways	U.S. $	Can. $	U.K. £
1. Green/brown/white	450.00	675.00	300.00
2. Flambé	400.00	600.00	250.00

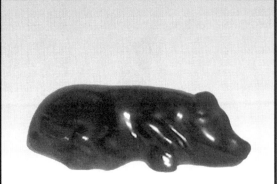

HN 800
Pig Snoozing - large

Model No.:	110			
Height:	2 ½" x 5 ½", 6.4 x 14.0 cm			
Size:	Large			
Colour:	See below			
Issued:	1. 1922-by 1946			
	2. and 3. c.1912			

Colourways	U.S. $	Can. $	U.K. £
1. Unknown	525.00	800.00	350.00
2. Flambé (illustrated)	525.00	800.00	350.00
3. Sung	1,500.00	2,250.00	900.00

HN 801
Pig Snoozing - small

Model No.:	110A			
Height:	1 ¼" x 3 ¾", 3.1 x 9.5 cm			
Size:	Small			
Colour:	See below			
Issued:	1. 1922-by 1946			
	2. 3. and 4. c.1912			

Colourways	U.S. $	Can. $	U.K. £
1. Tan	450.00	675.00	300.00
2. Blue (illustrated)	450.00	675.00	300.00
3. Flambé	450.00	675.00	300.00
4. Sung	1,500.00	2,250.00	900.00

HN 802
Pigs
Snoozing - Both Pigs' Ears Up

Model No.:	61	
Height:	4" x 7", 10.1 x 17.8 cm	
Colour:	See below	
Issued:	1. 1923-1936	
	2. 1912-1936	
Varieties:	HN 213, 238	

Colourways	U.S. $	Can. $	U.K. £
1. Black/white		Very Rare	
2. Flambé (illustrated)	1,200.00	1,800.00	750.00

HN 803
Hare
Crouching - Style One

Model No.:	119	
Height:	2" x 4 ½", 5.1 x 11.4 cm	
Colour:	See below	
Issued:	1. 1923-by 1946	
	2. and 3. 1913-by 1946	
Varieties:	HN 107, 126, 142, 273	

Colourways	U.S. $	Can. $	U.K. £
1. Black/white	450.00	675.00	300.00
2. Flambé	375.00	550.00	250.00
3. Sung (illustrated)	900.00	1,350.00	600.00

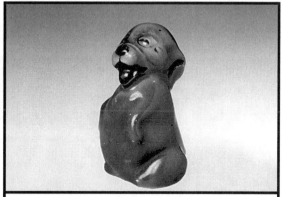

HN 804
'Bonzo' Character Dog
Style One - lying - orange / cream

Model No.:	392	
Designer:	Charles Noke	
Height:	1", 2.5 cm	
Colour:	Pale orange and cream	
Issued:	1922-1936	

Description	U.S. $	Can. $	U.K. £
Style one, orange/cream	1,500.00	2,250.00	1,000.00

HN 805A
'Bonzo' Character Dog
Style Two - large mouth - green / purple

Model No.:	389	
Designer:	Charles Noke	
Height:	2 ½", 6.4 cm	
Colour:	Green and purple	
Issued:	1923-1936	
Varieties:	HN 809, 811	

Description	U.S. $	Can. $	U.K. £
Style two, green/purple	1,500.00	2,250.00	1,000.00

HN 805B
'Bonzo' Character Dog
Style Three - small mouth - blue

Model No.:	387
Designer:	Charles Noke
Height:	2", 5.1 cm
Colour:	Blue with brown face and highlights
Issued:	1923-1936
Varieties:	HN 808, 810, 812

Description	U.S. $	Can. $	U.K. £
Style three, blue	1,500.00	2,250.00	1,000.00

HN 806
Duck
Standing - white

Model No.:	395
Height:	2 ½", 6.4 cm
Size:	Small
Colour:	See below
Issued:	1. 1923-1968
	2. 1922-1996
Varieties:	HN 807, 2591

Colourways	U.S. $	Can. $	U.K. £
1. White/brown/black	125.00	175.00	75.00
2. Flambé	125.00	175.00	85.00

HN 807
Drake
Standing - green

Model No.:	395
Height:	2 ½", 6.4 cm
Size:	Small
Colour:	See below
Issued:	1. 1923-1977
	2. 1922-1996
Varieties:	HN 806, 2591

Colourways	U.S. $	Can. $	U.K. £
1. Green/brown/white	125.00	175.00	75.00
2. Flambé	125.00	175.00	85.00

HN 808
'Bonzo' Character Dog
Style Three - small mouth - yellow / brown

Model No.:	387
Designer:	Charles Noke
Height:	2", 5.1 cm
Colour:	Yellow with brown spots
Issued:	1923-1936
Varieties:	HN 805B, 810, 812

Description	U.S. $	Can. $	U.K. £
Style three, yellow/brown	1,500.00	2,250.00	1,000.00

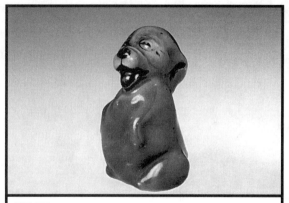

HN 809
'Bonzo' Character Dog
Style Two - large mouth - yellow

Model No.:	389
Designer:	Charles Noke
Height:	2 ½", 6.4 cm
Colour:	Yellow
Issued:	1933-1936
Varieties:	HN 805A, 811

Description	U.S. $	Can. $	U.K. £
Style two, yellow	1,500.00	2,250.00	1,000.00

HN 810
'Bonzo' Character Dog
Style Three - small mouth - green

Model No.:	387
Designer:	Charles Noke
Height:	2", 5.1 cm
Colour:	Green
Issued:	1923-1936
Varieties:	HN 805B, 808, 812

Description	U.S. $	Can. $	U.K. £
Style three, green	1,500.00	2,250.00	1,000.00

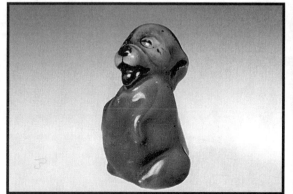

HN 811
'Bonzo' Character Dog
Style Two - large mouth - blue

Model No.:	389
Designer:	Charles Noke
Height:	2 ½", 6.4 cm
Colour:	Blue
Issued:	1923-1936
Varieties:	HN 805A, 809

Description	U.S. $	Can. $	U.K. £
Style two, blue	1,500.00	2,250.00	1,000.00

HN 812
'Bonzo' Character Dog
Style Three - small mouth - orange

Model No.:	387
Designer:	Charles Noke
Height:	2", 5.1 cm
Colour:	Orange
Issued:	1923-1936
Varieties:	HN 805B, 808, 810

Description	U.S. $	Can. $	U.K. £
Style three, orange	1,500.00	2,250.00	1,000.00

HN 813
Miniature Bird

Model No.:	396
Height:	Unknown
Colour:	White
Issued:	1923-by 1946
Varieties:	HN 867, 868, 869, 870, 871, 872, 873, 874

Description	U.S. $	Can. $	U.K. £
Miniature bird		Rare	

HN 814
'Bonzo' Character Dog
Style Four - black buttons

Model No.:	393
Designer:	Charles Noke
Height:	2″, 5.1 cm
Colour:	Cream-yellow with black buttons and jacket edge
Issued:	1923-by 1946
Varieties:	HN 815, 826

Description	U.S. $	Can. $	U.K. £
Style four, black buttons	1,500.00	2,250.00	1,000.00

HN 815
'Bonzo' Character Dog
Style Four - red buttons

Model No.:	393
Designer:	Charles Noke
Height:	2″, 5.1 cm
Colour:	Cream-yellow with red buttons and jacket edge
Issued:	1923-by 1946
Varieties:	HN 814, 826

Description	U.S. $	Can. $	U.K. £
Style four, red buttons	1,500.00	2,250.00	1,000.00

*

HN 818
'Ooloo' Character Cat
Black

Model No.:	400
Designer:	Charles Noke
Height:	3″, 7.6 cm
Colour:	Black with white face
Issued:	1923-1932
Varieties:	HN 819, 827, 828, 829; Also called 'Lucky' K12, HN 971 on ashtray

Description	U.S. $	Can. $	U.K. £
Black cat	525.00	800.00	350.00

HN 819
'Ooloo' Character Cat
White

Model No.:	400
Designer:	Charles Noke
Height:	3", 7.6 cm
Colour:	White
Issued:	1923-1932
Varieties:	HN 818, 827, 828, 829; Also called 'Lucky' K12, HN 971 on ashtray

Description	U.S. $	Can. $	U.K. £
White cat	1,200.00	1,800.00	800.00

HN 820
Character Kitten
Curled - Style One - ginger head

Model No.:	397
Designer:	Unknown
Height:	1", 2.5 cm
Colour:	White body, ginger head
Issued:	1923-1936
Varieties:	HN 821, 822
Derivative:	Onyx pin tray (Model No. 397A)

Description	U.S. $	Can. $	U.K. £
White/ginger kitten		Very Rare	

HN 821
Character Kitten
Curled - Style One - brown head

Model No.:	397
Designer:	Unknown
Height:	1", 2.5 cm
Colour:	White front, brown back and head
Issued:	1923-1936
Varieties:	HN 820, 822
Derivative:	Onyx pin tray (Model No. 397A)

Description	U.S. $	Can. $	U.K.
White/brown kitten		Very Rare	

HN 822
Character Kitten
Curled - Style One - black head

Model No.:	397
Designer:	Unknown
Height:	1", 2.5 cm
Colour:	White body and black head
Issued:	1923-1936
Varieties:	HN 820, 821
Derivative:	Onyx pin tray (Model No. 397A)

Description	U.S. $	Can. $	U.K. £
White/black kitten		Very Rare	

HN 823
Character Kitten
Curled - Style Two - white

Model No.: 398
Height: 1 ¼", 3.2 cm
Colour: See below
Issued: 1. 1923-1936
　　　　 2. c.1930
Varieties: HN 824, 825

Colourways	U.S. $	Can. $	U.K. £
1. White/brown	Very Rare		
2. Chinese Jade	Very Rare		

HN 824
Character Kitten
Curled - Style Two - black

Model No.: 398
Height: 1 ¼", 3.2 cm
Colour: See below
Issued: 1. 1923-1936
　　　　 2. c.1930
Varieties: HN 823, 825

Colourways	U.S. $	Can. $	U.K. £
1. Black	Very Rare		
2. Chinese Jade (illustrated)	Very Rare		

HN 825
Character Kitten
Curled - Style Two - ginger

Model No.: 398
Height: 1 ¼", 3.2 cm
Colour: See below
Issued: 1. 1923-1936
　　　　 2. c.1930
Varieties: HN 823, 824

Colourways	U.S. $	Can. $	U.K. £
1. White/ginger	Very Rare		
2. Chinese Jade	Very Rare		

HN 826
'Bonzo' Character Dog
Style Four - red

Model No.: 393
Designer: Charles Noke
Height: 2", 5.1 cm
Colour: Red
Issued: 1923-1936
Varieties: HN 814, 815

Description	U.S. $	Can. $	U.K. £
Style four, red	1,500.00	2,250.00	1,000.00

HN 827
'Ooloo' Character Cat
Ginger

Model No.: 400
Designer: Charles Noke
Height: 3", 7.6 cm
Colour: Ginger
Issued: 1923-1932
Varieties: HN 818, 819, 828, 829; Also called
            'Lucky' K12, HN 971 on ashtray

Description	U.S. $	Can. $	U.K. £
Ginger cat	1,200.00	1,800.00	800.00

HN 828
'Ooloo' Character Cat
Tabby

Model No.: 400
Designer: Charles Noke
Height: 3", 7.6 cm
Colour: Tabby
Issued: 1923-1932
Varieties: HN 818, 819, 827, 829; Also called
            'Lucky' K12, HN 971 on ashtray

Description	U.S. $	Can. $	U.K. £
Tabby cat	1,200.00	1,800.00	800.00

HN 829
'Ooloo' Character Cat
Black / white

Model No.: 400
Designer: Charles Noke
Height: 3", 7.6 cm
Colour: Black and white
Issued: 1923-1932
Varieties: HN 818, 819, 827, 828; Also called
            'Lucky' K12, HN 971 on ashtray

Description	U.S. $	Can. $	U.K. £
Black/white cat	525.00	800.00	350.00

*

HN 831
Beagle Puppy

Model No.:   407
Height: 2 ¼", 5.7 cm
Colour: See below
Issued: 1. 1923-by 1946
              2. c.1925
Derivatives: Onyx calendar,
              Sterling silver place card holder

Colourways		U.S. $	Can. $	U.K. £
1.	White/browns	900.00	1350.00	600.00
2.	Chinese Jade	1,100.00	1,650.00	750.00

HN 832
Pekinese Puppy
Seated

Model No.:	406
Height:	2 ½", 6.4 cm
Colour:	See below
Issued:	1. 1923-by 1946
	2. and 3. c.1923
Derivatives:	Trinket boxes, onyx calendar

Colourways	U.S. $	Can. $	U.K. £
1. Golden brown/black	375.00	550.00	250.00
2. Chinese Jade		Very Rare	
3. Flambé		Very Rare	

HN 833
Pekinese Puppy
Standing

Model No.:	405
Height:	2", 5.1 cm
Colour:	See below
Issued:	1. 1923-by 1946
	2. and 3. c.1923
Derivatives:	Trinket boxes

Colourways	U.S. $	Can. $	U.K. £
1. Brown/black/tan	375.00	550.00	250.00
2. Chinese Jade		Very Rare	
3. Flambé		Very Rare	

HN 834
Pekinese Puppy
Curled - dark brown

Model No.:	403
Height:	1", 2.5 cm
Colour:	Pale brown with dark brown nose and tips of ears
Issued:	1923-by 1946
Varieties:	HN 835, 836
Derivative:	Ashtray

Description	U.S. $	Can. $	U.K. £
Dark brown puppy	600.00	900.00	400.00

HN 835
Pekinese Puppy
Curled - light brown

Model No.:	403
Height:	1", 2.5 cm
Colour:	Light brown
Issued:	1923-by 1946
Varieties:	HN 834, 836
Derivative:	Ashtray

Description	U.S. $	Can. $	U.K. £
Light brown puppy	600.00	900.00	400.00

HN 836
Pekinese Puppy
Curled - pale brown

Model No.:	403
Height:	1", 2.5 cm
Colour:	Pale brown
Issued:	1923-by 1946
Varieties:	HN 834, 835
Derivative:	Ashtray

Description	U.S. $	Can. $	U.K. £
Pale brown puppy	600.00	900.00	400.00

HN 837
Pomeranian
Curled - brown

Model No.:	402
Height:	1", 2.5 cm
Colour:	Brown
Issued:	1923-by 1946
Varieties:	HN 838, 839

Colourways	U.S. $	Can. $	U.K. £
Brown	600.00	900.00	400.00

HN 838
Pomeranian
Curled - light brown

Model No.:	402
Height:	1", 2.5 cm
Colour:	Light brown
Issued:	1923-by 1946
Varieties:	HN 837, 839

Colourways	U.S. $	Can. $	U.K. £
Light brown	600.00	900.00	400.00

HN 839
Pomeranian
Curled - white / grey

Model No.:	402
Height:	1", 2.5 cm
Colour:	White and grey
Issued:	1923-by 1946
Varieties:	HN 837, 838

Colourways	U.S. $	Can. $	U.K. £
White/grey	600.00	900.00	400.00

HN 840
Character Duck
Style One - Large - yellow / white

Model No.:	415
Height:	3", 7.6 cm
Size:	Large
Colour:	Pale yellow body, white head
Issued:	1924-by 1946
Varieties:	HN 842, 844

Colourways	U.S. $	Can. $	U.K. £
Yellow/white, large	600.00	900.00	400.00

HN 841
Character Duck
Style One - Small - yellow / black

Model No.:	415A
Height:	2 ½", 6.4 cm
Size:	Small
Colour:	Pale yellow body, black wings, white head
Issued:	1924-by 1946
Varieties:	HN 843, 845
Derivative:	Onyx pin tray (square, round and oblong bases)

Colourways	U.S. $	Can. $	U.K. £
Yellow/black, small	450.00	675.00	300.00

HN 842
Character Duck
Style One - Large - yellow / brown

Model No.:	415
Height:	3", 7.6 cm
Size:	Large
Colour:	Yellow body, black wings, brown head
Issued:	1924-by 1946
Varieties:	HN 840, 844

Colourways	U.S. $	Can. $	U.K. £
Yellow/brown, large	600.00	900.00	400.00

HN 843
Character Duck
Style One - Small - yellow / brown

Model No.:	415A
Height:	2 ½", 6.4 cm
Size:	Small
Colour:	Yellow body with brown highlights
Issued:	1924-by 1946
Varieties:	HN 841, 845
Derivative:	Onyx pin tray (square, round and oblong bases)

Colourways	U.S. $	Can. $	U.K. £
Yellow/brown, small	450.00	675.00	300.00

HN 844
Character Duck
Style One - Large - orange / black

Model No.:	415		
Height:	3", 7.6 cm		
Size:	Large		
Colour:	Orange body, black and brown highlights		
Issued:	1924-by 1946		
Varieties:	HN 840, 842		

Colourways	U.S. $	Can. $	U.K. £
Orange/black, large	600.00	900.00	400.00

HN 845
Character Duck
Style One - Small - orange / black

Model No.:	415A	
Height:	2 ½", 6.4 cm	
Size:	Small	
Colour:	Orange body, black / brown highlights	
Issued:	1924-by 1946	
Varieties:	HN 841, 843	
Derivative:	Onyx pin tray (square, round and oblong bases)	

Colourways	U.S. $	Can. $	U.K. £
Orange/black, small	450.00	675.00	300.00

HN 846
Toucan on Tree Stump (flower holder)

Model No.:	432
Height:	Unknown
Colour:	Unknown
Issued:	1924-1936

Description	U.S. $	Can. $	U.K. £
Toucan (flower holder)		Very Rare	

HN 847
Bird on Tree Stump (flower holder)

Model No.:	430
Height:	Unknown
Colour:	Yellow and orange
Issued:	1924-1936

Description	U.S. $	Can. $	U.K. £
Bird (flower holder)		Very Rare	

HN 848
Heron on Grass Perch (flower holder)

Model No.:	437
Height:	5 ½", 13.8 cm
Colour:	Grey with black highlights, green base
Issued:	1924-1936

Description	U.S. $	Can. $	U.K. £
Heron (flower holder)	1,500.00	2,200.00	1,000.00

HN 849
Duck and Ladybird (flower holder)

Model No.:	435
Height:	4 ½", 11.4 cm
Colour:	White duck, green base
Issued:	1924-1936

Description	U.S. $	Can. $	U.K. £
Duck/ladybird (flower holder)		Very Rare	

HN 850
Duckling on a Rock (flower holder)

Model No.:	438
Height:	Unknown
Colour:	Yellow with brown wing tips, brown white and green base
Issued:	1924-1936

Description	U.S. $	Can. $	U.K. £
Duckling (flower holder)		Very Rare	

HN 851
Robin on Tree Stump (flower holder)

Model No.:	Unknown
Height:	Unknown
Colour:	Red and brown robin, black base
Issued:	1924-1936
Varieties:	HN 860

Description	U.S. $	Can. $	U.K. £
Robin (flower holder)		Very Rare	

HN 852
Penguin on Rocks (flower holder)

Model No.:	441
Height:	6 ½", 16.5 cm
Colour:	1. Black and white penguin, blue rocks
	2. Pearl glaze
Issued:	1924-1936
Varieties:	HN 856

Colourways	U.S. $	Can. $	U.K. £
1. Black/white		Very Rare	
2. Pearl		Very Rare	

HN 853
Mallard Drake on Rocks (flower holder)

Model No.:	436
Height:	Unknown
Colour:	Unknown
Issued:	1924-1936

Description	U.S. $	Can. $	U.K. £
Mallard drake (flower holder)		Very Rare	

HN 854
Budgerigar on Branch (flower holder)

Model No.:	429
Height:	6 ½", 16.5 cm
Colour:	Pearlized budgerigar, green base
Issued:	1924-1936

Description	U.S. $	Can. $	U.K. £
Budgerigar (flower holder)		Very Rare	

HN 855
Wren on Tree Stump (flower holder)

Model No.:	431
Height:	Unknown
Colour:	Blue, green and grey bird on brown base
Issued:	1924-1936

Description	U.S. $	Can. $	U.K. £
Wren (flower holder)		Very Rare	

HN 856
Penguin on Rocks (flower holder)

Model No.:	441
Height:	6 ½", 16.5 cm
Colour:	Black and white penguin on brown and green rocks
Issued:	1924-1936
Varieties:	HN 852

Description	U.S. $	Can. $	U.K. £
Penguin (flower holder)		Very Rare	

HN 857
Cormorant Nesting on Tree Stump (flower holder)

Model No.:	439
Height:	Unknown
Colour:	White bird on brown base
Issued:	1924-1936

Description	U.S. $	Can. $	U.K. £
Cormorant (flower holder)		Very Rare	

HN 858
Kingfisher on Tree Stump (flower holder)
Style One

Model No.:	227
Height:	3", 7.6 cm
Colour:	See below
Issued:	1. 1924-1936
	2. c.1918-1936
Varieties:	HN 165

Colourways	U.S. $	Can. $	U.K. £
1. Green/blue/brown	525.00	800.00	350.00
2. Flambé	750.00	1,100.00	500.00

HN 859
Tortoise on Rocks (flower holder)

Model No.:	434
Height:	Unknown
Colour:	Green and white
Issued:	1924-by 1946

Description	U.S. $	Can. $	U.K. £
Tortoise (flower holder)		Very Rare	

HN 860
Robin on Tree Stump (flower holder)

Model No.:	Unknown		
Height:	Unknown		
Colour:	Black and green with yellow highlights		
Issued:	1924-by 1946		
Varieties:	HN 851		

Description	U.S. $	Can. $	U.K. £
Robin (flower holder)		Very Rare	

HN 861
Polar Bear
Standing - Style One

Model No.:	433		
Height:	4 ½ " x 8", 11.4 x 20.3 cm		
Colour:	See below		
Issued:	1. 1924-by 1946		
	2. Unknown		

Colourways	U.S. $	Can. $	U.K. £
1. White	1,275.00	1,900.00	850.00
2. Red		Very Rare	

HN 862A
Kingfisher on Stand with Primroses

Model No.:	44A		
Height:	4 ½", 11.4 cm		
Colour:	Green, malachite blue and orange bird, yellow flowers		
Issued:	1924-1936		
Varieties:	HN 862B with kingcup flowers		

Description	U.S. $	Can. $	U.K. £
Kingfisher/primroses	400.00	600.00	275.00

HN 862B
Kingfisher on Stand with Kingcups

Model No.	44B		
Height:	4 ½", 11.4 cm		
Colour:	Green, malachite blue and orange bird, yellow flowers		
Issued:	1924-1936		
Varieties:	HN 862A with primrose flowers		

Description	U.S. $	Can. $	U.K. £
Kingfisher/kingcups	400.00	600.00	275.00

HN 863
Character Duck
Style Two - yellow / white

Model No.: 425
Height: 2 ½", 6.4 cm
Colour: Yellow body, white head
Issued: 1924-by 1946
Varieties: HN 864, 865

Colourways	U.S. $	Can. $	U.K. £
Yellow/white	375.00	550.00	250.00

HN 864
Character Duck
Style Two - yellow / brown

Model No.: 425
Height: 2 ½", 6.4 cm
Colour: Yellow body, brown head
Issued: 1924-by 1946
Varieties: HN 863, 865

Colourways	U.S. $	Can. $	U.K. £
Yellow/brown	375.00	550.00	250.00

HN 865
Character Duck
Style Two - brown

Model No.: 425
Height: 2 ½", 6.4 cm
Colour: Brown body and head
Issued: 1924-by 1946
Varieties: HN 863, 864

Colourways	U.S. $	Can. $	U.K. £
Brown	375.00	550.00	250.00

HN 866
Character Fox

Model No.: 442
Height: Unknown
Colour: Light brown with dark brown highlights
Issued: 1924-by 1946
Derivatives: Onyx pin tray

Description	U.S. $	Can. $	U.K. £
Character fox		Rare	

HN 867
Miniature Bird
Grey / brown

Model No.:	396
Height:	Unknown
Colour:	Grey back and wings, brown head
Issued:	1924-by 1946
Varieties:	HN 813, 868, 869, 870, 871, 872, 873, 874

Colourways	U.S. $	Can. $	U.K. £
Grey/brown		Rare	

HN 868
Miniature Bird
Green

Model No.:	396
Height:	Unknown
Colour:	Green back and head
Issued:	1924-by 1946
Varieties:	HN 813, 867, 869, 870, 871, 872, 873, 874

Colourways	U.S. $	Can. $	U.K. £
Green		Rare	

HN 869
Miniature Bird
Green / yellow

Model No.:	396
Height:	Unknown
Colour:	Green-black back and head, yellow breast
Issued:	1924-by 1946
Varieties:	HN 813, 867, 868, 870, 871, 872, 873, 874

Colourways	U.S. $	Can. $	U.K. £
Green/yellow		Rare	

HN 870
Miniature Bird
Green / grey

Model No.:	396
Height:	Unknown
Colour:	Green-black head, grey wings, yellow breast
Issued:	1924-by 1946
Varieties:	HN 813, 867, 868, 869, 871, 872, 873, 874

Colourways	U.S. $	Can. $	U.K. £
Green/grey		Rare	

HN 871
Miniature Bird
Brown

Model No.:	396
Height:	Unknown
Colour:	Brown back and wings
Issued:	1924-by 1946
Varieties:	HN 813, 867, 868, 869, 870, 872, 873, 874

Colourways	U.S. $	Can. $	U.K. £
Brown		Rare	

HN 872
Miniature Bird
Green / red

Model No.:	396
Height:	Unknown
Colour:	Green back, red head
Issued:	1924-by 1946
Varieties:	HN 813, 867, 868, 869, 870, 871, 873, 874

Colourways	U.S. $	Can. $	U.K. £
Green/red		Rare	

HN 873
Miniature Bird
Blue

Model No.:	396
Height:	Unknown
Colour:	Blue back
Issued:	1924-by 1946
Varieties:	HN 813, 867, 868, 869, 870, 871, 872, 874

Colourways	U.S. $	Can. $	U.K. £
Blue		Rare	

HN 874
Miniature Bird
Green / mauve

Model No.:	396
Height:	Unknown
Colour:	Green back, mauve breast, blue head
Issued:	1924-by 1946
Varieties:	HN 813, 867, 868, 869, 870, 871, 872, 873

Colourways	U.S. $	Can. $	U.K. £
Green/mauve		Rare	

For an illustration of the Miniature Birds see page 143.

HN 875
Kingfisher on Tree Stump (flower holder)
Style Two

Model No.:	446		
Height:	4", 10.1 cm		
Colour:	Blue		
Issued:	1924-1936		

Description	U.S. $	Can. $	U.K. £
Kingfisher (flower holder)		Rare	

HN 876
Tiger on a Rock
Style One

Model No.:	106		
Designer:	Charles Noke		
Height:	3 ½" x 9", 8.9 x 22.9 cm		
Colour:	See below		
Issued:	1. 1924-by 1946		
	2. c.1913		

Colourways	U.S. $	Can. $	U.K. £
1. Browns/black	1,800.00	2,700.00	1,200.00
2. Flambé	1,500.00	2,250.00	1,000.00

Note: Charles Noke impressed on rock.

HN 877
Cockatoo on Rock

Model No.:	68		
Designer:	Leslie Harradine		
Height:	6", 15.2 cm		
Colour:	See below		
Issued:	1. 1924-1936		
	2. c.1912-1936		
Varieties:	HN 185, 191, 192, 200		
Derivative:	Onyx pin tray		

Colourways	U.S. $	Can. $	U.K. £
1. Blue/orange	375.00	550.00	250.00
2. Flambé	750.00	1,100.00	500.00

HN 878
Cockerel
Seated - Style Two - white

Model No.:	451		
Height:	4", 10.1 cm		
Colour:	White		
Issued:	1924-1936		
Varieties:	HN 879, 880		

Description	U.S. $	Can. $	U.K. £
White cockerel	275.00	400.00	175.00

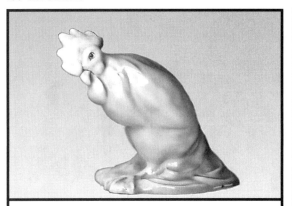

HN 879
Cockerel
Seated - Style Two - blue

Model No.:	451
Height:	4", 10.1 cm
Colour:	Blue and green
Issued:	1924-1936
Varieties:	HN 878, 880

Description	U.S. $	Can. $	U.K. £
Blue cockerel	275.00	400.00	175.00

HN 880
Cockerel
Seated - Style Two - yellow

Model No.:	451
Height:	4", 10.1 cm
Colour:	Yellow, black and red
Issued:	1924-1936
Varieties:	HN 878, 879

Description	U.S. $	Can. $	U.K. £
Yellow cockerel	275.00	400.00	175.00

HN 881
Bulldog
Seated - Style Three

Model No.:	122
Height:	2 ¾", 7.0 cm
Size:	Small
Colour:	See below
Issued:	1 and 2. 1938-by 1946
	3 and 4. c.1913-by 1946
Varieties:	On lid of lustre bowl HN 987

Colourways	U.S. $	Can. $	U.K. £
1. Brindle		Very Rare	
2. Cream/brown	2,000.00	3,000.00	1,250.00
3. Chinese Jade	2,250.00	3,500.00	1,500.00
4. Flambé	1,500.00	2,250.00	1,000.00

HN 882
Penguin
Style Two

Model No.:	459		
Height:	6 ¾', 17.2 cm		
Colour:	See below		
Issued:	1. 1925-by 1946		
	2. c.1925-by 1961		

Colourways	U.S. $	Can. $	U.K. £
1. Green head		Rare	
2. Flambé	750.00	1,100.00	500.00

HN 883
Two Cuddling Orang-Outangs

Model No.:	486
Designer:	Leslie Harradine
Size:	5 ½" x 7", 14.0 x 17.8 cm
Colour:	See below
Issued:	1. 1925-1936
	2. c.1913-1936

Colourways	U.S. $	Can. $	U.K. £
1. Natural colours		Very Rare	
2. Flambé (illustrated)	3,000.00	4,500.00	2,000.00
3. Sung	3,750.00	5,500.00	2,500.00

HN 884
Character Parrot on Pillar
Style One

Model No.:	465
Height:	Unknown
Colour:	Blue and orange
Issued:	1925-1936

Description	U.S. $	Can. $	U.K. £
HN 884, Style One		Rare	

Character Parrot on Pillar
Style Two
Model No.: 466
Height: Unknown

HN 885
Colour: Pink, purple and orange
Issued: 1925-1936
Varieties: HN 886, 888

HN 886
Colour: Red, blue and orange
Issued: 1925-1936
Varieties: HN 885, 888

HN 888
Colour: Pale blue and yellow
Issued: 1925-1936
Varieties: HN 885, 886

Description	U.S. $	Can. $	U.K. £
HN 885		Rare	
HN 886		Rare	
HN 888		Rare	

*HN 887 Cockatoo not issued.

HN 889
Greyhound
Seated - black/white
Model No.: 80
Designer: Charles Noke
Height: 5", 12.7 cm
Colour: See below
Issued: 1. 1925-by 1946; 2. c.1913-by 1946
Varieties: HN 890

Colourways	U.S. $	Can. $	U.K. £
1. Black/white	1,100.00	1,600.00	750.00
2. Flambé	975.00	1,450.00	650.00

Note: First produced in the 1890s as part of a vellum piece.

HN 890
Greyhound
Seated - brown /cream
Model No.: 80
Designer: Charles Noke
Height: 5", 12.7 cm
Colour: See below
Issued: 1. 1925-by 1946; 2. c.1913-by 1946
Varieties: HN 889

Colourways	U.S. $	Can. $	U.K. £
1. Brown/cream	1,100.00	1,600.00	750.00
2. Flambé	975.00	1,450.00	650.00

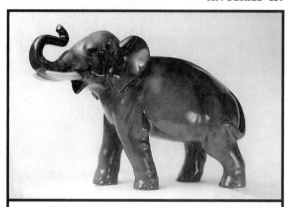

HN 891A
Elephant, Trunk in salute - Style One - medium

Model No.:	489A
Designer:	Charles Noke
Height:	6", 15.2 cm
Colour:	See below
Issued:	1. 1926-1943; 2a. c.1926-1950; 2b. 1962-1996

Colourways	U.S. $	Can. $	U.K. £
1. Olive-grey (earthenware)	600.00	900.00	400.00
2a. Flambé (original)	525.00	800.00	350.00
2b. Flambé (re-issue)	200.00	300.00	125.00
3. Sung	1,100.00	1,600.00	750.00

HN 891B
Elephant, Trunk in salute - Style One - small

Model No.:	489B
Designer:	Charles Noke
Height:	4 ½", 11.4 cm
Size:	Small
Colour:	See below
Issued:	1. 1926-1943; 2. c.1926-1962; 3. c.1926
Varieties:	HN 941, 2644

Colourways	U.S. $	Can. $	U.K. £
1. Silver-grey (china)	525.00	800.00	350.00
2. Flambé	450.00	675.00	300.00
3. Sung	1,050.00	1,500.00	700.00

HN 892
Character Pig - Laughing
Style One - red

Model No.:	494
Height:	2 ½", 6.4 cm
Colour:	See below
Issued:	1. 1926-by 1946
	2. Unknown
Varieties:	HN 893

Colourways	U.S. $	Can. $	U.K. £
1. Red/black spots		Rare	
2. Flambé		Rare	

HN 893
Character Pig - Laughing
Style One - green

Model No.:	494
Height:	2 ½", 6.4 cm
Colour:	See below
Issued:	1. 1926-by 1946
	2. Unknown
Varieties:	HN 892

Colourways	U.S. $	Can. $	U.K. £
1. Green/black spots		Rare	
2. Flambé		Rare	

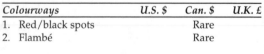

HN 894
Character Pig - Crying
Style Two
Model No.: 495
Height: 2 ½″, 6.4 cm
Colour: See below
Issued: 1. 1926-by 1946
2. Unknown

Colourways	U.S. $	Can. $	U.K. £
1. Unknown		Rare	
2. Flambé (illustrated)		Rare	

HN 895
Character Pig
Style Three
Model No.: 496
Height: 2 ½″, 6.4 cm
Colour: Unknown
Issued: 1926-by 1946

Description	U.S. $	Can. $	U.K. £
Style three		Rare	

Photograph
not available
at press time

HN 896
Character Pig
Style Four
Model No.: Unknown
Height: Unknown
Colour: Unknown
Issued: 1926-by 1946

Description	U.S. $	Can. $	U.K. £
Style four		Rare	

Photograph
not available
at press time

HN 897
Character Pig
Style Five
Model No.: Unknown
Height: Unknown
Colour: Unknown
Issued: 1926-1936

Description	U.S. $	Can. $	U.K. £
Style five		Rare	

HN 898
Alsatian's Head
Pencil Holder

Model No.: 509
Height: 3", 7.6 cm
Colour: Brown
Issued: 1926-1936
Derivative: Onyx pin tray

Description	U.S. $	Can. $	U.K. £
Pencil holder	750.00	1,100.00	500.00

HN 899
Alsatian
Seated, with collar

Model No.: 497
Height: 3 ¾", 9.5 cm
Colour: See below
Issued: 1926-by 1946
Varieties: On lid of lustre bowl HN 986 (Flambé)
Derivatives: Onyx calendar, onyx pin tray

Colourways	U.S. $	Can. $	U.K. £
1. Natural colours	900.00	1,350.00	600.00
2. Flambé (illustrated)	750.00	1,100.00	500.00

HN 900
Fox Terrier
Seated - Style One - white/brown/ginger

Model No.: 511
Height: 3 ½", 8.9 cm
Colour: White, brown and ginger
Issued: 1926-by 1946
Varieties: HN 901
Derivative: Onyx pin tray

Colourways	U.S. $	Can. $	U.K. £
White/brown/ginger		Very Rare	

HN 901
Fox Terrier
Seated - Style One - white/black/brown

Model No.: 511
Height: 3 ½" , 8.9 cm
Colour: White, black and brown
Issued: 1926-by 1946
Varieties: HN 900
Derivative: Card holder; Onyx pin tray

Colourways	U.S. $	Can. $	U.K. £
White/black/brown		Very Rare	

HN 902
Character Pig
Style Six - black

Model No.:	510		
Height:	Unknown		
Colour:	White with black patches		
Issued:	1926-1936		
Varieties:	HN 903		

Description	U.S. $	Can. $	U.K. £
Style six - black		Rare	

HN 903
Character Pig
Style Six - brown

Model No.:	510		
Height:	Unknown		
Colour:	White with brown patches		
Issued:	1926-1936		
Varieties:	HN 902		

Description	U.S. $	Can. $	U.K. £
Style six - brown		Rare	

HN 904
Terrier Puppy
Begging - Style One

Model No.:	515		
Height:	3 ¼", 8.3 cm		
Colour:	White with black and brown patches		
Issued:	1926-by 1946		
Derivatives:	Marble ashtray		

Description	U.S. $	Can. $	U.K. £
Terrier puppy		Very Rare	

HN 905
Frog
Style Two

Model No.:	516		
Height:	1 ½", 3.8 cm		
Colour:	See below		
Issued:	1. 1926-1936		
	2. Unknown		

Colourways	U.S. $	Can. $	U.K. £
1. Green/ivory throat		Rare	
2. Flambé (illustrated)		Rare	

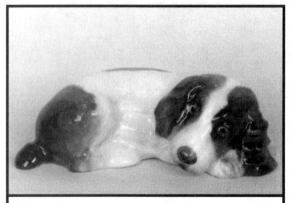

HN 906
Spaniel Puppy - Dark Brown Patches

Model No.:	514
Height:	1 ½", 3.8 cm
Colour:	White with dark brown patches
Issued:	1926-1936
Varieties:	HN 907

Colourways	U.S. $	Can. $	U.K. £
Dark brown patches	850.00	1,300.00	575.00

HN 907
Spaniel Puppy - Light Brown Patches

Model No.:	514
Height:	1 ½", 3.8 cm
Colour:	White with light brown patches
Issued:	1926-1936
Varieties:	HN 906

Colourways	U.S. $	Can. $	U.K. £
Light brown patches	850.00	1,300.00	575.00

HN 908
Spaniel Puppy's Head
Pencil Holder

Model No.:	520
Height:	3", 7.6 cm
Colour:	1. Blue roan
	2. Liver and white
Issued:	1926-1936

Colourways	U.S. $	Can. $	U.K. £
1. Blue roan	750.00	1,100.00	500.00
2. Liver and white	750.00	1,100.00	500.00

NOTES ON PRICING

- Animal figures are not as plentiful as pretty ladies or character figures and caution in pricing must prevail.

- In the pricing tables N/A (not available) indicates that the animal figure was not available in that particular market.

- Italicized prices are an indication only and form a starting point for discussion on the final price, which may be lower or higher depending on supply and demand.

- Rarity classification provides a range for the collector to work with.

Rarity Class	Rare	Very Rare	Extremely Rare
U.S. $	1,100./1,500.	1,500./2,250.	2,250./3,250.
Can. $	1,650./2,200.	2,250./3,250.	3,250./4,500.
U.K. £	750./1,000.	1,000./1,500.	1,500./2,250.

- Always remember that when dealing with rare animal figures you need two willing parties, a buyer and a seller. One without the other will not work and only when they agree do you have a market price.

HN 909
Fox Terrier
Standing - Style One

Model No.:	554
Height:	4", 10.1 cm
Size:	Medium
Colour:	See below
Issued:	1. 1927-by 1946
	2. Unknown
Varieties:	HN 923

Colourways	U.S. $	Can. $	U.K. £
1. White/dark brown	550.00	825.00	350.00
2. Flambé	750.00	1,100.00	500.00

HN 910
Fox Terrier
Seated- Style Two

Model No.:	553
Height:	1. 5 ¼", 13.3 cm
	2. 4 ½", 11.4 cm
Size:	Medium
Colour:	See below
Issued:	1. 1927-by 1946
	2. c.1927
Varieties:	HN 924

Colourways	U.S. $	Can. $	U.K. £
1. White/black/brown	550.00	825.00	350.00
2. Flambé	750.00	1,100.00	500.00

HN 911
Tiger
Lying

Model No.:	533
Designer:	Charles Noke
Height:	2 ½" x 7 ½", 6.4 cm x 19.1 cm
Colour:	See below
Issued:	1. 1927-by 1946
	2. c.1926

Colourways	U.S. $	Can. $	U.K. £
1. Browns	750.00	1,100.00	500.00
2. Flambé	1,125,00	1,700.00	750.00

HN 912
Tiger, Seated

Model No.:	530
Designer:	Charles Noke
Height:	6 ¼", 15.9 cm
Colour:	See below
Issued:	1. 1927-1940 2. c.1926-1940

Colourways	U.S. $	Can. $	U.K. £
1. Golden brown/brown	750.00	1,100.00	500.00
2. Flambé	1,275.00	2,000.00	850.00
3. Sung	4,500.00	6,750.00	3,000.00

Note: Model 530 was also used to produced HN 919 Leopard.

HN 913
Character Toucan With Hat
Style One

Model No.:	548
Height:	1 ½", 3.84 cm
Colour:	Green and black body, yellow beak, red and yellow hat
Issued:	1927-by 1946

Description	U.S. $	Can. $	U.K. £
Style one		Rare	

HN 914
Character Toucan With Hat
Style Two

Model No.:	546
Height:	1 ½", 3.84 cm
Colour:	Green and black body, red and yellow hat
Issued:	1927-by 1946

Description	U.S. $	Can. $	U.K. £
Style two		Rare	

HN 915
Character Toucan With Hat
Style Three

Model No.:	549
Height:	1 ½", 3.84 cm
Colour:	Turquoise body, red hat
Issued:	1927-by 1946

Description	U.S. $	Can. $	U.K. £
Style three		Rare	

HN 916
Character Toucan With Hat
Style Four

Model No.:	550
Height:	1 ½", 3.84 cm
Colour:	Black and orange body, brown hat
Issued:	1927-by 1946

Description	U.S. $	Can. $	U.K. £
Style four		Rare	

HN 917
Character Toucan With Hat
Style Five

Model No.:   551
Height: 1 ½", 3.84 cm
Colour: Blue body, red and yellow hat
Issued: 1927-by 1946

Description	U.S. $	Can. $	U.K. £
Style five		Rare	

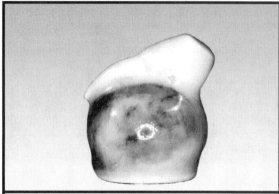

HN 918
Character Toucan With Hat
Style Six

Model No.:   547
Height: 1 ½", 3.84 cm
Colour: See below
Issued: 1. 1927-by 1946
              2. c.1930

Colourways	U.S. $	Can. $	U.K. £
1. Purple/black/yellow/red		Rare	
2. Chinese Jade (illustrated)		Rare	

HN 919
Leopard
Seated

Model No.:   530
Designer: Charles Noke
Height: 6 ½", 16.5 cm
Colour: Brown with black spots
Issued: 1927-1940

Description	U.S. $	Can. $	U.K. £
Leopard	900.00	1,350.00	600.00

Note: Model 530 was also used to produce HN 912 Tiger.

HN 920
Foxes
Curled - Style Two

Model No.:   528
Height: 3" x 6", 7.6 x 15.2 cm
Colour: See below
Issued: 1. 1927-by 1946
              2. c.1926
Varieties: HN 925

Description	U.S. $	Can. $	U.K. £
1. Brown/black		Rare	
2. Flambé		Rare	

HN 921
Alsatian
Seated, without collar

Model No.:	525
Height:	1. 7", 17.8 cm
	2. 8 ¼", 21.0 cm
Colour:	See below
Issued:	1. 1927-by 1946
	2. c.1927

Colourways	U.S. $	Can. $	U.K. £
1. Natural colours	1,100.00	1,650.00	750.00
2. Flambé	1,100.00	1,650.00	750.00

HN 922
Wilfred the Rabbit

Model No.:	559
Designer:	Charles Noke
Height:	4", 10.1 cm
Colour:	Light brown and white rabbit, yellow trumpet
Issued:	1927-1936

Description	U.S. $	Can. $	U.K. £
Wilfred the rabbit	2,000.00	3,000.00	1,250.00

HN 923
Fox Terrier
Standing - Style One

Model No.:	554
Height:	4", 10.1 cm
Size:	Medium
Colour:	See below
Issued:	1. 1927-by 1946
	2. Unknown
Varieties:	HN 909

Colourways	U.S. $	Can. $	U.K. £
1. White/light brown	550.00	825.00	350.00
2. Flambé	750.00	1,100.00	500.00

HN 924
Fox Terrier
Seated - Style Two

Designer:	553
Height:	1. 5 ¼", 13.3 cm
	2. 4 ½", 11.4 cm
Size:	Medium
Colour:	See below
Issued:	1. 1927-by 1946
	2. c.1927
Varieties:	HN 910

Colourways	U.S. $	Can. $	U.K. £
1. White/light brown	550.00	825.00	350.00
2. Flambé	750.00	1,100.00	500.00

HN 925
Foxes
Curled - Style Two

Model No.:	528
Height:	3″ x 6″, 7.6 x 15.2 cm
Colour:	See below
Issued:	1. 1927-by 1946
	2. c.1926
Varieties:	HN 920

Colourways	U.S. $	Can. $	U.K. £
1. Grey/brown		Rare	
2. Flambé		Rare	

HN 926
Foxes
Curled - Style Three

Model No.:	545
Height:	1 ¾″, 5.1 cm
Size:	Miniature
Colour:	See below
Issued:	1. 1927-by 1946
	2. c.1927

Colourways	U.S. $	Can. $	U.K. £
1. Brown/black	525.00	800.00	350.00
2. Flambé	750.00	1,100.00	500.00

HN 927
Pekinese (two)

Model No.:	544
Height:	2 ½″ x 4 ½″, 6.4 cm x 11.4 cm
Colour:	See below
Issued:	1. 1927-by 1946
	2 and 3. c.1927

Colourways	U.S. $	Can. $	U.K. £
1. Natural colours	1,000.00	1,500.00	650.00
2. Chinese Jade		Very Rare	
3. Flambé		Very Rare	

HN 928
Ousel Bowl

Model No.:	Unknown
Height:	7″, 17.8 cm
Colour:	Green, blue, brown and orange
Issued:	1927-by 1946

Description	U.S. $	Can. $	U.K. £
Ousel bowl	1,500.00	2,250.00	1,000.00

Note: The bird forms a covered bowl.

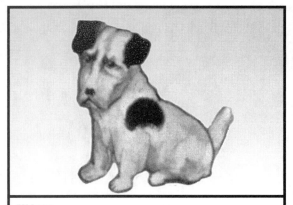

HN 929
Fox Terrier Puppy
Seated - white/black patches

Model No.:	570
Height:	Unknown
Colour:	White with black patches
Issued:	1927-by 1946
Varieties:	HN 931

Colourways	U.S. $	Can. $	U.K. £
White, black patches		Very Rare	

HN 930
Alsatian Puppy

Model No.:	568
Height:	2 ½", 6.4 cm
Colour:	Brown
Issued:	1927-by 1946

Description	U.S. $	Can. $	U.K. £
Alsatian puppy		Very Rare	

HN 931
Fox Terrier Puppy
Seated - brown

Model No.:	570
Height:	Unknown
Colour:	Brown
Issued:	1927-by 1946
Varieties:	HN 929

Colourways	U.S. $	Can. $	U.K. £
Brown		Very Rare	

HN 932
Scottish Terrier
Seated - Style One - steel grey

Model No.:	569
Height:	Unknown
Colour:	Steel grey
Issued:	1927-by 1946
Varieties:	HN 933, 934

Colourways	U.S. $	Can. $	U.K. £
Steel grey		Very Rare	

HN 933
Scottish Terrier
Seated - Style One - black

Model No.:	569
Height:	Unknown
Colour:	Black
Issued:	1927-by 1946
Varieties:	HN 932, 934

Colourways	U.S. $	Can. $	U.K. £
Black		Very Rare	

HN 934
Scottish Terrier
Seated - Style One - brown

Model No.:	569
Height:	Unknown
Colour:	Brown
Issued:	1927-by 1946
Varieties:	HN 932, 933

Colourways	U.S. $	Can. $	U.K. £
Brown		Very Rare	

HN 935
Pip, Squeak and Wilfred Tray

Model No.:	564
Designer:	Charles Noke
Height:	4", 10.1 cm
Colour:	Brown, black and white, cream tray
Issued:	1927-1936

Description	U.S. $	Can. $	U.K. £
Pip, Squeak, Wilfred	2,000.00	3,000.00	1,250.00

Note: On base "Daily Mirror."

HN 936
Teal Duck

Model No.:	Unknown
Height:	Unknown
Colour:	Unknown
Issued:	1927-by 1946

Description	U.S. $	Can. $	U.K. £
Teal duck		Very Rare	

HN 937
Alsatian
Standing on plinth

Model No.:	572	
Height:	Unknown	
Colour:	Brown	
Issued:	1927-by 1946	

Description	U.S. $	Can. $	U.K. £
Alsatian, standing		Extremely Rare	

HN 938
Alsatian
Lying on plinth

Model No.:	571	
Height:	Unknown	
Colour:	Brown	
Issued:	1927-by 1946	

Description	U.S. $	Can. $	U.K. £
Alsatian, lying		Extremely Rare	

HN 939
Bears Drinking - dark brown

Model No.:	561	
Height:	3", 7.6 cm	
Colour:	Dark brown	
Issued:	1927-1936	
Varieties:	HN 940	

Colourways	U.S. $	Can. $	U.K. £
Dark brown	3,000.00	4,500.00	2,000.00

HN 940
Bears Drinking - light brown

Model No.:	561	
Height:	3", 7.6 cm	
Colour:	Light brown	
Issued:	1927-1936	
Varieties:	HN 939	

Colourways	U.S. $	Can. $	U.K. £
Light brown	3,000.00	4,500.00	2,000.00

HN 941
Elephant, Trunk in salute - Style One

Model No.:	489B
Designer:	Charles Noke
Height:	4 ½", 11.4 cm
Size:	Small
Colour:	See below
Issued:	1. 1927-by 1946; 2. and 3. c.1926-1962
Varieties:	HN 891B, 2644

Colourways	U.S. $	Can. $	U.K. £
1. Black/white	525.00	800.00	350.00
2. Flambé	450.00	675.00	300.00
3. Sung	1,050.00	1,500.00	700.00

HN 942
Fox Terrier
Standing - Style Three - light brown patches

Model No.:	581
Height:	6", 15.2 cm
Size:	Large
Colour:	White with light brown patches
Issued:	1927-1936
Varieties:	HN 944

Colourways	U.S. $	Can. $	U.K. £
Light brown patches	650.00	1,000.00	400.00

HN 943
Fox Terrier
Standing - Style Two - light brown patches

Model No.:	580
Height:	5 ½", 14.0 cm - Large
Colour:	See below
Issued:	1. 1927-1940
	2. and 3. c.1927-by 1946
Varieties:	HN 945

Colourways	U.S. $	Can. $	U.K. £
1. White/light brown	650.00	1,000.00	400.00
2. Chinese Jade	1,875.00	2,750.00	1,250.00
3. Flambé	1,100.00	1,650.00	750.00

HN 944
Fox Terrier
Standing - Style Three - dark brown patches

Model No.:	581
Height:	6", 15.2 cm
Size:	Large
Colour:	White with dark brown patches
Issued:	1927-1936
Varieties:	HN 942

Colourways	U.S. $	Can. $	U.K. £
Dark brown patches	650.00	1,000.00	400.00

HN 945
Fox Terrier
Standing - Style Two - black-brown patches

Model No.:	580
Height:	5 ½", 14.0 cm
Size:	Large
Colour:	See below
Issued:	1. 1927-1940, 2. c.1927-by 1946
Varieties:	HN 943

Colourways	U.S. $	Can. $	U.K. £
1. White/black-brown	650.00	1,000.00	400.00
2. Chinese Jade	1,875.00	2,750.00	1,250.00
3. Flambé	1,100.00	1,650.00	750.00

HN 946
Peruvian Penguin - Medium

Model No.:	585
Designer:	Charles Noke
Height:	7 ¾", 19.7 cm - medium
Colour:	See below
Issued:	1. 1927-by 1946; 2. c.1936-1961
Varieties:	HN 1190

Colourways	U.S. $	Can. $	U.K. £
1. Black/white	975.00	1,450.00	650.00
2. Flambé	750.00	1,100.00	500.00

Note: Flambé models incorporate a rock as the base. Naturalistic models are free standing,

HN 947
King Penguin

Model No.:	591
Height:	7 ½", 19.0 cm
Colour:	See below
Issued:	1. 1927-by 1946
	2. c.1927
Varieties:	HN 1189

Colourways	U.S. $	Can. $	U.K. £
1. Silver-grey	975.00	1,450.00	650.00
2. Flambé	750.00	1,100.00	500.00

HN 948
Bulldog
Seated - Style Four

Model No.:	135
	Flambé: 135A
Height:	6", 15.2 cm
Colour:	See below
Issued:	1. 1927-by 1946 2. and 3. c.1913
Varieties:	HN 129

Colourways	U.S. $	Can. $	U.K. £
1. Dark brown	3,500.00	5,250.00	2,000.00
2. Flambé	2,250.00	3,375.00	1,500.00
3. Sung	3,500.00	5,250.00	2,000.00

CHARACTER ELEPHANT

Height: Unknown
Issued: 1928-by 1946

	HN 949 Style One	HN 950 Style Two	HN 951 Style Two	HN 952 Style One
Model No.:	596	595	595	596
Colour:	Orange	Yellow	Brown and blue	Pink
Varieties:	HN 952	HN 951	HN 950	HN 949
Currency	*HN 949*	*HN 950*	*HN 951*	*HN 952*
U.S. $				
Can. $	Very Rare	Very Rare	Very Rare	Very Rare
U.K. £				

Terrier Puppy
Seated

HN 953

Model No.:	597
Height:	Unknown
Colour:	Black, brown and white
Issued:	1928-by 1946
Varieties:	HN 954

HN 954

Model No.:	597
Height:	Unknown
Colour:	Black, dark brown and white
Issued:	1928-by 1946
Varieties:	HN 953

Description	U.S. $	Can. $	U.K. £
HN 953		Extremely Rare	
HN 954		Extremely Rare	

HN 955
Brown Bear
Style One

Model No.:	592
Height:	5", 12.7 cm
Colour:	See below
Issued:	1. 1928-by 1946
	2. c.1928

Colourways	U.S. $	Can. $	U.K. £
1. Brown	1,150.00	1,700.00	750.00
2. Flambé		Very Rare	

HN 956
Mallard Drake, Standing

Model No.:	137
Height:	1. 5 ½", 14.0 cm
	2. 6 ½", 16.5 cm
Size:	Medium
Colour:	See below
Issued:	1. 1928-by 1946
	2. 1913-1996
Varieties:	HN 114, 115, 116, 1191, 2555, 2647

Colourways	U.S. $	Can. $	U.K. £
1. Unknown	400.00	600.00	250.00
2. Flambé	200.00	300.00	125.00

HN 957
King Charles Spaniel - liver and white

Model No.:	532	
Height:	4 ¾" 12.1 cm	
Colour:	Liver and white	
Issued:	1928-by 1946	
Varieties:	HN 958	

Colourways	U.S. $	Can. $	U.K. £
Liver and white		Very Rare	

HN 958
King Charles Spaniel - black and white

Model No.:	532	
Height:	4 ¾", 12.1 cm	
Colour:	Black and white	
Issued:	1928-by 1946	
Varieties:	HN 957	

Colourways	U.S. $	Can. $	U.K. £
Black and white		Very Rare	

*

HN 960
Character Ape with Book
Eyes open

Model No.:	604	
Designer:	Charles Noke	
Height:	4", 10.1 cm	
Colour:	Brown	
Issued:	1928-1936	

Description	U.S. $	Can. $	U.K. £
Ape, eyes open	1,275.00	1,900.00	850.00

HN 961
Character Ape with Book
Eyes closed

Model No.:	604
Designer:	Charles Noke
Height:	4", 10.1 cm
Colour:	Brown
Issued:	1928-1936

Description	U.S. $	Can. $	U.K. £
Ape, eyes closed	1,275.00	1,900.00	850.00

HN 962
Great Dane's Head
Pencil Holder

Model No.:	529
Height:	3", 7.6 cm
Colour:	Grey and white
Issued:	1928-1936
Derivative:	Onyx calendar

Description	U.S. $	Can. $	U.K. £
Pencil holder	750.00	1,100.00	500.00

HN 963
Fox
Seated - Style Four

Model No.:	599
Height:	5 ½", 14.0 cm
Size:	Medium
Colour:	Brown with black ear tips
Issued:	1928-by 1946

Description	U.S. $	Can. $	U.K. £
Fox, seated	525.00	800.00	350.00

HN 964
Scottish Terrier
Standing - Style One - black

Model No.:	78
Height:	4", 10.1 cm
Colour:	See below
Issued:	1. 1928-by 1946
	2. c.1913
Varieties:	HN 965

Colourways	U.S. $	Can. $	U.K. £
1. Black	1,100.00	1,600.00	700.00
2. Flambé		Very Rare	

HN 965
Scottish Terrier
Standing - Style One - brown

Model No.:	78		
Height:	4", 10.1 cm		
Colour:	See below		
Issued:	1. 1928-by 1946		
	2. c.1913		
Varieties:	HN 964		

Colourways	U.S. $	Can. $	U.K. £
1. Brown	1,100.00	1,600.00	700.00
2. Flambé		Very Rare	

HN 966
Elephant, Trunk in salute

Model No.:	489		
Designer:	Charles Noke		
Height:	7", 17.8 cm		
Size:	Large		
Colour:	See below		
Issued:	1. 1928-by 1946		
	2. and 3. c.1926-1962		

Colourways	U.S. $	Can. $	U.K. £
1. Brown/grey (matt)		Extremely Rare	
2. Chinese Jade	2,250.00	3,375.00	1,500.00
3. Flambé	600.00	900.00	400.00

HN 967
Cat, Seated - Style One

Model No.:	9		
Designer:	Charles Noke		
Height:	4 ½", 11.4 cm		
Colour:	See below		
Issued:	1. 1928-by 1946		
	2. 1920-1996		
Varieties:	HN 109, 120		

Colourways	U.S. $	Can. $	U.K. £
1. Brown/white	750.00	1,100.00	500.00
2. Flambé	175.00	250.00	100.00
3. Sung		Extremely Rare	

HN 968
Pig
Snorting - large

Model No.:	72		
Height:	2 ½" x 5 ½", 6.4 x 14.0 cm		
Size:	Large		
Colour:	See below		
Issued:	1. 1928-1936		
	2. c.1912-1936		

Colourways	U.S. $	Can. $	U.K. £
1. Black/white	675.00	1,000.00	450.00
2. Flambé	750.00	1,100.00	500.00

HN 968A
Pig
Snorting - small

Model No.:	72A
Height:	2" x 4 ½", 5.0 x 11.9 cm
Size:	Small
Colour:	See below
Issued:	1. 1928-1936
	2. c.1928-1936

Colourways	U.S. $	Can. $	U.K. £
1. Black/white	525.00	800.00	350.00
2. Flambé	600.00	900.00	400.00

HN 969
Rabbits

Model No.:	249
Height:	3 ½", 8.9 cm
Colour:	See below
Issued:	1. 1928-by 1946
	2. c.1919
Varieties:	HN 209, 217, 218, 219

Colourways	U.S. $	Can. $	U.K. £
1. White/brown	900.00	1,350.00	600.00
2. Flambé		Very Rare	

HN 970
Dachshund
Standing - Style Two

Model No.:	36
Height:	4 ½" x 6 ½", 11.4 x 6.5 cm
Colour:	See below
Issued:	1928-by 1946

Colourways	U.S. $	Can. $	U.K. £
Brown		Rare	

HN 971
'Ooloo' Character Cat
Ashtray

Model No.:	400
Height:	3", 7.6 cm
Colour:	Black and white cat, yellow tray
Issued:	1928-by 1946

Description	U.S. $	Can. $	U.K. £
Ashtray		Rare	

HN 972
Character Ape in Dunce's Cap with Book

Model No.:	640
Designer:	Charles Noke
Height:	5 ½", 14.0 cm
Colour:	See below
Issued:	1. 1928-1936
	2. c.1929-1937

Colourways	U.S. $	Can. $	U.K. £
1. Dark brown/white	2,250.00	3,500.00	1,500.00
2. Flambé (illustrated)	1,650.00	2,500.00	1,100.00

HN 973
Character Duck
Style Three - yellow/brown/black

Model No.:	647
Height:	6", 15.2 cm
Size:	Large
Colour:	See below
Issued:	1. 1930-by 1946
	2. c.1930
Varieties:	HN 974

Colourways	U.S. $	Can. $	U.K. £
1. Yellow/brown/black	1,000.00	1,500.00	700.00
2. Flambé		Very Rare	

HN 974
Character Duck
Style Three - lemon-yellow

Model No.:	647
Height:	6", 15.2 cm
Size:	Large
Colour:	See below
Issued:	1. 1930-by 1946
	2. c.1930
Varieties:	HN 973

Colourways	U.S. $	Can. $	U.K. £
1. Lemon-yellow	1,000.00	1,500.00	700.00
2. Flambé		Very Rare	

HN 975
English Setter with Collar

Model No.:	646
Height:	6", 15.2 cm
Colour:	Black and white
Issued:	1930-by 1946
Varieties:	Also called 'Red Setter with Collar'
	HN 976

Description	U.S. $	Can. $	U.K. £
English setter	1,275.00	1,900.00	850.00

HN 976
Red Setter with Collar

Model No.:	646
Height:	6", 15.2 cm
Colour:	Light brown
Issued:	1930-by 1946
Varieties:	Also called 'English Setter with Collar' HN 975

Description	U.S. $	Can. $	U.K. £
Red setter	1,275.00	1,900.00	850.00

HN 977
Drake
Resting

Model No.:	654
Height:	3 ¾" x 7 ¼", 9.5 x 18.4 cm
Size:	Large
Colour:	See below
Issued:	1. 1930-by 1946
	2. c.1929-1961
Varieties:	HN 1192

Colourways	U.S. $	Can. $	U.K. £
1. Green/white/brown	600.00	900.00	400.00
2. Flambé	600.00	900.00	400.00

HN 978
Fox
Curled - Style Two

Model No.:	653
Height:	Unknown
Colour:	See below
Issued:	2. 1930-by 1946
	2. c.1929

Colourways	U.S. $	Can. $	U.K. £
1. Brown		Very Rare	
2. Flambé		Very Rare	

HN 979
Hare
Lying, legs stretched behind - brown

Model No.:	656
Height:	3" x 7 ½", 7.6 x 19.1 cm
Size:	Large
Colour:	See below
Issued:	1. 1930-by 1946
	2. 1929-1962
Varieties:	HN 984, 985, 1071, 2593

Colourways	U.S. $	Can. $	U.K. £
1. Brown/white/black	375.00	550.00	250.00
2. Flambé	450.00	675.00	300.00

HN 980
Aberdeen Terrier - black

Model No.:	657
Height:	3" x 5", 7.6 x 12.7 cm
Colour:	Black
Issued:	1930-by 1946
Varieties:	HN 981

Colourways	U.S. $	Can. $	U.K. £
Black	650.00	1,000.00	425.00

HN 981
Aberdeen Terrier - grey

Model No.:	657
Height:	3" x 5", 7.6 x 12.7 cm
Colour:	Grey with brown highlights
Issued:	1930-by 1946
Varieties:	HN 980

Colourways	U.S. $	Can. $	U.K. £
Grey	650.00	1,000.00	425.00

HN 982
Sealyham - Standing - Style One

Model No.:	658
Height:	3", 7.6 cm
Colour:	See below
Issued:	1 to 3. 1930-1936
	4. c.1930
Varieties:	HN 983

Colourways	U.S. $	Can. $	U.K. £
1. White/black patches	675.00	1,000.00	450.00
2. White/brown patches	675.00	1,000.00	450.00
3. Light tan	825.00	1,250.00	550.00
4. Flambé		Very Rare	

HN 983
Sealyham
Standing - Style One - light brown patches

Model No.:	658
Height:	3", 7.6 cm
Colour:	See below
Issued:	1. 1930-1936
	2. c.1930
Varieties:	HN 982

Colourways	U.S. $	Can. $	U.K. £
1. White/light brown	825.00	1,250.00	550.00
2. Flambé		Very Rare	

HN 984
Hare
Lying, legs stretched behind - white

Model No.:	656
Height:	3″ x 7 ½″, 7.6 x 19.1 cm
Size:	Large
Colour:	See below
Issued:	1. 1930-by 1946
	2. 1929-1962
Varieties:	HN 979, 985, 1071, 2593

Colourways	U.S. $	Can. $	U.K. £
1. White	375.00	550.00	250.00
2. Flambé	450.00	675.00	300.00

HN 985
Hare
Lying, legs stretched behind - grey

Model No.:	656
Height:	3″ x 7 ½″, 7.6 x 19.1 cm
Size:	Large
Colour:	See below
Issued:	1. 1930-by 1946
	2. 1929-1962
Varieties:	HN 979, 984, 1071, 2593

Colourways	U.S. $	Can. $	U.K. £
1. Grey	375.00	550.00	250.00
2. Flambé	450.00	675.00	300.00

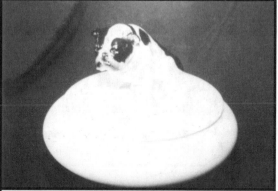

HN 986
Alsatian Seated on Lid of a Lustre Bowl

Model No.:	497A
Height:	5″, 12.7 cm (includes bowl)
Colour:	Brown dog on mother of pearl bowl
Issued:	1930-by 1946
Varieties:	HN 899 (without bowl)

Description	U.S. $	Can. $	U.K. £
Alsatian / lustre bowl	2,000.00	3,000.00	1,350.00

HN 987
Bulldog Seated on Lid of a Lustre Bowl

Model No.:	122
Height:	4″, 10.1 cm (includes bowl)
Colour:	White bulldog with dark brown patches, mother of pearl bowl
Issued:	1930-by 1946
Varieties:	HN 881 (without bowl)

Description	U.S. $	Can. $	U.K. £
Bulldog / lustre bowl	2,500.00	3,750.00	1,650.00

HN 988
Airedale Terrier
Standing

Model No.:	685
Height:	8", 8", 20.3 x 20.3 cm
Size:	Large
Colour:	Light brown
Issued:	1930-1936
Varieties:	HN 996

Colourways	U.S. $	Can. $	U.K. £
Light brown	1,250.00	1,850.00	800.00

HN 989
Scottish Terrier
Standing - Style Two - black/grey

Model No.:	Unknown
Height:	3 ½" x 6 ¾", 8.9 x 17.1 cm
Colour:	Black with grey highlights
Issued:	1930-1936
Varieties:	HN 992

Colourways	U.S. $	Can. $	U.K. £
Black/grey	1,350.00	2,000.00	900.00

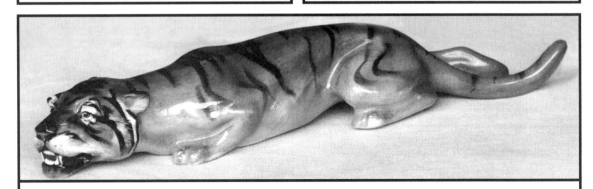

Tiger
Stalking - Style One

	HN 990	HN 991A	HN 991B
Model No.:	680	680A	680B
Designer:	Charles Noke		
Colour:	Brown		
Issued:	1930-by 1946		
Size:	Large	Medium	Small
Length:	7 ½", 19.1 cm	5 ½", 14.0 cm	Unknown

Currency	Large	Medium	Small
U.S. $	675.00	600.00	525.00
Can. $	1,000.00	900.00	800.00
U.K. £	450.00	400.00	350.00

HN 992
Scottish Terrier
Standing - Style Two - brown/black

Model No.:	Unknown
Height:	3 ½" x 6 ¾", 8.9 x 17.1 cm
Colour:	Brown and black
Issued:	1930-by 1946
Varieties:	HN 989

Colourways	U.S. $	Can. $	U.K. £
Black/brown	1,350.00	2,000.00	900.00

HN 993
Cat Asleep on Cushion

Model No.:	24
Height:	1 ¾", 4.4 cm
Colour:	Black and blue
Issued:	1930-1936

Description	U.S. $	Can. $	U.K. £
Cat asleep on cushion		Extremely Rare	

HN 994
Fox on Pedestal

Model No.:	21
Height:	6", 15.2 cm
Colour:	See below
Issued:	1. 1930-1936
	2. c.1912-1936

Colourways	U.S. $	Can. $	U.K. £
1. Brown		Very Rare	
2. Flambé		Very Rare	

HN 995
Pekinese
Standing

Model No.:	689
Height:	3 ½" x 5", 8.9 x 12.7 cm
Colour:	See below
Issued:	1. 1930-1937
	2. c.1930
Varieties:	HN 1003

Colourways	U.S. $	Can. $	U.K. £
1. Brown/black	1,150.00	1,700.00	750.00
2. Chinese Jade	2,250.00	3,500.00	1,500.00

HN 996
Airedale Terrier
Standing

Model No.:	685
Height:	8" x 8", 20.3 x 20.3 cm
Size:	Large
Colour:	Light brown with black highlights
Issued:	1930-1936
Varieties:	HN 988

Colourways	U.S. $	Can. $	U.K. £
Light brown/black	1,250.00	1,850.00	800.00

HN 997
Airedale Terrier
Seated

Model No.:	686
Height:	5", 12.7 cm
Colour:	White with black and dark brown patches on ears, eyes and body
Issued:	1930-by 1946

Description	U.S. $	Can. $	U.K. £
Airedale terrier, seated	1,250.00	1,850.00	800.00

HN 998
King Penguin and Chick

Model No.:	239
Height:	5 ½", 14.0 cm
Colour:	See below
Issued:	1. 1930-by 1946
	2. c.1918-1961
Varieties:	HN 198, 297

Colourways	U.S. $	Can. $	U.K. £
1. Green/yellow	900.00	1,350.00	600.00
2. Flambé (illustrated)	825.00	1,250.00	550.00

HN 999
Persian Cat
Seated - Style One

Model No.:	690
Height:	5", 12.7 cm
Colour:	Black and white
Issued:	1930-1985
Varieties:	HN 2539

Description	U.S. $	Can. $	U.K. £
Black/white cat	175.00	250.00	125.00

HN 1000
Cocker Spaniel Ch. 'Lucky Star of Ware'

Model No.:	709
Designer:	Frederick Daws
Height:	6 ½", 16.5 cm
Size:	Large
Colour:	Black with grey highlights
Issued:	1931-1960
Varieties:	HN 1002, 1108, 1134, 1186; Also called 'Lucky Pride of Ware'

Description	U.S. $	Can. $	U.K. £
Black, large	450.00	675.00	300.00

HN 1001
Cocker Spaniel with Pheasant

Model No.:	714
Designer:	Frederick Daws
Height:	6 ½" x 7 ¾", 16.5 x 19.7 cm
Size:	Large
Colour:	White with brown markings, reddish-brown and green pheasant
Issued:	1931-1968
Varieties:	HN 1137

Description	U.S. $	Can. $	U.K. £
White/brown, large	500.00	750.00	325.00

HN 1002
Cocker Spaniel

Model No.:	709
Designer:	Frederick Daws
Height:	6 ½", 16.5 cm
Size:	Large
Colour:	Liver and white
Issued:	1931-1960
Varieties:	HN 1000, 1108, 1134, 1186; Also called 'Lucky Star of Ware' and 'Lucky Pride of Ware'

Description	U.S. $	Can. $	U.K. £
Liver/white, large	600.00	900.00	400.00

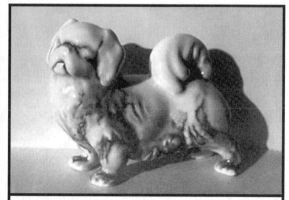

HN 1003
Pekinese
Standing

Model No.:	689
Height:	3 ½" x 5", 8.9 x 12.7 cm
Colour:	See below
Issued:	1. 1931-1937
	2. c.1930
Varieties:	HN 995

Colourways	U.S. $	Can. $	U.K. £
1. Dark brown	1,150.00	1,700.00	750.00
2. Chinese Jade	2,250.00	3,500.00	1,500.00

HN 1004
Blue Tit and Blossom

Model No.:	721
Height:	2 ½", 6.4 cm
Colour:	Browns, white, flowers, dark brown and green base
Issued:	1931-1937

Description	U.S. $	Can. $	U.K. £
Blue tit	975.00	1,450.00	650.00

HN 1005
Thrush and Blossom

Model No.:	716
Height:	2 ½", 6.4 cm
Colour:	Browns, yellow, white flowers, dark brown and green base
Issued:	1931-1937

Description	U.S. $	Can. $	U.K. £
Thrush	975.00	1,450.00	650.00

*

HN 1007
Rough Haired Terrier Ch. 'Crackley Startler'

Model No.:	725
Designer:	Frederick Daws
Height:	7 ½", 19.1 cm
Size:	Large
Colour:	White with black and brown markings
Issued:	1931-1955
Varieties:	Also known as 'Crackley Hunter'

Description	U.S. $	Can. $	U.K. £
Rough-haired terrier	750.00	1,100.00	500.00

HN 1008
Scottish Terrier Ch. 'Albourne Arthur'

Model No.:	720
Designer:	Frederick Daws
Height:	7", 17.8 cm
Size:	Large
Colour:	Black
Issued:	1931-1955

Description	U.S. $	Can. $	U.K. £
Scottish terrier	1,100.00	1,650.00	700.00

HN 1009
Hare and Leverets

Model No.:	731
Designer:	Unknown
Length:	5", 12.7 cm
Colour:	Brown
Issued:	1931-1937

Description	U.S. $	Can. $	U.K. £
Hare and leverets		Very Rare	

PEKINESE CH. 'BIDDEE OF IFIELD'- Standing

Designer:	Frederick Daws
Colour:	Golden brown with black highlights

	HN 1010	HN 1011	HN 1012
Model No.:	734	734A	734B
Height:	7", 17.8 cm	6 ½", 16.5 cm	3", 11.4 cm
Size:	Extra large	Large	Medium
Issued:	1931-1955	1931-1955	1931-1985
Derivative:	—	—	Bookend

Currency	Extra Large	Large	Small
U.S. $	1,275.00	825.00	100.00
Can. $	1,900.00	1,250.00	150.00
U.K. £	850.00	550.00	65.00

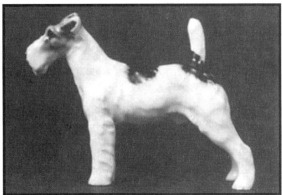

HN 1013
Rough-Haired Terrier Ch. 'Crackley Startler'

Model No.:	725A
Designer:	Frederick Daws
Height:	5 ½", 17.8 cm
Size:	Medium
Colour:	White with black and brown markings
Issued:	1931-1960
Varieties:	Also called 'Crackley Hunter'
Derivative:	Bookend

Description	U.S. $	Can. $	U.K. £
Medium	350.00	525.00	225.00

HN 1014
Rough-Haired Terrier Ch. 'Crackley Startler'

Model No.:	725B
Designer:	Frederick Daws
Height:	3 ¾", 13.3 cm
Size:	Small
Colour:	White with black and brown markings
Issued:	1931-1985
Varieties:	Also called 'Crackley Hunter'

Description	U.S. $	Can. $	U.K. £
Small	150.00	225.00	100.00

HN 1015
Scottish Terrier Ch. 'Albourne Arthur'

Model No.:	720A
Designer:	Frederick Daws
Height:	5", 16.5 cm
Size:	Medium
Colour:	Black
Issued:	1931-1960
Derivative:	Bookend

Description	U.S. $	Can. $	U.K. £
Medium	350.00	525.00	225.00

HN 1016
Scottish Terrier Ch. 'Albourne Arthur'

Model No.:	720B
Designer:	Frederick Daws
Height:	3 ½", 12.7 cm
Size:	Small
Colour:	Black
Issued:	1931-1985

Description	U.S. $	Can. $	U.K. £
Small	150.00	225.00	100.00

SCOTTISH TERRIER - Seated - Style Two
Colour: Black

HN 1017
Model No.:   733
Height: 7", 17.8 cm
Size: Large
Issued: 1931-1946

Description	U.S. $	Can. $	U.K. £
Large	1,750.00	2,600.00	1,150.00

HN 1018
Model No.:   733A
Height: 5", 12.7 cm
Size: Medium
Issued: 1931-by 1946

Description	U.S. $	Can. $	U.K. £
1. Natural	900.00	1,350.00	600.00
2. Flambé	900.00	1,350.00	600.00

HN 1019
Model No.:   733B
Height: 3 ½", 8.9 cm
Size: Small
Issued: 1931-by 1946

Description	U.S. $	Can. $	U.K. £
Small	750.00	1,100.00	500.00

HN 1020
Cocker Spaniel Ch. 'Lucky Star of Ware'
Model No.:   709A
Designer: Frederick Daws
Height: 5", 17.8 cm
Size: Medium
Colour: See below
Issued: 1. 1931-1985   2. c.1937
Varieties: Also called 'Lucky Pride of Ware,' and
             Spaniel HN 1036, 1109, 1135, 1187

Colourways	U.S. $	Can. $	U.K. £
1. Black/grey	125.00	175.00	80.00
2. Flambé	900.00	1,350.00	600.00

HN 1021
Cocker Spaniel Ch. 'Lucky Star of Ware'
Model No.:   709B
Designer: Frederick Daws
Height: 3 ½", 8.9 cm
Size: Small
Colour: Black coat with grey markings
Issued: 1931-1968
Varieties: Also called 'Lucky Pride of Ware,' and
             Spaniel HN 1037, 1078, 1136, 1188

Description	U.S. $	Can. $	U.K. £
Small	150.00	225.00	100.00

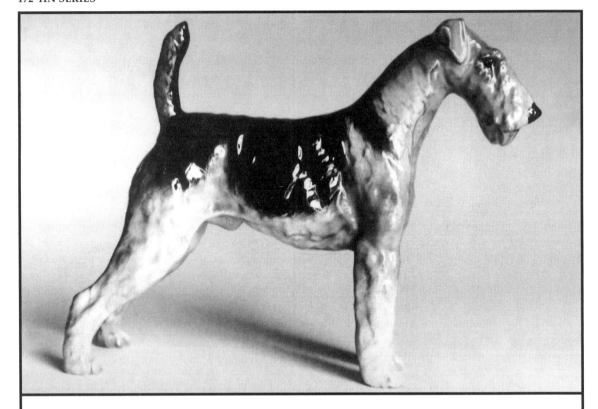

AIREDALE TERRIER CH. 'COTSFORD TOPSAIL'

Designer: Frederick Daws
Colour: 1. Natural; Dark brown and black coat, light brown underbody
2. Flambé

		HN 1022	HN 1023	HN 1024
Model No.:		738	738A	738B
Height:		8″, 20.3 cm	5 ¼″, 13.3 cm	4″, 10.1 cm
Size:		Large	Medium	Small
Issued:	1. Natural	1931-1960	1931-1985	1931-1968
	2. Flambé	c.1931	c.1931	N/A

	Large		Medium		Small	
Currency	Natural	Flambé	Natural	Flambé	Natural	Flambé
U.S. $	1,000.00	1,350.00	200.00	1,100.00	275.00	N/A
Can. $	1,500.00	2,000.00	300.00	1,650.00	400.00	N/A
U.K. £	650.00	900.00	125.00	700.00	175.00	N/A

ENGLISH FOXHOUND CH. 'TRING RATTLER'

Designer: Frederick Daws
Colour: White, black and brown

	HN 1025	HN 1026	HN 1027
Model No.:	740	740A	740B
Height:	8", 20.3 cm	5", 12.7 cm	4", 10.1 cm
Size:	Large	Medium	Small
Issued: 1. Natural	1931-1955	1931-1960	1931-1956
2. Flambé	—	—	Unknown

	Large		Medium		Small	
Currency	Natural	Flambé	Natural	Flambé	Natural	Flambé
U.S. $	1,750.00	N/A	750.00	N/A	500.00	
Can. $	2,600.00	N/A	1,100.00	N/A	750.00	Very
U.K. £	1,150.00	N/A	500.00	N/A	325.00	Rare

COCKER SPANIEL WITH PHEASANT

Designer: Frederick Daws
Colour: White coat with dark brown markings,
             red brown and green pheasant

HN 1028

Model No.:   714A
Height: 5 ¼", 13.3 cm
Size: Medium
Issued: 1931-1985
Varieties: HN 1138
Derivative: Bookend

HN 1029

Model No.:   714B
Height: 3 ½", 8.9 cm
Size: Small
Issued: 1931-1968
Varieties: HN 1062, 2600

Description	U.S. $	Can. $	U.K. £
HN 1028 — medium	175.00	250.00	125.00
HN 1029 — small	200.00	300.00	150.00

SEALYHAM, CH. 'SCOTIA STYLIST ' - standing

Designer: Frederick Daws
Colour: White with light brown patches

HN 1030

Model No.:   748
Height: 5 ½" x 9", 14.0 x 22.9 cm
Size: Large
Issued: White - 1931-1955
             Flambé - c.1931

HN 1031

Model No.:   748A
Height: 4", 10.1 cm
Size: Medium
Issued: 1931-1955
Derivative: Bookend

HN 1032

Model No.:   748B
Height: 3", 12.7 cm
Size: Small
Issued: 1931-1960

Description	U.S. $	Can. $	U.K. £
HN 1030 — white	1,250.00	1,875.00	800.00
HN 1030 — flambé	2,250.00	3,500.00	1,500.00
HN 1031 — medium	275.00	400.00	175.00
HN 1032 — small	225.00	350.00	150.00

CAIRN CH. 'CHARMING EYES'

Designer: Frederick Daws
Colour: Grey with black markings

	HN 1033	HN 1034	HN 1035
Model No.:	750	750A	750B
Height:	7", 17.8 cm	4 ½", 11.4 cm	3 ¼", 8.3 cm
Size:	Large	Medium	Small
Issued: 1. Natural	1931-1955	1931-1960	1. 1931-1985
2. Flambé	N/A	N/A	2. c.1931
Varieties:	HN 1104	HN 1105	HN 1106
Derivative:	—	Bookend	—

Currency	Large		Medium		Small	
	Natural	Flambé	Natural	Flambé	Natural	Flambé
U.S. $	1,250.00	N/A	400.00	N/A	150.00	750.00
Can. $	1,875.00	N/A	600.00	N/A	225.00	1,100.00
U.K. £	800.00	N/A	250.00	N/A	100.00	500.00

HN 1036
Cocker Spaniel - Medium

Model No.:	709A
Designer:	Frederick Daws
Height:	5 ¼", 13.3 cm
Colour:	See below
Issued:	1. 1931-1985; 2. c.1937
Varieties:	HN 1109, 1135, 1187, Also called 'Lucky Pride of Ware' and 'Lucky Star of Ware' HN 1020

Colourways	U.S. $	Can. $	U.K. £
1. White/light brown	125.00	175.00	80.00
2. Flambé	900.00	1,350.00	600.00

HN 1037
Cocker Spaniel

Model No.:	709B
Designer:	Frederick Daws
Height:	3 ½", 8.9 cm
Size:	Small
Colour:	White, light brown patches
Issued:	1931-1968
Varieties:	HN 1078, 1136, 1188; Also called 'Lucky Pride of Ware' and 'Lucky Star of Ware' HN 1021

Description	U.S. $	Can. $	U.K. £
Small	150.00	225.00	100.00

HN 1038
Scottish Terrier
Begging - Style One

Model No.:	Unknown
Height:	Unknown
Colour:	Unknown
Issued:	1931-by 1946

Description	U.S. $	Can. $	U.K. £
Scottish terrier		Extremely Rare	

PEKINESE CH. 'BIDDEE OF IFIELD'
Seated

Designer: Frederick Daws
Colour: Butterscotch coat with black highlight

HN 1039

Model No.:   752
Height: 7", 17.8 cm
Size: Large
Issued: 1931-by 1946

HN 1040

Model No.:   752B
Height: 3", 7.6 cm
Size: Small
Issued: 1. Natural - 1931-by 1946
             2. Flambé - c.1931

Description	U.S. $	Can. $	U.K. £
HN 1039 — Natural	1,500.00	2,250.00	1,000.00
HN 1040 — Natural	750.00	1,100.00	500.00
HN 1040 — Flambé		Very Rare	

HN 1041
Sealyham Ch. 'Scotia Stylist' - Lying - Style One

Model No.:   753
Designer: Frederick Daws
Height: Unknown
Size: Large
Colour: White with light brown patches over
             the ears and eyes
Issued: 1931-by 1946

Description	U.S. $	Can. $	U.K. £
Large	1,500.00	2,250.00	1,000.00

BULLDOG
Standing

Designer: Frederick Daws
Colour: Brown and white

	HN 1042	**HN 1043**	**HN 1044**
Model No.:	754	754A	754B
Height:	5 ½", 14.0 cm	4 ¾", 12.1 cm	3 ¼", 8.3 cm
Size:	Large	Medium	Small
Issued:	1931-1960	1931-1960	1931-1968
Varieties:	HN 1045, 1072	HN 1046, 1073	HN 1047, 1074
Derivative:	—	Bookend	—

Currency	Large	Medium	Small
U.S. $	1,200.00	650.00	300.00
Can. $	1,750.00	1,000.00	450.00
U.K. £	750.00	425.00	200.00

HN 1045
Bulldog
Standing

Model No.:	754
Designer:	Frederick Daws
Height:	5 ¼", 13.3 cm
Size:	Large
Colour:	Brown and white
Issued:	1931-1960
Varieties:	HN 1042, 1072

Description	U.S. $	Can. $	U.K. £
Large	1,200.00	1,750.00	750.00

HN 1046
Bulldog
Standing

Model No.:	754A
Designer:	Frederick Daws
Height:	4 ¾", 12.1 cm
Size:	Medium
Colour:	Brown and white
Issued:	1931-1960
Varieties:	HN 1043, 1073

Description	U.S. $	Can. $	U.K. £
Medium	500.00	750.00	300.00

HN 1047
Bulldog
Standing

Model No.:	754B
Designer:	Frederick Daws
Height:	3 ¼", 8.3 cm
Size:	Small
Colour:	Brown and white
Issued:	1931-1985
Varieties:	HN 1044, 1074

Description	U.S. $	Can. $	U.K. £
Small	185.00	275.00	125.00

HN 1048
West Highland Terrier
Style One

Model No.:	756
Height:	6 ½" x 9", 16.5 x 22.9 cm
Size:	Large
Colour:	White with brown highlights
Issued:	1931-1931

Description	U.S. $	Can. $	U.K. £
Large		Only three known to exist.	

Note: Sold at auction, Phillips, London, October 2000, for £1,125.00.

ENGLISH SETTER CH. 'MAESYDD MUSTARD'

Designer: Frederick Daws
Colour: Off white coat with black highlights

		HN 1049	HN 1050	HN 1051
Model No.:		770	770A	770B
Height:		7 ½", 19.0 cm	5 ¼", 13.3 cm	4", 10.1 cm
Size:		Large	Medium	Small
Issued:	1.	1931-1960	1931-1985	1931-1968
	2.	Unknown (flambé)	—	—
Varieties:				
Also called:				
English Setter		HN 2620	HN 2621	HN 2622
Gordon Setter		HN 1079	HN 1080	HN 1081
Irish Setter		HN 1054	HN 1055	HN 1056
Ch. 'Pat O'Moy'				

Currency	Large		Medium		Small	
	Natural	*Flambé*	*Natural*	*Flambé*	*Natural*	*Flambé*
U.S. $	900.00	1,200.00	200.00	—	275.00	—
Can. $	1,350.00	1,800.00	300.00	—	400.00	—
U.K. £	600.00	800.00	125.00	—	175.00	—

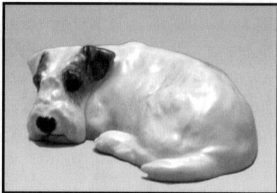

HN 1052
Sealyham Ch. 'Scotia Stylist'
Lying

Model No.:	753A
Designer:	Frederick Daws
Height:	Unknown
Size:	Medium
Colour:	White with light brown patches over ears and eyes
Issued:	1931-by 1946

Description	U.S. $	Can. $	U.K. £
Medium	1,150.00	1,700.00	750.00

HN 1053
Sealyham Ch. 'Scotia Stylist'
Lying

Model No.:	753B
Designer:	Frederick Daws
Height:	Unknown
Size:	Small
Colour:	White with light brown patches over ears and eyes
Issued:	1931-by 1946

Description	U.S. $	Can. $	U.K. £
Small	750.00	1,100.00	500.00

NOTES ON PRICING

- Animal figures are not as plentiful as pretty ladies or character figures and caution in pricing must prevail.

- In the pricing tables N/A (not available) indicates that the animal figure was not available in that particular market.

- Italicized prices are an indication only and form a starting point for discussion on the final price, which may be lower or higher depending on supply and demand.

- Rarity classification provides a range for the collector to work with.

Rarity Class	Rare	Very Rare	Extremely Rare
U.S. $	1,100./1,500.	1,500./2,250.	2,250./3,250.
Can. $	1,650./2,200.	2,250./3,250.	3,250./4,500.
U.K. £	750./1,000.	1,000./1,500.	1,500./2,250.

- Always remember that when dealing with rare animal figures you need two willing parties, a buyer and a seller. One without the other will not work and only when they agree do you have a market price.

IRISH SETTER CH. 'PAT O'MOY'

Designer: Frederick Daws
Colour: Reddish-brown

		HN 1054	**HN 1055**	**HN 1056**
Model No.:		770	770A	770B
Height:		7 ½", 19.0 cm	5", 12.7 cm	4", 10.1 cm
Size:		Large	Medium	Small
Issued:	1.	1931-1960	1931-1985	1931-1968
	2.	Unknown (flambé)	—	—
Varieties:				
Also called:				
English Setter		HN 2620	HN 2621	HN 2622
English Setter Ch.				
'Maesydd Mustard'		HN 1049	HN 1050	HN 1051
Gordon Setter		HN 1079	HN 1080	HN 1081
Derivative:		—	Bookend	—

Currency	Large		Medium		Small	
	Natural	Flambé	Natural	Flambé	Natural	Flambé
U.S. $	1,100.00	1,200.00	200.00	—	275.00	—
Can. $	1,650.00	1,800.00	300.00	—	400.00	—
U.K. £	700.00	800.00	125.00	—	175.00	—

COLLIE CH. 'ASHSTEAD APPLAUSE'

Designer: Frederick Daws
Colour: Dark and light brown coat, white chest, shoulders and feet

	HN 1057	HN 1058	HN 1059
Model No.:	779	779A	779B
Height:	7 ½", 19.1 cm	5", 12.7 cm	3 ½", 11.4 cm
Size:	Large	Medium	Small
Issued:	1931-1960	1931-1985	1931-1969

Currency	Large	Medium	Small
U.S. $	1,000.00	200.00	250.00
Can. $	1,500.00	300.00	375.00
U.K. £	650.00	125.00	150.00

*

HN 1062
Cocker Spaniel with Pheasant

Model No.:	714B
Designer:	Frederick Daws
Height:	3 ½", 8.9 cm
Size:	Small
Colour:	White with black markings, reddish-brown pheasant
Issued:	1931-1968
Varieties:	HN 1029, 2600

Description	U.S. $	Can. $	U.K. £
Cocker spaniel/pheasant	200.00	300.00	125.00

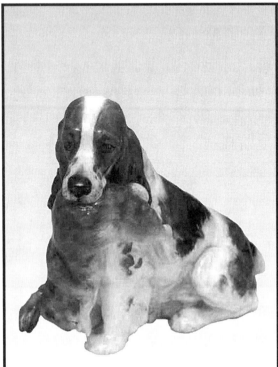

COCKER SPANIEL WITH HARE

Colour:	Brown and white dog, brown hare

HN 1063

Model No.:	784
Height:	5", 12.7 cm
Size:	Large
Issued:	1931-1935

HN 1064

Model No.:	784A
Height:	4", 10.1 cm
Size:	Small
Issued:	1931-1935

Description	U.S. $	Can. $	U.K. £
HN 1063 — large		Very Rare	
HN 1064 — small		Very Rare	

GREYHOUND
Standing

Colour: Golden brown with dark brown markings, cream chest and feet

	HN 1065	HN 1066	HN 1067
Model No.:	792	792A	792B
Height:	8 ½", 21.6 cm	6", 15.2 cm	4 ½", 11.4 cm
Size:	Large	Medium	Small
Issued:	1931-1955	1931-1955	1931-1960
Varieties:	HN 1075	HN 1076	HN 1077

Currency	Large	Medium	Small
U.S. $	1,500.00	1,000.00	750.00
Can. $	2,250.00	1,500.00	1,100.00
U.K. £	1,000.00	650.00	500.00

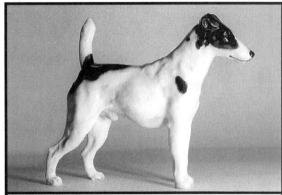

HN 1068
Smooth-Haired Terrier Ch. 'Chosen Don of Notts'

Model No.:	791
Designer:	Frederick Daws
Height:	8 ½", 21.6 cm
Size:	Large
Colour:	White, black patches on eyes, ears and back
Issued:	1931-by 1952
Varieties:	HN 2512

Description	U.S. $	Can. $	U.K. £
Large	2,500.00	3,750.00	1,650.00

HN 1069
Smooth-Haired Terrier Ch. 'Chosen Don of Notts'

Model No.:	791A
Designer:	Frederick Daws
Height:	6", 15.2 cm
Size:	Medium
Colour:	White, black patches on eyes, ears and back
Issued:	1932-1960
Varieties:	HN 2513

Description	U.S. $	Can. $	U.K. £
Medium	1,350.00	2,000.00	900.00

HN 1070
Smooth-Haired Terrier Ch. 'Chosen Don of Notts'

Model No.:	791B
Designer:	Frederick Daws
Height:	5", 12.7 cm
Size:	Small
Colour:	White, black patches on eyes, ears and back
Issued:	1931-1952
Varieties:	HN 2514

Description	U.S. $	Can. $	U.K. £
Small	1,500.00	2,250.00	1,000.00

HN 1071
Hare
Lying, legs stretched behind - brown

Model No.:	656
Height:	3" x 7 ½", 7.6 cm x 19.1 cm
Size:	Large
Colour:	See below
Issued:	1. 1932-1941
	2. 1929-1962
Varieties:	HN 979, 984, 985, 2593

Colourways	U.S. $	Can. $	U.K. £
1. Brown/white	375.00	550.00	250.00
2. Flambé	450.00	675.00	300.00

BULLDOG
Standing

Designer: Frederick Daws
Colour: White, brown collar, gold (tan) studs

	HN 1072	HN 1073	HN 1074
Model No.:	754	754A	754B
Height:	6″, 15.2 cm	5″, 12.7 cm	3 ¼″, 8.2 cm
Size:	Large	Medium	Small
Issued:	1932-1960	1932-1960	1932-1985
Varieties:	HN 1042, 1045	HN 1043, 1046	HN 1044, 1047

Currency	Large	Medium	Small
U.S. $	1,200.00	650.00	200.00
Can. $	1,750.00	1,000.00	300.00
U.K. £	750.00	425.00	140.00

GREYHOUND
Standing

Colour: White with dark brown patches on eyes, ears and back

	HN 1075	HN 1076	HN 1077
Model No.:	792	792A	792B
Height:	8 ½″, 21.6 cm	6″, 15.2 cm	4 ½″, 11.4 cm
Size:	Large	Medium	Small
Issued:	1932-1955	1932-1955	1932-1955
Varieties:	HN 1065	HN 1066	HN 1067

Currency	Large	Medium	Small
U.S. $	1,500.00	1,000.00	750.00
Can. $	2,250.00	1,500.00	1,100.00
U.K. £	1,000.00	650.00	500.00

HN 1078
Cocker Spaniel

Model No.:	709B
Designer:	Frederick Daws
Height:	3", 7.6 cm
Size:	Small
Colour:	White with black markings
Issued:	1932-1968
Varieties:	HN 1037, 1136, 1188; Also called 'Lucky Pride of Ware' and 'Lucky Star of Ware' HN 1021

Description	U.S. $	Can. $	U.K. £
Small	185.00	275.00	125.00

HN 1079
Gordon Setter - Large

Model No.:	770
Designer:	Frederick Daws
Height:	8", 20.3 cm
Colour:	Dark brown coat, light brown underbody
Issued:	1. 1932-1955; 2. Unknown
Varieties:	English Setter HN 2620, English Setter Ch. 'Maesydd Mustard' HN 1049, Irish Setter Ch. 'Pat O'Moy' HN 1054

Description	U.S. $	Can. $	U.K. £
1. Natural	3,500.00	5,000.00	2,250.00
2. Flambé	1,200.00	1,800.00	800.00

HN 1080
Gordon Setter - Medium

Model No.:	770A
Designer:	Frederick Daws
Height:	5", 12.7 cm
Colour:	Dark brown coat, light brown underbody
Issued:	1932-1955
Varieties:	English Setter HN 2621, English Setter Ch. 'Maesydd Mustard' HN 1050, Irish Setter Ch. 'Pat O'Moy' HN 1055

Description	U.S. $	Can. $	U.K. £
Medium	1,250.00	2,000.00	850.00

HN 1081
Gordon Setter - Small

Model No.:	770B
Designer:	Frederick Daws
Height:	4", 10.1 cm
Colour:	Dark brown coat, light brown underbody
Issued:	1932-1960
Varieties:	English Setter HN 2622, English Setter Ch. 'Maesydd Mustard' HN 1051, Irish Setter Ch. 'Pat O'Moy' HN 1055

Description	U.S. $	Can. $	U.K. £
Small	800.00	1,200.00	525.00

HN 1082
Tiger
Stalking - Style Two - extra large

Model No.:	809
Designer:	Charles Noke
Height:	5 ¾" x 13 ¼", 14.6 cm x 33.5 cm
Size:	Extra large
Colour:	See below
Issued:	1. 1933-by 1946 2. 1950-1996
Varieties:	HN 2646, Tiger on Alabaster Base HN 1126

Colourways	U.S. $	Can. $	U.K. £
1. Natural	1,250.00	2,000.00	850.00
2. Flambé	825.00	1,250.00	550.00

HN 1083
Tiger
Stalking - Style Two - medium

Model No.:	809A
Designer:	Charles Noke
Height:	3 ¼" x 7", 8.3 x 17.8 cm
Size:	Medium
Colour:	Brown with dark brown stripes
Issued:	1933-by 1946

Description	U.S. $	Can. $	U.K. £
Medium	900.00	1,350.00	600.00

HN 1084
Tiger
Stalking - Style Two - small

Model No.:	809B
Designer:	Charles Noke
Height:	2", 5.1 cm
Size:	Small
Colour:	Brown with dark brown stripes
Issued:	1933-by 1946

Description	U.S. $	Can. $	U.K. £
Small	675.00	1,000.00	450.00

Note: Mould 809B was also used to produce HN 1094 Leopard.

HN 1085
Lion
Standing - Style One - large

Model No.:	801
Designer:	Charles Noke
Height:	9" x 13", 22.9 cm x 33.0 cm
Size:	Large
Colour:	Brown coat, dark brown mane
Issued:	1933-by 1946
Varieties:	Lion on alabaster base HN 1125

Description	U.S. $	Can. $	U.K. £
Large	2,000.00	3,000.00	1,250.00

HN 1086
Lion
Standing - Style One - small

Model No.:	801A
Designer:	Charles Noke
Height:	5", 12.7 cm
Size:	Small
Colour:	Brown coat, dark brown mane
Issued:	1931-by 1946

Description	U.S. $	Can. $	U.K. £
Small	1,000.00	1,500.00	650.00

Photograph
not available
at press time

HN 1087
Drake on Ashtray

Model No.:	395
Height:	3 ½", 8.9 cm
Colour:	Green drake, cream ashtray
Issued:	1934-by 1946

Description	U.S. $	Can. $	U.K. £
HN 1087A — Fluted		Rare	
HN 1087B — Plain		Rare	

HN 1088
Duck on Ashtray

Model No.:	Unknown
Height:	3 ½", 8.9 cm
Colour:	White duck, cream ashtray
Issued:	1934-by 1946

Description	U.S. $	Can. $	U.K. £
HN 1088A — fluted		Rare	
HN 1088B — plain		Rare	

HN 1089
Robin on Ashtray

Model No.:	155
Height:	3", 7.6 cm
Colour:	Dark brown bird with red breast, cream ashtray
Issued:	1934-by 1946

Description	U.S. $	Can. $	U.K. £
HN 1089A — fluted	225.00	350.00	150.00
HN 1089B — plain	225.00	350.00	150.00

HN 1090
Mouse on Ashtray

Model No.:	1164B	
Height:	3", 7.6 cm	
Colour:	Grey mouse on cream ashtray	
Issued:	1934-by 1946	

Description	U.S. $	Can. $	U.K. £
HN 1090A — fluted		Rare	
HN 1090B — plain		Rare	

HN 1091
Lop-eared Rabbit on Ashtray

Model No.:	1165	
Height:	3 ½", 8.9 cm	
Colour:	Brown and white rabbit on cream ashtray	
Issued:	1934-by 1946	

Description	U.S. $	Can. $	U.K. £
HN 1091A — fluted		Rare	
HN 1091B — plain		Rare	

HN 1092
Comical Bird on Ashtray

Model No.:	366	
Height:	Unknown	
Colour:	Black, white and orange	
Issued:	1934-by 1946	

Description	U.S. $	Can. $	U.K. £
HN 1092A — fluted		Rare	
HN 1092B — plain		Rare	

Note: Model illustrated is the Comical Bird which
sits on the ashtray.

HN 1093
Squirrel on Ashtray

Model No.:	115	
Height:	3", 7.6 cm	
Colour:	Brown squirrel on cream ashtray	
Issued:	1934-by 1946	

Description	U.S. $	Can. $	U.K. £
HN 1093A — fluted		Rare	
HN 1093B — plain		Rare	

HN 1094
Leopard
Standing

Model No.:	809B
Designer:	Charles Noke
Height:	2", 5.1 cm
Colour:	Browns
Issued:	1934-by 1946

Description	U.S. $	Can. $	U.K. £
Leopard, standing		Very Rare	

Note: Mould 809B was also used to produce HN 1084 Tiger.

HN 1095
Kingfisher on Ashtray

Model No.:	Unknown
Height:	3", 7.6 cm
Colour:	Unknown
Issued:	1934-by 1946

Description	U.S. $	Can. $	U.K. £
HN 1095A— fluted		Rare	
HN 1095B — plain		Rare	

HN 1096
Character Fox with Stolen Goose

Model No.:	857
Designer:	Charles Noke
Height:	4 ¾", 12.1 cm
Colour:	Green cloak and hat, brown fox
Issued:	1934-by 1946
Varieties:	HN 1102

Colourways	U.S. $	Can. $	U.K. £
Green cloak		Very Rare	

HN 1097
Character Dog Running with Ball

Model No.:	853
Height:	2 ", 12.7 cm
Colour:	White with light brown patches over eyes and ears, light and dark brown patches on back, yellow and red striped ball
Issued:	1934-1985
Varieties:	Also known with plain ball

Description	U.S. $	Can. $	U.K. £
Striped ball	125.00	175.00	85.00
Plain ball		Very Rare	

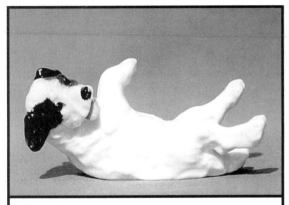

HN 1098
Character Dog Lying on Back

Model No.:	854	
Height:	2", 11.4 cm	
Colour:	White with brown and black patches over ears and eyes	
Issued:	1934-1959	

Description	U.S. $	Can. $	U.K. £
Dog, lying on back	250.00	375.00	175.00

HN 1099
Character Dog Yawning

Model No.:	856	
Height:	4", 10.1 cm	
Colour:	White with brown patches over ears and eyes, black patches on back	
Issued:	1934-1985	

Description	U.S. $	Can. $	U.K. £
Dog, yawning	125.00	175.00	85.00

Note: Model also known with left front paw tucked under.

HN 1100
Bull Terrier
Standing - Style One

Model No.:	852	
Height:	4", 10.1 cm	
Colour:	White with brown patches over eyes and ears, black patches on back	
Issued:	1934-1959	

Description	U.S. $	Can. $	U.K. £
Bull terrier	300.00	450.00	200.00

HN 1101
Character Dog Lying, Panting

Model No.:	866	
Height:	2 ¼", 5.7 cm	
Colour:	White with brown patches over ears and eyes, black patches on back	
Issued:	1934-1959	

Description	U.S. $	Can. $	U.K. £
Dog, lying/panting	200.00	300.00	135.00

HN 1102
Character Fox with Stolen Goose

Model No.:	857
Designer:	Charles Noke
Height:	4 ¾", 12.1 cm
Colour:	Red cloak, black hat, grey chicken
Issued:	1934-by 1946
Varieties:	HN 1096

Colourways	U.S. $	Can. $	U.K. £
Red cloak		Very Rare	

HN 1103
Character Dog with Ball

Model No.:	855
Height:	2 ½", 10.2 cm
Colour:	White with light and dark brown patches maroon ball
Issued:	1934-1985

Description	U.S. $	Can. $	U.K. £
Dog with ball	125.00	175.00	85.00

Note: This model is also known with a doll in place of the ball.

HN 1104
Cairn
Standing - Large

Model No.:	750
Designer:	Frederick Daws
Height:	7", 17.8 cm
Size:	Large
Colour:	Black (earthenware)
Issued:	1937-1955
Varieties:	Also called Cairn Ch. 'Charming Eyes' HN 1033

Description	U.S. $	Can. $	U.K. £
Large	1,450.00	2,250.00	950.00

HN 1105
Cairn
Standing - Medium

Model No.:	750A
Designer:	Frederick Daws
Height:	4 ½", 11.4 cm
Size:	Medium
Colour:	Black (earthenware)
Issued:	1937-1960
Varieties:	Also called Cairn Ch. 'Charming Eyes' HN 1034

Description	U.S. $	Can. $	U.K. £
Medium	600.00	900.00	400.00

HN 1106
Cairn, Standing

Model No.:	750B
Designer:	Frederick Daws
Height:	3", 7.6 cm
Size:	Small
Colour:	See below
Issued:	1. 1937-1960; 2. c.1931
Varieties:	Also called Cairn Ch. 'Charming Eyes' HN 1035

Colourways	U.S. $	Can. $	U.K. £
1. Black (earthenware)	300.00	450.00	200.00
2. Flambé	750.00	1,100.00	500.00

HN 1107
Scottish Terrier
Standing - Style Three

Model No.:	Unknown
Height:	6 ¾" x 11", 17.2 x 27.9 cm
Size:	Large
Colour:	Black (earthenware)
Issued:	1934-by 1946

Description	U.S. $	Can. $	U.K. £
Large		Very Rare	

HN 1108
Cocker Spaniel - Large

Model No.:	709
Designer:	Frederick Daws
Height:	6 ½", 16.5 cm
Colour:	White with black markings
Issued:	1937-1960
Varieties:	HN 1002, 1134, 1186; Also called 'Lucky Star of Ware' and 'Lucky Pride of Ware' HN 1000

Description	U.S. $	Can. $	U.K. £
Large	600.00	900.00	400.00

HN 1109
Cocker Spaniel - Medium

Model No.:	709A
Designer:	Frederick Daws
Height:	5", 12.7 cm
Colour:	See below
Issued:	1. 1937-1985; 2. c.1937
Varieties:	HN 1036, 1135, 1187, Also called 'Lucky Pride of Ware' and 'Lucky Star of Ware' HN 1020
Derivative:	Bookend

Colourways	U.S. $	Can. $	U.K. £
1. White/black	150.00	225.00	100.00
2. Flambé	900.00	1,350.00	600.00

HN 1110
Scottish Terrier
Standing - Style Four

Model No.:	873
Designer:	Frederick Daws
Height:	7", 17.8 cm
Size:	Large
Colour:	Black (earthenware)
Issued:	1937-by 1946

Description	U.S. $	Can. $	U.K. £
Large	1,500.00	2,250.00	1,000.00

HN 1111
Dalmatian Ch. 'Goworth Victor'

Model No.:	900
Designer:	Frederick Daws
Height:	7 ¾", 19.7 cm
Size:	Large
Colour:	White with black spots, black ears
Issued:	1937-1955

Description	U.S. $	Can. $	U.K. £
Large	2,500.00	3,750.00	1,650.00

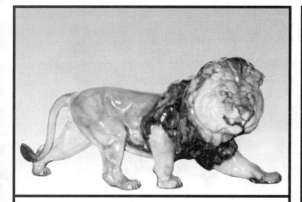

HN 1112
Lion
Standing - Style Two

Model No.:	Unknown
Designer:	Charles Noke
Height:	16", 40.6 cm (length)
Size:	Large
Colour:	Brown with dark brown mane (china)
Issued:	1937-1946
Varieties:	HN 1119 Lion on the Rock

Description	U.S. $	Can. $	U.K. £
Large	2,000.00	3,000.00	1,250.00

HN 1113
Dalmatian Ch. 'Goworth Victor'

Model No.:	900A
Designer:	Frederick Daws
Height:	5 ½", 14.0 cm
Size:	Medium
Colour:	White with black spots, black ears
Issued:	1937-1985

Description	U.S. $	Can. $	U.K. £
Medium	250.00	375.00	150.00

HN 1114
Dalmatian Ch. 'Goworth Victor'

Model No.:	900B
Designer:	Frederick Daws
Height:	4 ¼", 10.8 cm
Size:	Small
Colour:	White with black spots, black ears
Issued:	1937-1968

Description	U.S. $	Can. $	U.K. £
Small	350.00	525.00	225.00

HN 1115
Alsatian Ch. 'Benign of Picardy'

Model No.:	925
Designer:	Frederick Daws
Height:	9", 22.9 cm
Size:	Large
Colour:	Dark brown coat with light brown underbody, black highlights
Issued:	1937-1960

Description	U.S. $	Can. $	U.K. £
Large	1,100.00	1,650.00	750.00

HN 1116
Alsatian Ch. 'Benign of Picardy'

Model No.:	925A
Designer:	Frederick Daws
Height:	6", 15.2 cm
Size:	Medium
Colour:	Dark brown coat with light brown underbody, black highlights
Issued:	1937-1985

Description	U.S. $	Can. $	U.K. £
Medium	200.00	300.00	135.00

HN 1117
Alsatian Ch. 'Benign of Picardy'

Model No.:	925B
Designer:	Frederick Daws
Height:	4 ½", 11.4 cm
Size:	Small
Colour:	Dark brown coat with light brown underbody, black highlights
Issued:	1937-1968

Description	U.S. $	Can. $	U.K. £
Small	250.00	375.00	150.00

Photograph
not available
at press time

HN 1118
Tiger on the Rock
Style Two

Model No.:	809
Designer:	Charles Noke
Height:	12", 30.5 cm
Colour:	Brown and black (earthenware)
Issued:	1937-by 1946
Varieties:	HN 1082 (without rock)

Description	U.S. $	Can. $	U.K. £
Tiger on rock	1,875.00	2,750.00	1,250.00

HN 1119
Lion on the Rock
Style One

Model No.:	Unknown
Designer:	Charles Noke
Height:	11", 27.9 cm
Colour:	Tan, brown and black (earthenware)
Issued:	1937-by 1946
Varieties:	Lion (standing) HN 1112

Description	U.S. $	Can. $	U.K. £
Lion on rock	1,875.00	2,750.00	1,250.00

HN 1120
Fighter Elephant - Large

Model No.:	626
Designer:	Charles Noke
Height:	12" x 9", 30.5 x 22.9 cm
Colour:	See below
Issued:	1. 1937-by 1946
	2. and 3. c.1929
Varieties:	HN 2640

Colourways	U.S. $	Can. $	U.K. £
1. Grey (earthenware)	1,250.00	1,850.00	850.00
2. Flambé	2,250.00	3,250.00	1,500.00
3. Sung	3,750.00	5,500.00	2,500.00

HN 1121
Elephant
Trunk down, curled

Model No.:	600
Designer:	Charles Noke
Height:	13", 33.0 cm
Size:	Large
Colour:	See below
Issued:	1. 1937-1960
	2. and 3. c.1938-1968

Colourways	U.S. $	Can. $	U.K. £
1. Grey (earthenware)	Very Rare		
2. Flambé	3,000.00	4,500.00	2,000.00
3. Sung	4,500.00	6,750.00	3,000.00

Photograph
not available
at press time

HN 1125
Lion on Alabaster Base

Model No.:	801
Designer:	Charles Noke
Height:	7", 17.8 cm
Size:	Extra large
Colour:	Tan
Issued:	1937-by 1946
Varieties:	HN 1085 (without base)

Description	U.S. $	Can. $	U.K. £
Lion on alabaster base		Very Rare	

HN 1126
Tiger on Alabaster Base

Model No.:	809
Designer:	Charles Noke
Height:	5 ¾" x 13 ¼", 14.6 x 33.5 cm
Size:	Extra large
Colour:	See below
Issued:	1937-by 1946
Varieties:	HN 1082, 2646

Description	U.S. $	Can. $	U.K. £
Tiger on alabaster base		Very Rare	

HN 1127
Dachshund Ch. 'Shrewd Saint'

Model No.:	938
Designer:	Frederick Daws
Height:	6", 15.2 cm
Size:	Large
Colour:	See below
Issued:	1. 1937-1955
	2. c.1937
Varieties:	Also called Dachshund HN 1139

Colourways	U.S. $	Can. $	U.K. £
1. Browns (earthenware)	750.00	1,200.00	500.00
2. Flambé	1,500.00	2,250.00	1,000.00

HN 1128
Dachshund Ch. 'Shrewd Saint'

Model No.:	938A
Designer:	Frederick Daws
Height:	4", 10.1 cm
Size:	Medium
Colour:	See below
Issued:	1. 1937-1985
	2. c.1937
Varieties:	Also called Dachshund HN 1140

Colourways	U.S. $	Can. $	U.K. £
1. Dark/light brown	150.00	225.00	100.00
2. Flambé	900.00	1,450.00	600.00

HN 1129
Dachshund Ch. 'Shrewd Saint'

Model No.:	938B
Designer:	Frederick Daws
Height:	3", 7.6 cm
Size:	Small
Colour:	See below
Issued:	1. 1937-1968
	2. c.1937
Varieties:	Also called Dachshund HN 1141

Colourways	U.S. $	Can. $	U.K. £
1. Dark/light brown	200.00	300.00	135.00
2. Flambé	750.00	1,100.00	500.00

HN 1130
Fox
Seated - Style Five

Model No.:	978
Designer:	Raoh Schorr
Height:	11", 27.9 cm
Size:	Extra large
Colour:	Brown and white
Issued:	1937-by 1946
Varieties:	HN 2527

Description	U.S. $	Can. $	U.K. £
Extra large	1,500.00	2,250.00	1,000.00

HN 1131
Staffordshire Bull Terrier
Style One

Model No.:	959
Designer:	Frederick Daws
Height:	9", 22.9 cm
Size:	Large
Colour:	White
Issued:	1937-by 1946
Varieties:	Also called Bull Terrier Ch. 'Bokos Brock' HN 1142

Description	U.S. $	Can. $	U.K. £
Large	2,500.00	3,750.00	1,600.00

HN 1132
Staffordshire Bull Terrier
Style One

Model No.:	959A
Designer:	Frederick Daws
Height:	6 ½", 16.5 cm
Size:	Medium
Colour:	White
Issued:	1937-1960
Varieties:	Also called Bull Terrier Ch. 'Bokos Brock' HN 1143

Description	U.S. $	Can. $	U.K. £
Medium	950.00	1,400.00	650.00

HN 1133
Staffordshire Bull Terrier
Style One

Model No.:	959B
Designer:	Frederick Daws
Height:	4 ½", 11.4 cm
Size:	Small
Colour:	White
Issued:	1937-by 1946
Varieties:	Also called Bull Terrier Ch. 'Bokos Brock' HN 1144

Description	U.S. $	Can. $	U.K. £
Small	1,500.00	2,250.00	1,000.00

HN 1134
Cocker Spaniel

Model No.:	709
Designer:	Frederick Daws
Height:	6 ½", 16.5 cm
Size:	Large
Colour:	Liver and white
Issued:	1937-by 1946
Varieties:	HN 1002, 1108, 1186; Also called 'Lucky Star of Ware' HN 1000 and 'Lucky Pride of Ware'

Description	U.S. $	Can. $	U.K. £
Large	600.00	900.00	400.00

HN 1135
Cocker Spaniel

Model No.:	709A
Designer:	Frederick Daws
Height:	5", 12.7 cm
Size:	Medium
Colour:	See below
Issued:	1. 1937-by 1946; 2. c.1937
Varieties:	HN 1036, 1109, 1187; Also called 'Lucky Pride of Ware' and 'Lucky Star of Ware' HN 1020

Colourways	U.S. $	Can. $	U.K. £
1. Liver/white	225.00	325.00	150.00
2. Flambé	900.00	1,350.00	600.00

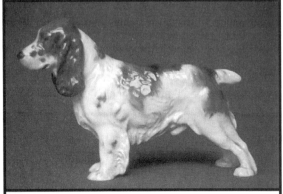

HN 1136
Cocker Spaniel

Model No.:	709B
Designer:	Frederick Daws
Height:	3", 7.6 cm
Size:	Small
Colour:	Liver and white
Issued:	1937-by 1946
Varieties:	HN 1037, 1078, 1188; Also called 'Lucky Pride of Ware' and 'Lucky Star of Ware' HN 1021

Description	U.S. $	Can. $	U.K. £
Small	250.00	375.00	175.00

HN 1137
Cocker Spaniel with Pheasant

Model No.:	714
Designer:	Frederick Daws
Height:	6 ½" x 7 ¾", 16.5 x 19.7 cm
Size:	Large
Colour:	White coat with black markings, red-brown pheasant
Issued:	1937-1968
Varieties:	HN 1001

Description	U.S. $	Can. $	U.K. £
Large	525.00	800.00	350.00

HN 1138
Cocker Spaniel with Pheasant

Model No.:	714A
Designer:	Frederick Daws
Height:	5 ¼", 13.3 cm
Size:	Medium
Colour:	White coat with black markings, red-brown pheasant
Issued:	1937-1985
Varieties:	HN 1028
Derivative:	Bookend

Description	U.S. $	Can. $	U.K. £
Medium	175.00	250.00	125.00

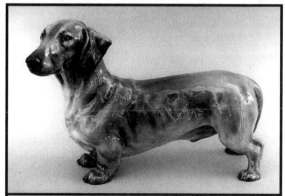

HN 1139
Dachshund
Standing - Style Three

Model No.:	938
Designer:	Frederick Daws
Height:	6", 15.2 cm
Size:	Large
Colour:	See below
Issued:	1. 1937-1955; 2. c.1937
Varieties:	Also called Dachshund Ch. 'Shrewd Saint' HN 1127

Colourways	U.S. $	Can. $	U.K. £
1. Brown	750.00	1,200.00	500.00
2. Flambé	1,500.00	2,250.00	1,000.00

HN 1140
Dachshund
Standing - Style Three

Model No.:	938A
Designer:	Frederick Daws
Height:	4", 10.1 cm
Size:	Medium
Colour:	See below
Issued:	1. 1937-1968; 2. c.1937
Varieties:	Also called Dachshund Ch. 'Shrewd Saint' HN 1128

Colourways	U.S. $	Can. $	U.K. £
1. Brown	275.00	400.00	185.00
2. Flambé	900.00	1,450.00	600.00

HN 1141
Dachshund
Standing - Style Three

Model No.:	938B
Designer:	Frederick Daws
Height:	2 ¾", 7.0 cm
Size:	Small
Colour:	See below
Issued:	1. 1937-1968; 2. c.1937
Varieties:	Also called Dachshund Ch. 'Shrewd Saint' HN 1129

Colourways	U.S. $	Can. $	U.K. £
1. Brown	250.00	400.00	165.00
2. Flambé	750.00	1,100.00	500.00

HN 1142
Bull Terrier Ch. 'Bokos Brock'

Model No.:	959
Designer:	Frederick Daws
Height:	9", 22.9 cm
Size:	Large
Colour:	Dark brown and white
Issued:	1937-by 1946
Varieties:	Also called Staffordshire Bull Terrier HN 1131

Description	U.S. $	Can. $	U.K. £
Large	3,750.00	5,600.00	2,500.00

HN 1143
Bull Terrier Ch. 'Bokos Brock'

Model No.:	959A
Designer:	Frederick Daws
Height:	6 ½", 16.5 cm
Size:	Medium
Colour:	Dark brown and white
Issued:	1937-1960
Varieties:	Also called Staffordshire Bull Terrier HN 1132

Description	U.S. $	Can. $	U.K. £
Medium	1,350.00	2,000.00	900.00

HN 1144
Bull Terrier Ch. 'Bokos Brock'

Model No.:	959B
Designer:	Frederick Daws
Height:	4 ½", 11.4 cm
Size:	Small
Colour:	Dark brown and white
Issued:	1937-by 1946
Varieties:	Also called Staffordshire Bull Terrier HN 1133

Description	U.S. $	Can. $	U.K. £
Small	2,000.00	3,000.00	1,350.00

HN 1145
Moufflon
Style One

Model No.:	952
Designer:	Raoh Schorr
Height:	6", 15.2 cm
Colour:	Green-bronze
Issued:	1937-1942
Varieties:	HN 1160, 1179

Colourways	U.S. $	Can. $	U.K. £
Green-bronze	325.00	475.00	225.00

HN 1146
Calf
Style One

Model No.:	946
Designer:	Raoh Schorr
Height:	2" x 5 ½", 5.1 x 14.0 cm
Colour:	Green-bronze
Issued:	1937-1942
Varieties:	HN 1161, 1173

Colourways	U.S. $	Can. $	U.K. £
Green-bronze	325.00	475.00	225.00

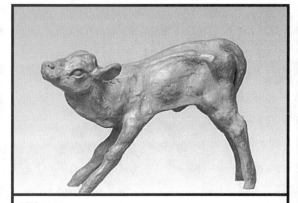

HN 1147
Calf
Style Two

Model No.:	947
Designer:	Raoh Schorr
Height:	6" x 9", 15.2 x 22.9 cm
Colour:	Green-bronze
Issued:	1937-1942
Varieties:	HN 1162, 1174

Colourways	U.S. $	Can. $	U.K. £
Green-bronze	325.00	475.00	225.00

HN 1148
Water Buffalo

Model No.:	948
Designer:	Raoh Schorr
Height:	7" x 12 ½", 17.8 x 31.7 cm
Colour:	Green-bronze
Issued:	1937-1942
Varieties:	HN 1163, 1175

Colourways	U.S. $	Can. $	U.K. £
Green-bronze	475.00	700.00	325.00

HN 1149
Donkey
Style One

Model No.:	949
Designer:	Raoh Schorr
Height:	6", 15.2 cm
Colour:	Green-bronze
Issued:	1937-1942
Varieties:	HN 1164, 1176

Colourways	U.S. $	Can. $	U.K. £
Green-bronze	325.00	475.00	225.00

HN 1150
Young Doe

Model No.:	950
Designer:	Raoh Schorr
Height:	4", 10.1 cm
Colour:	Green-bronze
Issued:	1937-1942
Varieties:	HN 1165, 1177

Colourways	U.S. $	Can. $	U.K. £
Green-bronze	325.00	475.00	225.00

HN 1151
Swiss Goat

Model No.:	951
Designer:	Raoh Schorr
Height:	5", 12.7 cm
Colour:	Green-bronze
Issued:	1937-1942
Varieties:	HN 1166, 1178

Colourways	U.S. $	Can. $	U.K. £
Green-bronze	325.00	475.00	225.00

HN 1152
Horse
Prancing

Model No.:	953
Designer:	Raoh Schorr
Height:	6 ¾", 17.2 cm
Colour:	Green-bronze
Issued:	1937-1942
Varieties:	HN 1167, 1180

Colourways	U.S. $	Can. $	U.K. £
Green-bronze	325.00	475.00	225.00

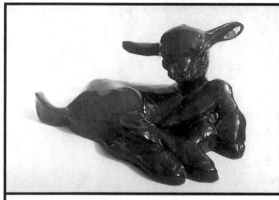

HN 1153
Moufflon
Style Two

Model No.:	954
Designer:	Raoh Schorr
Height:	2″, 5.1 cm
Colour:	Green-bronze
Issued:	1937-1942
Varieties:	HN 1168, 1181

Colourways	U.S. $	Can. $	U.K. £
Green-bronze	325.00	475.00	225.00

HN 1154
Jumping Goat

Model No.:	955
Designer:	Raoh Schorr
Height:	6 ¾″, 17.2 cm
Colour:	Green-bronze
Issued:	1937-1942
Varieties:	HN 1169, 1182

Colourways	U.S. $	Can. $	U.K. £
Green-bronze	325.00	475.00	225.00

Photograph
not available
at press time

HN 1155
Donkey
Style Two

Model No.:	956
Designer:	Raoh Schorr
Height:	6″, 15.2 cm
Colour:	Green-bronze
Issued:	1937-1942
Varieties:	HN 1170, 1183

Colourways	U.S. $	Can. $	U.K. £
Green-bronze	325.00	475.00	225.00

HN 1156
'Suspicion'
Doe

Model No.:	957
Designer:	Raoh Schorr
Height:	8 ¼″, 21.0 cm
Colour:	Green-bronze
Issued:	1937-1942
Varieties:	HN 1171, 1184

Colourways	U.S. $	Can. $	U.K. £
Green-bronze	325.00	475.00	225.00

HN 1157
Antelope

Model No.:	958
Designer:	Raoh Schorr
Height:	6", 15.2 cm
Colour:	Green-bronze
Issued:	1937-1942
Varieties:	HN 1172, 1185

Colourways	U.S. $	Can. $	U.K. £
Green-bronze	325.00	475.00	225.00

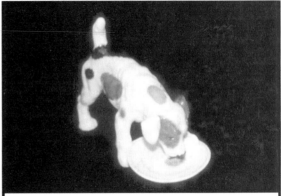

HN 1158
Character Dog with Plate

Model No.:	963
Designer:	Unknown
Height:	3 ¼", 12.7 cm
Colour:	White with black and light brown patches
Issued:	1937-1985

Description	U.S. $	Can. $	U.K. £
Dog with plate	125.00	175.00	75.00

HN 1159
Character Dog with Bone

Model No.:	962
Designer:	Unknown
Height:	3 ¾", 9.5 cm
Colour:	White with black and light brown patches on back, light brown patch over left ear
Issued:	1937-1985

Description	U.S. $	Can. $	U.K. £
Dog with bone	125.00	175.00	75.00

HN 1160
Moufflon
Style One

Model No.:	952
Designer:	Raoh Schorr
Height:	6", 15.2 cm
Colour:	Cream (matt)
Issued:	1937-1942
Varieties:	HN 1145, 1179

Colourways	U.S. $	Can. $	U.K. £
Cream (matt)	325.00	475.00	225.00

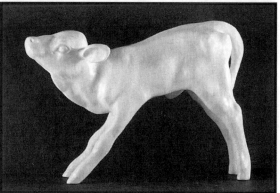

HN 1161
Calf
Style One

Model No.:	946
Designer:	Raoh Schorr
Height:	2" x 5 ½", 5.1 x 14.0 cm
Colour:	Cream (matt)
Issued:	1937-1942
Varieties:	HN 1146, 1173

Colourways	U.S. $	Can. $	U.K. £
Cream (matt)	325.00	475.00	225.00

HN 1162
Calf
Style Two

Model No.:	947
Designer:	Raoh Schorr
Height:	6" x 9", 15.2 x 22.9 cm
Colour:	Cream (matt)
Issued:	1937-1942
Varieties:	HN 1147, 1174

Colourways	U.S. $	Can. $	U.K. £
Cream (matt)	325.00	475.00	225.00

HN 1163
Water Buffalo

Model No.:	948
Designer:	Raoh Schorr
Height:	7" x 12 ½", 17.8 x 31.7 cm
Colour:	Cream (matt)
Issued:	1937-1942
Varieties:	HN 1148, 1175

Colourways	U.S. $	Can. $	U.K. £
Cream (matt)	475.00	700.00	325.00

HN 1164
Donkey
Style One

Model No.:	949
Designer:	Raoh Schorr
Height:	6", 15.2 cm
Colour:	Cream (matt)
Issued:	1937-1942
Varieties:	HN 1149, 1176

Colourways	U.S. $	Can. $	U.K. £
Cream (matt)	325.00	475.00	225.00

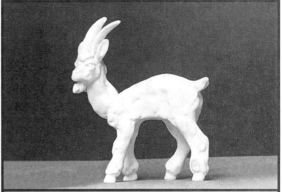

HN 1165
Young Doe

Model No.:	950
Designer:	Raoh Schorr
Height:	4", 10.1 cm
Colour:	Cream (matt)
Issued:	1937-1942
Varieties:	HN 1150, 1177

Colourways	U.S. $	Can. $	U.K. £
Cream (matt)	325.00	475.00	225.00

HN 1166
Swiss Goat

Model No.:	951
Designer:	Raoh Schorr
Height:	5", 12.7 cm
Colour:	Cream (matt)
Issued:	1937-1942
Varieties:	HN 1151, 1178

Colourways	U.S. $	Can. $	U.K. £
Cream (matt)	325.00	475.00	225.00

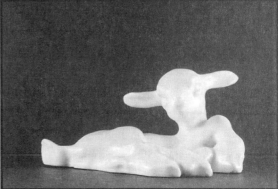

HN 1167
Horse
Prancing

Model No.:	953
Designer:	Raoh Schorr
Height:	6 ¾", 17.2 cm
Colour:	Cream (matt)
Issued:	1937-1942
Varieties:	HN 1152, 1180

Colourways	U.S. $	Can. $	U.K. £
Cream (matt)	325.00	475.00	225.00

HN 1168
Moufflon
Style Two

Model No.:	954
Designer:	Raoh Schorr
Height:	2 ½" x 5", 6.4 x 12.7 cm
Colour:	Cream (matt)
Issued:	1937-1942
Varieties:	HN 1153, 1181

Colourways	U.S. $	Can. $	U.K. £
Cream (matt)	325.00	475.00	225.00

HN 1169
Jumping Goat

Model No.:	955
Designer:	Raoh Schorr
Height:	6 ¾", 17.2 cm
Colour:	Cream (matt)
Issued:	1937-1942
Varieties:	HN 1154, 1182

Colourways	U.S. $	Can. $	U.K. £
Cream (matt)	325.00	475.00	225.00

Photograph
not available
at press time

HN 1170
Donkey
Style Two

Model No.:	956
Designer:	Raoh Schorr
Height:	6", 15.2 cm
Colour:	Cream (matt)
Issued:	1937-1942
Varieties:	HN 1155, 1183

Colourways	U.S. $	Can. $	U.K. £
Cream (matt)	325.00	475.00	225.00

HN 1171
'Suspicion'
Doe

Model No.:	957
Designer:	Raoh Schorr
Height:	8 ¼", 21.0 cm
Colour:	Cream (matt)
Issued:	1937-1942
Varieties:	HN 1156, 1184

Colourways	U.S. $	Can. $	U.K. £
Cream (matt)	325.00	475.00	225.00

HN 1172
Antelope

Model No.:	958
Designer:	Raoh Schorr
Height:	6", 15.2 cm
Colour:	Cream (matt)
Issued:	1937-1942
Varieties:	HN 1157, 1185

Colourways	U.S. $	Can. $	U.K. £
Cream (matt)	325.00	475.00	225.00

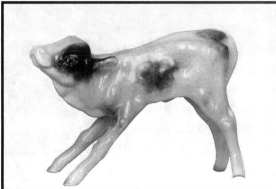

HN 1173
Calf
Style One

Model No.:	946
Designer:	Raoh Schorr
Height:	2″ x 5 ½″, 5.1 x 14.0 cm
Colour:	Light brown
Issued:	1937-1942
Varieties:	HN 1146, 1161

Colourways	U.S. $	Can. $	U.K. £
Natural colours	325.00	475.00	225.00

HN 1174
Calf
Style Two

Model No.:	947
Designer:	Raoh Schorr
Height:	6″ x 9″, 15.2 x 22.9 cm
Colour:	Natural colours
Issued:	1937-1942
Varieties:	HN 1147, 1162

Colourways	U.S. $	Can. $	U.K. £
Natural colours	325.00	475.00	225.00

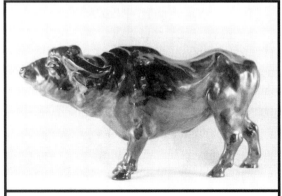

HN 1175
Water Buffalo

Model No.:	948
Designer:	Raoh Schorr
Height:	7″ x 12 ½″, 17.8 x 31.7 cm
Colour:	Brown with black highlights
Issued:	1937-1942
Varieties:	HN 1148, 1163

Colourways	U.S. $	Can. $	U.K. £
Natural colours	475.00	700.00	325.00

HN 1176
Donkey
Style One

Model No.:	949
Designer:	Raoh Schorr
Height:	6″, 15.2 cm
Colour:	Natural colours
Issued:	1937-1942
Varieties:	HN 1149, 1164

Colourways	U.S. $	Can. $	U.K. £
Natural colours	325.00	475.00	225.00

HN 1177
Young Doe

Model No.:	950
Designer:	Raoh Schorr
Height:	4", 10.1 cm
Colour:	Natural colours
Issued:	1937-1942
Varieties:	HN 1150, 1165

Colourways	U.S. $	Can. $	U.K. £
Natural colours	325.00	475.00	225.00

HN 1178
Swiss Goat

Model No.:	951
Designer:	Raoh Schorr
Height:	5", 12.7 cm
Colour:	Natural colours
Issued:	1937-1942
Varieties:	HN 1151, 1166

Colourways	U.S. $	Can. $	U.K. £
Natural colours	325.00	475.00	225.00

HN 1179
Moufflon
Style One

Model No.:	952
Designer:	Raoh Schorr
Height:	6", 15.2 cm
Colour:	Natural colours
Issued:	1937-1942
Varieties:	HN 1145, 1160

Colourways	U.S. $	Can. $	U.K. £
Natural colours	325.00	475.00	225.00

HN 1180
Horse
Prancing

Model No.:	953
Designer:	Raoh Schorr
Height:	6 ¾", 17.2 cm
Colour:	White and brown body, grey mane
Issued:	1937-1942
Varieties:	HN 1152, 1167

Colourways	U.S. $	Can. $	U.K. £
Natural colours	325.00	475.00	225.00

HN 1181
Moufflon
Style Two

Model No.:	954
Designer:	Raoh Schorr
Height:	2", 5.1 cm
Colour:	Natural colours
Issued:	1937-1942
Varieties:	HN 1153, 1168

Colourways	U.S. $	Can. $	U.K. £
Natural colours	325.00	475.00	225.00

HN 1182
Jumping Goat

Model No.:	955
Designer:	Raoh Schorr
Height:	6 ¾", 17.2 cm
Colour:	Brown and white goat on grey base
Issued:	1937-1942
Varieties:	HN 1154, 1169

Colourways	U.S. $	Can. $	U.K. £
Natural colours	325.00	475.00	225.00

Photograph
not available
at press time

HN 1183
Donkey
Style Two

Model No.:	956
Designer:	Raoh Schorr
Height:	6", 15.2 cm
Colour:	Natural colours
Issued:	1937-1942
Varieties:	HN 1155, 1170

Colourways	U.S. $	Can. $	U.K. £
Natural colours	325.00	475.00	225.00

HN 1184
'Suspicion'
Doe

Model No.:	957
Designer:	Raoh Schorr
Height:	8 ¼", 21.0 cm
Colour:	Natural colours
Issued:	1937-1942
Varieties:	HN 1156, 1171

Colourways	U.S. $	Can. $	U.K. £
Natural colours	325.00	475.00	225.00

HN 1185
Antelope

Model No.:	958
Designer:	Raoh Schorr
Height:	6", 15.2 cm
Colour:	Brown with black highlights
Issued:	1937-1942
Varieties:	HN 1157, 1172

Colourways	U.S. $	Can. $	U.K. £
Natural colours	325.00	475.00	225.00

HN 1186
Cocker Spaniel

Model No.:	709
Designer:	Frederick Daws
Height:	6 ¼", 15.9 cm
Size:	Large
Colour:	Golden brown with dark brown highlights
Issued:	1937-1960
Varieties:	HN 1002, 1108, 1134; Also called 'Lucky Pride of Ware' and 'Lucky Star of Ware' HN 1000

Description	U.S. $	Can. $	U.K. £
Large	600.00	900.00	400.00

HN 1187
Cocker Spaniel

Model No.:	709A
Designer:	Frederick Daws
Height:	5", 12.7 cm
Size:	Medium
Colour:	See below
Issued:	1937-1985
Varieties:	HN 1036, 1135, 1109; Also called 'Lucky Pride of Ware' and 'Lucky Star of Ware' HN 1020

Colourways	U.S. $	Can. $	U.K. £
1. Browns	150.00	225.00	100.00
2. Flambé	900.00	1,350.00	600.00

HN 1188
Cocker Spaniel

Model No.:	709B
Designer:	Frederick Daws
Height:	3 ½", 8.9 cm
Size:	Small
Colour:	Golden brown with dark brown highlights
Issued:	1937-1969
Varieties:	HN 1037, 1078, 1136; Also called 'Lucky Pride of Ware' and 'Lucky Star of Ware' HN 1021

Description	U.S. $	Can. $	U.K. £
Small	175.00	250.00	125.00

HN 1189
King Penguin

Model No.:	591
Height:	7 ½", 19.0 cm
Colour:	See below
Issued:	1. 1937-by 1946
	2. c.1927
Varieties:	HN 947

Description	U.S. $	Can. $	U.K. £
1. Black/white/orange	675.00	1,000.00	450.00
2. Flambé	750.00	1,100.00	500.00

HN 1190
Peruvian Penguin

Model No.:	585
Designer:	Charles Noke
Height:	7 ¾", 19.7 cm
Size:	Medium
Colour:	See below
Issued:	1. 1936-by 1946
	2. c.1936-1961
Varieties:	HN 946

Colourways	U.S. $	Can. $	U.K. £
1. Black/white	675.00	1,000.00	450.00
2. Flambé	750.00	1,100.00	500.00

Note: Naturalistic models have no base.

HN 1191
Mallard Drake
Standing - Green head

Model No.:	137
Height:	5 ½", 14.0 cm
Size:	Medium
Colour:	See below
Issued:	1. 1937-by 1960
	2. 1913-1996
Varieties:	HN 114, 115, 116, 956, 2555, 2647

Colourways	U.S. $	Can. $	U.K. £
1. Green/brown/white	400.00	600.00	250.00
2. Flambé	200.00	300.00	125.00

HN 1192
Drake
Resting

Model No.:	654
Height:	3 ¾" x 7 ¼", 9.5 x 18.4 cm
Size:	Large
Colour:	See below
Issued:	1. 1937-by 1946
	2. c.1929-1961
Varieties:	HN 977

Colourways	U.S. $	Can. $	U.K. £
1. White/black/green	600.00	900.00	400.00
2. Flambé	600.00	900.00	400.00

HN 1193
Tern (male)

Model No.:	231
Height:	2 ½" x 8 ½", 6.4 x 21.6 cm
Colour:	See below
Issued:	1. 1937-by 1946
	2. c.1912
Varieties:	HN 168; Also called 'Tern' (female)
	HN 167, 1194

Colourways	U.S. $	Can. $	U.K. £
1. White/black	300.00	450.00	200.00
2. Flambé	750.00	1,100.00	500.00

HN 1194
Tern (female)

Model No.:	231
Height:	2 ½" x 8 ½", 6.4 x 21.6 cm
Colour:	See below
Issued:	1. 1937-by 1946
	2. c.1912
Varieties:	HN 167; Also called 'Tern' (male)
	HN 168, 1193

Colourways	U.S. $	Can. $	U.K. £
1. White/grey	300.00	450.00	200.00
2. Flambé	750.00	1,100.00	500.00

HN 1195
Black-Headed Gull (male)

Model No.:	235
Height:	3 ¾", 9.5 cm
Colour:	White with black head and wing tips
Issued:	1937-by 1946
Varieties:	HN 212, Also called 'Seagull' (female)
	HN 212, 1196

Description	U.S. $	Can. $	U.K. £
Black-headed gull (male)	375.00	550.00	250.00

HN 1196
Seagull (female)

Model No.:	235
Height:	3 ¾", 9.5 cm
Colour:	White with grey wings and black tail feathers
Issued:	1937-by 1946
Varieties:	HN 212; Also called 'Black-Headed Gull' (male) HN 211, 1195

Description	U.S. $	Can. $	U.K. £
Seagull (female)	375.00	550.00	250.00

HN 1197
Gannet

Model No.:	243
Height:	6 ½", 16.5 cm
Colour:	See below
Issued:	1. 1937-by 1946
	2. c.1919
Varieties:	HN 195

Colourways	U.S. $	Can. $	U.K. £
1. Lemon/grey	675.00	1,000.00	450.00
2. Flambé		Very Rare	

HN 1198
Drake
Standing

Model No.:	307
Height:	13", 33.0 cm
Size:	Large
Colour:	Unknown
Issued:	1937-by 1952
Varieties:	HN 248, 249, 252, 2635

Description	U.S. $	Can. $	U.K. £
Drake	1,500.00	2,250.00	1,000.00

HN 1199
Peruvian Penguin - large

Model No.:	769
Designer:	Charles Noke
Height:	12", 30.1 cm (large)
Colour:	See below
Issued:	1. 1937-by 1946; 2. c.1946-1962
Varieties:	HN 2633

Colourways	U.S. $	Can. $	U.K. £
1. Black/white	1,875.00	2,800.00	1,250.00
2. Flambé	2,250.00	3,350.00	1,500.00

Note: Flambé models incorporate a rock as the base.
Naturalistic models are free standing.

HN 1407
The Winner
Style One

Model No.:	Unknown
Designer:	G. D'Illiers
Height:	6 ¾", 17.2 cm
Colour:	Grey horse
Issued:	1930-1938

Description	U.S. $	Can. $	U.K. £
The Winner		Extremely Rare	

*

BUTTERFLIES

HN2605
CAMBERWELL BEAUTY BUTTERFLY

HN2604
PEACOCK BUTTERFLY

HN2607
RED ADMIRAL BUTTERFLY

HN2606
SWALLOWTAIL BUTTERFLY

BIRDS

HN267
COCKEREL, CROUCHING

HN124
COCKEREL, CROUCHING

HN122
FANTAIL PIGEONS

HN125
GUINEA FOWL

HN131
KINGFISHER ON ROCK

HN884
CHARACTER PARROT ON PILLAR

HN136
SWALLOW ON ROCK

BIRDS

HN2541
KINGFISHER ON A TREE STUMP

COLOURWAY OF HN295
PELICAN, BEAK DOWN

HN2552
THRUSH CHICKS (TWO)

HN2547
BUDGERIGARS ON A TREE STUMP

HN3509
DOWNY WOODPECKER

HN2556
DUCK, HEAD STRETCHED FORWARD

BIRDS

K21
PENGUIN, STYLE FOUR

HN3502
KING EIDER

K22
PENGUIN, STYLE FIVE

K23
PENGUIN, STYLE SIX

K20 PENGUIN
WITH CHICK UNDER WING

HN133
PENGUINS

K24
PENGUIN, STYLE SEVEN

BIRDS

K29
BALTIMORE ORIOLE

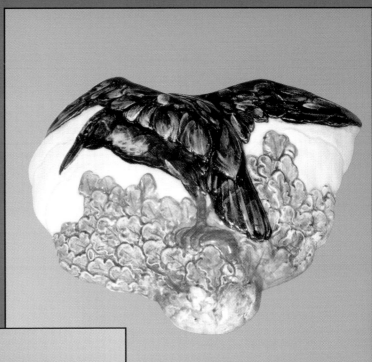

D5772B
CROW WALL POCKET

D5772A
OWL WALL POCKET

K31
BULLFINCH

HORSES

DA237
'PEAKSTONE LADY MARGARET' (SHIRE HORSE)

HN2623
PUNCH PEON, CHESTNUT SHIRE

HN2569
GUDE GREY MARE

HN2538
MERELY A MINOR – WHITE

HN2534
PRIDE OF THE SHIRES AND FOAL

HN2533
CHESTNUT MARE AND FOAL

HORSES

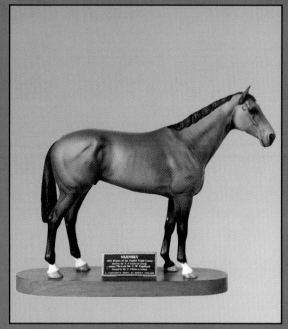

DA16
'NIJINSKY'

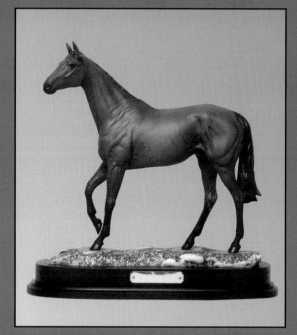

DA218
'RED RUM'

DA188
'MR. FRISK'

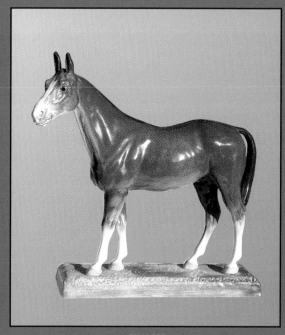

HN2537
MERELY A MINOR – BROWN

DA1
BARN OWL (TYTO ALBA)

HN 2500
Cerval

Model No.	966
Designer:	Raoh Schorr
Height:	5", 12.7 cm
Colour:	White (matt)
Issued:	1937-1937

Colourways	U.S. $	Can. $	U.K. £
White (matt)	325.00	475.00	225.00

HN 2501
Lynx

Model No.	966
Designer:	Raoh Schorr
Height:	4 ½" x 7", 11.4 x17.8 cm
Colour:	White-cream (matt)
Issued:	1937-1937

Colourways	U.S. $	Can. $	U.K. £
White-cream (matt)	325.00	475.00	225.00

HN 2502
Deer
Style One - green

Model No.	994
Designer:	Raoh Schorr
Height:	2 ½", 6.4 cm
Colour:	Green (matt)
Issued:	1937-1937
Varieties:	HN 2503

Colourways	U.S. $	Can. $	U.K. £
Green (matt)	325.00	475.00	225.00

HN 2503
Deer
Style One - white

Model No.:	994
Designer:	Raoh Schorr
Height:	2", 5.1 cm
Colour:	White (matt)
Issued:	1937-1937
Varieties:	HN 2502

Colourways	U.S. $	Can. $	U.K. £
White (matt)	325.00	475.00	225.00

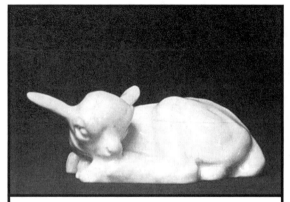

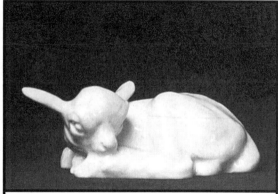

HN 2504
Lamb
Style One - green

Model No.:	995
Designer:	Raoh Schorr
Height:	1 ½″, 3.8 cm
Colour:	Green (matt)
Issued:	1937-1937
Varieties:	HN 2505

Colourways	U.S. $	Can. $	U.K. £
Green (matt)	325.00	475.00	225.00

HN 2505
Lamb
Style One - white

Model No.:	995
Designer:	Raoh Schorr
Height:	1 ½″, 3.8 cm
Colour:	White (matt)
Issued:	1937-1937
Varieties:	HN 2504

Colourways	U.S. $	Can. $	U.K. £
White (matt)	325.00	475.00	225.00

HN 2506
Asiatic Elephant

Model No.:	993
Designer:	Raoh Schorr
Height:	12″, 30.5 cm
Colour:	Green (matt)
Issued:	1937-1937

Colourways	U.S. $	Can. $	U.K. £
Green (matt)	1,500.00	2,250.00	1,000.00

HN 2507
Zebu Cow

Model No.:	997
Designer:	Raoh Schorr
Height:	11 ½″, 29.2 cm
Colour:	Green (matt)
Issued:	1937-1937

Colourways	U.S. $	Can. $	U.K. £
Green (matt)	450.00	675.00	300.00

HN 2508
Sealyham
Seated

Model No.:	986
Designer:	Unknown
Height:	3", 7.6 cm
Colour:	White with brown patches over eyes and ears
Issued:	1938-1959

Description	U.S. $	Can. $	U.K. £
Sealyham, seated	250.00	375.00	150.00

HN 2509
Sealyham
Standing - Style Two

Model No.:	985
Designer:	Unknown
Height:	2 ½", 6.3 cm
Colour:	White with light brown patches over eyes and ears
Issued:	1938-1959

Description	U.S. $	Can. $	U.K. £
Sealyham, standing	250.00	375.00	150.00

HN 2510
Character Dog Running

Model No.:	989
Designer:	Unknown
Height:	2 ¾", 7.0 cm
Colour:	White with light brown patches over ears and eyes, black and brown patch on back
Issued:	1938-1959

Description	U.S. $	Can. $	U.K. £
Dog, running	350.00	525.00	225.00

HN 2511
Bull Terrier
Standing - Style Two

Model No.:	988
Designer:	Unknown
Height:	4", 10.1 cm
Colour:	White with light and dark brown patches over eyes, ears and back
Issued:	1938-1959

Description	U.S. $	Can. $	U.K. £
Bull terrier	350.00	525.00	225.00

SMOOTH-HAIRED TERRIER CH. 'CHOSEN DON OF NOTTS'

Designer: Frederick Davis
Colour: White with dark brown patches on ears

	HN 2512	HN 2513	HN 2514
Model No.:	791	791A	791B
Height:	8 ½", 21.6 cm	6", 15.2 cm	4 ½", 11.4 cm
Size:	Large	Medium	Small
Issued:	1938-1952	1938-1960	1938-1952
Varieties:	HN 1068	HN 1069	HN 1070

Currency	Large	Medium	Small
U.S. $	2,750.00	1,450.00	1,450.00
Can. $	4,000.00	2,200.00	2,200.00
U.K. £	1,800.00	950.00	950.00

HN 2515
Springer Spaniel Ch. 'Dry Toast'

Model No.:	1009	
Designer:	Frederick Daws	
Height:	8", 20.3 cm	
Size:	Large	
Colour:	White coat with dark brown markings	
Issued:	1938-1955	

Description	U.S. $	Can. $	U.K. £
Large	1,200.00	1,750.00	800.00

HN 2516
Springer Spaniel Ch. 'Dry Toast'

Model No.:	1009A	
Designer:	Frederick Daws	
Height:	5", 12.7 cm	
Size:	Medium	
Colour:	White coat with dark brown markings	
Issued:	1938-1968	

Description	U.S. $	Can. $	U.K. £
Medium	300.00	450.00	200.00

HN 2517
Springer Spaniel Ch. 'Dry Toast'

Model No.:	1009B	
Designer:	Frederick Daws	
Height:	3 ¾", 9.5 cm	
Size:	Small	
Colour:	White coat with dark brown markings	
Issued:	1938-1985	

Description	U.S. $	Can. $	U.K. £
Small	200.00	300.00	135.00

HN 2518
Pride of the Shires and Foal

Model No.:	1018	
Designer:	W. M. Chance	
Height:	9 ¾" x 14", 24.8 x 35.5 cm	
Size:	Large	
Colour:	Brown mare, light brown foal	
Issued:	1938-1960	
Varieties:	HN 2523, 2528	

Description	U.S. $	Can. $	U.K. £
Large	750.00	1,100.00	500.00

HN 2519
Gude Grey Mare and Foal

Model No.:	1016
Designer:	W. M. Chance
Height:	7 ½", 19.0 cm
Size:	Large
Colour:	White mare with grey markings on legs, light brown foal with white stockings,
Issued:	1938-1960

Description	U.S. $	Can. $	U.K. £
Large	750.00	1,100.00	500.00

HN 2520
Farmer's Boy

Model No.:	1013
Designer:	W. M. Chance
Height:	8 ½", 21.6 cm
Size:	Large
Colour:	White horse, rider in brown and green
Issued:	1938-1960

Description	U.S. $	Can. $	U.K. £
Farmer's Boy	1,500.00	2,250.00	1,000.00

HN 2521
Dapple Grey and Rider

Model No.:	1017
Designer:	W. M. Chance
Height:	7 ¼", 18.4 cm
Size:	Large
Colour:	White horse, rider in red and brown
Issued:	1938-1960

Description	U.S. $	Can. $	U.K. £
Dapple grey/rider	3,000.00	4,500.00	2,000.00

HN 2522
Chestnut Mare and Foal

Model No.:	1020
Designer:	W. M. Chance
Height:	6 ½", 16.5 cm
Size:	Large
Colour:	Chestnut mare with white stockings, fawn coloured foal with white stockings
Issued:	1938-1960

Description	U.S. $	Can. $	U.K. £
Large	750.00	1,100.00	500.00

HN 2523
Pride of the Shires and Foal

Model No.:	1018
Designer:	W. M. Chance
Height:	9 ¾" x 14", 24.8 x 35.5 cm
Size:	Large
Colour:	White mare, grey markings on legs and hind quarters, light brown foal with white stockings
Issued:	1938-1960
Varieties:	HN 2518, 2528

Description	U.S. $	Can. $	U.K. £
Large	750.00	1,100.00	500.00

HN 2524
American Foxhound - large

Model No.:	1026
Designer:	Frederick Daws
Height:	8", 20.3 cm
Size:	Large
Colour:	White with black and brown markings
Issued:	1938-1955

Description	U.S. $	Can. $	U.K. £
Large	2,000.00	3,000.00	1,350.00

HN 2525
American Foxhound - medium

Model No.:	1026A
Designer:	Frederick Daws
Height:	5", 12.7 cm
Size:	Medium
Colour:	White with black and brown markings
Issued:	1938-1960

Description	U.S. $	Can. $	U.K. £
Medium	850.00	1,250.00	575.00

HN 2526
American Foxhound - small

Model No.:	1026B
Designer:	Frederick Daws
Height:	4", 10.1 cm
Size:	Small
Colour:	White with black and brown markings
Issued:	1938-1952

Description	U.S. $	Can. $	U.K. £
Small	650.00	1,000.00	425.00

HN 2527
Fox
Seated - Style Five

Model No.:	978
Designer:	Raoh Schorr
Height:	11", 27.9 cm
Size:	Extra large
Colour:	Brown and white
Issued:	1938-by 1946
Varieties:	HN 1130

Description	U.S. $	Can. $	U.K. £
Extra large	1,500.00	2,250.00	1,000.00

HN 2528
Pride of the Shires and Foal

Model No.:	1018
Designer:	W. M. Chance
Height:	9 ¾" x 14", 24.8 x 35.5 cm
Size:	Large
Colour:	Brown mare, light fawn foal
Issued:	1939-1960
Varieties:	HN 2518, 2523

Description	U.S. $	Can. $	U.K. £
Large	675.00	1,000.00	450.00

HN 2529
English Setter with Pheasant

Model No.:	1028
Designer:	Frederick Daws
Height:	8", 20.3 cm
Colour:	Grey with black markings, red-brown pheasant, yellow-brown leaves on base
Issued:	1939-1985
Varieties:	HN 2599

Description	U.S. $	Can. $	U.K. £
English setter/pheasant	600.00	900.00	400.00

HN 2530
Merely a Minor - brown

Model No.:	1039
Designer:	Frederick Daws
Height:	12", 30.5 cm
Size:	Large
Colour:	Brown with white stockings and nose
Issued:	1939-1960
Varieties:	HN 2531

Colourways	U.S. $	Can. $	U.K. £
Brown	600.00	900.00	400.00

HN 2531
Merely a Minor - grey

Model No.:	1039
Designer:	Frederick Daws
Height:	12", 30.5 cm
Size:	Large
Colour:	Grey
Issued:	1939-1960
Varieties:	HN 2530

Colourways	U.S. $	Can. $	U.K. £
Grey	600.00	900.00	400.00

HN 2532
Gude Grey Mare and Foal

Model No.:	1016A
Designer:	W. M. Chance
Height:	5 ½", 14.0 cm
Size:	Small
Colour:	White mare with grey markings on legs, light brown foal with white stockings
Issued:	1940-1967

Description	U.S. $	Can. $	U.K. £
Small	600.00	900.00	400.00

HN 2533
Chestnut Mare and Foal

Model No.:	1020B
Designer:	W. M. Chance
Height:	5", 12.7 cm
Size:	Small
Colour:	Chestnut brown mare with white stockings, fawn coloured foal with white stockings
Issued:	1940-1960

Description	U.S. $	Can. $	U.K. £
Small	525.00	800.00	350.00

HN 2534
Pride of the Shires and Foal

Model No.:	1018A
Designer:	W. M. Chance
Height:	6 ½", 16.5 cm
Size:	Small
Colour:	Brown mare, light brown foal
Issued:	1940-1960
Varieties:	HN 2536

Description	U.S. $	Can. $	U.K. £
Small	525.00	800.00	350.00

HN 2535
Tiger on a Rock
Style Three

Model No.:	1038
Designer:	Charles Noke
Height:	4" x 9", 10.1 x 22.9 cm
Colour:	Browns, charcoal rock
Issued:	1940-1960

Description	U.S. $	Can. $	U.K. £
Tiger on rock	1,050.00	1,600.00	700.00

HN 2536
Pride of the Shires and Foal

Model No.:	1018A
Designer:	W. M. Chance
Height:	6 ½", 16.5 cm
Size:	Small
Colour:	White mare, grey markings on legs and hind quarters, light brown foal white stockings
Issued:	1940-1960
Varieties:	HN 2534

Description	U.S. $	Can. $	U.K. £
Small	525.00	800.00	350.00

HN 2537
Merely a Minor - brown

Model No.:	1039A
Designer:	Frederick Daws
Height:	9 ¼", 24.0 cm
Size:	Medium
Colour:	Brown with white stockings and nose
Issued:	1940-1960
Varieties:	HN 2538

Colourways	U.S. $	Can. $	U.K. £
Brown	525.00	800.00	350.00

HN 2538
Merely a Minor - white

Model No.:	1039A
Designer:	Frederick Daws
Height:	9 ¼", 24.0 cm
Size:	Medium
Colour:	White with dark grey markings on legs and neck
Issued:	1940-1960
Varieties:	HN 2537

Colourways	U.S. $	Can. $	U.K. £
White	525.00	800.00	350.00

HN 2539
Persian Cat
Seated - Style One

Model No.:	690
Height:	5", 12.7 cm
Colour:	1. Dark grey with white highlights
	2. White
Issued:	1940-1968
Varieties:	HN 999

Colourways	U.S. $	Can. $	U.K. £
1. Dark grey	500.00	750.00	325.00
2. White	500.00	750.00	325.00

HN 2540
Kingfisher on a Tree Stump - large

Model No.:	1053
Height:	4 ½", 11.4 cm
Size:	Large
Colour:	Sea-green and blue feathers, brown breast, green and grey base
Issued:	1940-1946

Description	U.S. $	Can. $	U.K. £
Large	300.00	450.00	200.00

HN 2541
Kingfisher on a Tree Stump — small

Model No.:	1053A
Height:	3 ½", 8.9 cm
Size:	Small
Colour:	Sea-green and blue feathers, brown breast, green and grey base
Issued:	1940-1946

Description	U.S. $	Can. $	U.K. £
Small	275.00	400.00	175.00

NOTES ON PRICING

- Animal figures are not as plentiful as pretty ladies or character figures and caution in pricing must prevail.

- In the pricing tables N/A (not available) indicates that the animal figure was not available in that particular market.

- Italicized prices are an indication only and form a starting point for discussion on the final price, which may be lower or higher depending on supply and demand.

- Rarity classification provides a range for the collector to work with.

Rarity Class	Rare	Very Rare	Extremely Rare
U.S. $	1,100./1,500.	1,500./2,250.	2,250./3,250.
Can. $	1,650./2,200.	2,250./3,250.	3,250./4,500.
U.K. £	750./1,000.	1,000./1,500.	1,500./2,250.

- Always remember that when dealing with rare animal figures you need two willing parties, a buyer and a seller. One without the other will not work and only when they agree do you have a market price.

HN 2542A
Baltimore Oriole
Style One
Model No.: 1051
Height: 4 ¼", 10.8 cm
Colour: Black and orange bird, brown base, white flowers, green leaves
Issued: 1940-1946

Description	U.S. $	Can. $	U.K. £
Style one	325.00	475.00	225.00

HN 2542B
Baltimore Oriole
Style Two
Model No.: 1051
Height: 4 ¼", 10.8 cm
Colour: Black and orange bird, brown base, white flowers
Issued: 1940-1946

Description	U.S. $	Can. $	U.K. £
Style two	325.00	475.00	225.00

HN 2543
Bluebird with Lupins
Style Two
Model No.: 1062
Height: 6", 15.2 cm
Colour: Blue and pink bird with mauve and green stump
Issued: 1941-1946

Description	U.S. $	Can. $	U.K. £
Bluebird with lupins	325.00	475.00	225.00

HN 2544
Mallard Drake with Spill Vase
Model No.: 1057
Height: 8", 20.3 cm
Colour: Green head, brown and white feathers, green spill and reeds
Issued: 1941-1946

Description	U.S. $	Can. $	U.K. £
Drake with spill vase	1,500.00	2,250.00	1,000.00

HN 2545
Cock Pheasant

Model No.:	1063
Height:	7", 17.8 cm
Size:	Small
Colour:	Red-brown plumage, blue-green head
Issued:	1941-1952
Varieties:	HN 2632

Description	U.S. $	Can. $	U.K. £
Cock pheasant	375.00	550.00	250.00

HN 2546
Yellow-Throated Warbler
Style Two

Model No.:	1058
Height:	4 ¾", 12.1 cm
Colour:	Blue feathers, black wing tips, yellow throat
Issued:	1941-1946

Description	U.S. $	Can. $	U.K. £
Yellow-throated warbler	325.00	475.00	225.00

HN 2547
Budgerigars on a Tree Stump

Model No.:	1054
Height:	6", 15.2 cm
Colour:	Green and yellow birds with black markings, green and beige base
Issued:	1941-1946

Description	U.S. $	Can. $	U.K. £
Budgerigars	400.00	600.00	275.00

HN 2548
Golden-Crested Wren
Style Two

Model No.:	1052
Height:	4 ½", 11.4 cm
Colour:	Green feathers with black markings, white flowers, brown base
Issued:	1941-1946

Description	U.S. $	Can. $	U.K. £
Golden-crested wren	325.00	475.00	225.00

HN 2549
English Robin
Style One

Model No.:	1060		
Height:	2 ½", 6.4 cm		
Colour:	Brown feathers, red breast, yellow flowers, green leaves, beige base		
Issued:	1941-1946		

Description	U.S. $	Can. $	U.K. £
English robin	250.00	375.00	175.00

HN 2550
Chaffinch
Style One

Model No.:	1066		
Height:	2 ½", 6.4 cm		
Colour:	Brown with black, pink and blue wing tips, blue head, yellow flowers, green base		
Issued:	1941-1946		

Description	U.S. $	Can. $	U.K. £
Chaffinch	375.00	550.00	250.00

HN 2551
Bullfinch
Style Two

Model No.:	1070		
Height:	5 ½", 14.0 cm		
Colour:	Blue and pale blue feathers, red breast		
Issued:	1941-1946		

Description	U.S. $	Can. $	U.K. £
Bullfinch	325.00	475.00	225.00

HN 2552
Thrush Chicks (two)

Model No.:	1071		
Height:	3", 7.6 cm		
Colour:	See below		
Issued:	1. 1941-1946		
	2. c.1941		

Colourways	U.S. $	Can. $	U.K. £
1. Brown/yellow/green	325.00	475.00	225.00
2. Flambé		Rare	

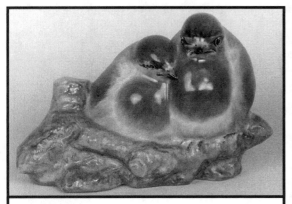

HN 2553
Robin Chicks (two)

Model No.:	1069
Height:	3", 7.6 cm
Colour:	Brown feathers, red breast, green base
Issued:	1941-1946

Description	U.S. $	Can. $	U.K. £
Robin chicks	325.00	475.00	225.00

HN 2554
Cardinal
Style Two

Model No.:	1059
Height:	6 ¾", 17.1 cm
Colour:	Red feathers with black markings, green leaves and stump, white flowers
Issued:	1941-1946

Description	U.S. $	Can. $	U.K. £
Cardinal	650.00	975.00	425.00

HN 2555
Mallard Drake
Standing - Green head

Model No.:	137
Height:	5 ½", 14.0 cm
Size:	Medium
Colour:	See below
Issued:	1. 1941-1946
	2. 1913-1996
Varieties:	HN 114, 115, 116, 956, 1191, 2647

Colourways	U.S. $	Can. $	U.K. £
1. Green/brown/white	400.00	600.00	250.00
2. Flambé	200.00	300.00	125.00

HN 2556
Duck
Head stretched forward

Model No.:	207
Height:	4", 10.1 cm
Colour:	See below
Issued:	1. 1941-1946
	2. c.1917
Varieties:	HN 150, 229

Colourways	U.S. $	Can. $	U.K. £
1. Brown/turquoise	375.00	550.00	250.00
2. Flambé	525.00	800.00	350.00

HN 2557
Welsh Corgi Ch. 'Spring Robin'
Large
Model No.: 1050
Designer: Frederick Daws
Height: 8", 20.3 cm
Size: Large
Colour: Golden brown with white and brown underbody
Issued: 1941-1955

Description	U.S. $	Can. $	U.K. £
Large	1,500.00	2,250.00	1,000.00

HN 2558
Welsh Corgi Ch. 'Spring Robin'
Medium
Model No.: 1050A
Designer: Frederick Daws
Height: 5", 12.7 cm
Size: Medium
Colour: Golden brown with white and brown underbody
Issued: 1941-1968

Description	U.S. $	Can. $	U.K. £
Medium	500.00	750.00	325.00

HN 2559
Welsh Corgi Ch. 'Spring Robin'
Small
Model No.: 1050B
Designer: Frederick Daws
Height: 3 ½", 8.9 cm
Size: Small
Colour: Golden brown with white and brown underbody
Issued: 1941-1985

Description	U.S. $	Can. $	U.K. £
Small	200.00	300.00	135.00

HN 2560
Great Dane Ch. 'Rebeller of Ouborough'
Model No.: 1077
Designer: Frederick Daws
Height: 8 ½", 21.6 cm
Size: Large
Colour: Light brown
Issued: 1941-1955

Description	U.S. $	Can. $	U.K. £
Large	1,750.00	2,600.00	1,150.00

HN 2561
Great Dane Ch. 'Rebeller of Ouborough'

Model No.:	1077A		
Designer:	Frederick Daws		
Height:	6", 15.2 cm		
Size:	Medium		
Colour:	Light brown		
Issued:	1941-1960		

Description	U.S. $	Can. $	U.K. £
Medium	800.00	1,200.00	525.00

HN 2562
Great Dane Ch. 'Rebeller of Ouborough'

Model No.:	1077B		
Designer:	Frederick Daws		
Height:	4 ½", 11.3 cm		
Size:	Small		
Colour:	Light brown		
Issued:	1941-1952		

Description	U.S. $	Can. $	U.K. £
Small	800.00	1,200.00	525.00

HN 2563
Pride of the Shires

Model No.:	1073		
Designer:	W. M. Chance		
Height:	9", 22.9 cm		
Size:	Large		
Colour:	Grey		
Issued:	1941-1960		

Description	U.S. $	Can. $	U.K. £
Large	1,000.00	1,500.00	650.00

HN 2564
Pride of the Shires

Model No.:	1073A		
Designer:	W. M. Chance		
Height:	6 3/8", 16.5 cm		
Size:	Small		
Colour:	Light brown horse, black mane, tail and legs, white nose and feet, green-brown base		
Issued:	1941-1960		

Description	U.S. $	Can. $	U.K. £
Small	750.00	1,100.00	500.00

HN 2565
Chestnut Mare - large

Model No.:	1074
Designer:	W. M. Chance
Height:	6 ½", 16.5 cm
Size:	Large
Colour:	Brown
Issued:	1941-1960

Description	U.S. $	Can. $	U.K. £
Large	1,000.00	1,500.00	650.00

HN 2566
Chestnut Mare - small

Model No.:	1074A
Designer:	W. M. Chance
Height:	5 ¼", 13.3 cm
Size:	Small
Colour:	Brown
Issued:	1941-1960

Description	U.S. $	Can. $	U.K. £
Small	750.00	1,100.00	500.00

HN 2567
Merely a Minor - small

Model No.:	1039B
Designer:	Frederick Daws
Height:	6 ½", 16.5 cm
Size:	Small
Colour:	White with grey markings on legs
Issued:	1941-1967
Varieties:	HN 2571

Description	U.S. $	Can. $	U.K. £
Small	500.00	750.00	325.00

HN 2568
Gude Grey Mare - large

Model No.:	1072
Designer:	W. M. Chance
Height:	8", 20.3 cm
Size:	Large
Colour:	White with grey markings on legs
Issued:	1941-1967

Description	U.S. $	Can. $	U.K. £
Large	1,000.00	1,500.00	650.00

HN 2569
Gude Grey Mare - medium

Model No.:	1072A
Designer:	W. M. Chance
Height:	5", 12.7 cm
Size:	Medium
Colour:	White with grey markings on legs
Issued:	1941-1967

Description	U.S. $	Can. $	U.K. £
Medium	600.00	900.00	400.00

HN 2570
Gude Grey Mare - small

Model No.:	1072B
Designer:	W. M. Chance
Height:	3 ¾", 9.5 cm
Size:	Small
Colour:	White with grey markings on legs
Issued:	1941-1967

Description	U.S. $	Can. $	U.K. £
Small	550.00	825.00	350.00

HN 2571
Merely a Minor - small

Model No.:	1039B
Designer:	Frederick Daws
Height:	6 ½", 16.5 cm
Size:	Small
Colour:	Light brown, white nose and feet, black tail
Issued:	1941-1967
Varieties:	HN 2567

Colourways	U.S. $	Can. $	U.K. £
Brown/white	500.00	750.00	325.00

HN 2572
Mallard Drake
Resting

Model No.:	1102
Height:	1 ½" x 2 ¾", 5.1 x 7.0 cm
Size:	Small
Colour:	Green head, brown wings, brown breast, white underbody white tail
Issued:	1941-1946

Description	U.S. $	Can. $	U.K. £
Mallard drake	150.00	225.00	95.00

HN 2573
Kingfisher
Style Two

Model No.:	1103
Designer:	Unknown
Height:	2 ½", 6.4 cm
Colour:	Turquoise, green and light brown feathers, black beak
Issued:	1941-1946

Description	U.S. $	Can. $	U.K. £
Kingfisher	300.00	450.00	200.00

HN 2574
Seagull on Rock

Model No.:	1108
Designer:	Unknown
Height:	2 ¼", 5.7 cm
Colour:	White head and breast, grey wings with black tail feathers
Issued:	1941-1946

Description	U.S. $	Can. $	U.K. £
Seagull on rock	300.00	450.00	200.00

HN 2575
Swan

Model No.:	1105
Designer:	Unknown
Height:	2 ¼", 5.7 cm
Colour:	White, black and orange beak
Issued:	1941-1946

Description	U.S. $	Can. $	U.K. £
Swan	450.00	675.00	300.00

HN 2576
Pheasant

Model No.:	1107
Designer:	Unknown
Height:	2 ½", 6.4 cm
Colour:	Red-brown feathers with green tail feathers, blue-green head, brown and green base
Issued:	1941-1946

Description	U.S. $	Can. $	U.K. £
Pheasant	300.00	450.00	200.00

HN 2577
Peacock

Model No.:	1106
Designer:	Unknown
Height:	2 ¾", 7.0 cm
Colour:	Dark turquoise breast, yellow, green and brown tail feathers
Issued:	1941-1946

Description	U.S. $	Can. $	U.K. £
Peacock	300.00	450.00	200.00

HN 2578
Dapple Grey

Model No.:	1134
Designer:	W. M. Chance
Height:	7 ½", 19.1 cm
Colour:	White with grey markings on legs
Issued:	1941-1960
Varieties:	Also called "Punch Peon," Chestnut Shire HN 2623

Description	U.S. $	Can. $	U.K. £
Dapple grey	750.00	1,100.00	500.00

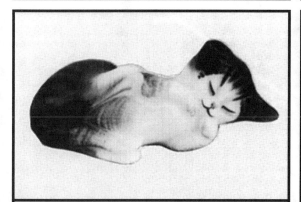

HN 2579
Character Kitten
Lying on back

Model No.:	1080
Designer:	Peggy Davies
Height:	1 ½", 3.8 cm
Colour:	Brown and white
Issued:	1941-1985

Description	U.S. $	Can. $	U.K. £
Kitten, on back	125.00	175.00	75.00

HN 2580
Character Kitten
Licking hind paw

Model No.:	1079
Designer:	Peggy Davies
Height:	2 ¼", 5.7 cm
Colour:	Brown and white
Issued:	1941-1985

Description	U.S. $	Can. $	U.K. £
Kitten, licking hind paw	125.00	175.00	75.00

HN 2581
Character Kitten
Sleeping

Model No.:	1085	
Designer:	Peggy Davies	
Height:	1 ½", 3.8 cm	
Colour:	Brown and white	
Issued:	1941-1985	

Description	U.S. $	Can. $	U.K. £
Kitten, sleeping	125.00	175.00	75.00

HN 2582
Character Kitten
On hind legs

Model No.:	1087	
Designer:	Peggy Davies	
Height:	2 ¾", 7.0 cm	
Colour:	Light brown and black coat with white underbody	
Issued:	1941-1985	

Description	U.S. $	Can. $	U.K. £
Kitten, on hind legs	125.00	175.00	75.00

HN 2583
Character Kitten
Licking front paw

Model No.:	1086	
Designer:	Peggy Davies	
Height:	2", 5.1 cm	
Colour:	Tan and white	
Issued:	1941-1985	

Description	U.S. $	Can. $	U.K. £
Kitten, licking front paw	125.00	175.00	75.00

HN 2584
Character Kitten
Looking up

Model No.:	1081	
Designer:	Peggy Davies	
Height:	2", 5.1 cm	
Colour:	Tan and white	
Issued:	1941-1985	

Description	U.S. $	Can. $	U.K. £
Kitten, looking up	125.00	175.00	75.00

HN 2585
Cocker Spaniel Lying in Basket

Model No.:	1155
Height:	2″, 5.1 cm
Colour:	White with brown and black markings, light brown basket
Issued:	1941-1985

Description	U.S. $	Can. $	U.K. £
Spaniel in basket	100.00	150.00	65.00

HN 2586
Cocker Spaniel Chewing Handle of Basket

Model No.:	1153
Height:	2 ¾″, 7.0 cm
Colour:	White with dark brown ears and patches on back, light brown patches over eyes, light brown basket
Issued:	1941-1985

Description	U.S. $	Can. $	U.K. £
Spaniel chewing basket	100.00	150.00	65.00

HN 2587
Terrier Sitting in Basket

Model No.:	1152
Height:	3″, 7.6 cm
Colour:	White with brown markings, brown basket
Issued:	1941-1985

Description	U.S. $	Can. $	U.K. £
Terrier in basket	100.00	150.00	65.00

HN 2588
Terrier Puppies in a Basket

Model No.:	1154
Height:	3″, 7.6 cm
Colour:	White with light and dark brown markings, brown basket
Issued:	1941-1985

Description	U.S. $	Can. $	U.K. £
Puppies in basket	100.00	150.00	65.00

HN 2589
Cairn Terrier
Begging
Model No.:   1131
Height: 4", 10.1 cm
Colour: Beige with black highlights
Issued: 1941-1985

Description	U.S. $	Can. $	U.K. £
Cairn terrier	100.00	150.00	65.00

HN 2590
Cocker Spaniels Sleeping
Model No.:   1132
Height: 1 ¾", 4.5 cm
Colour: White dog with brown markings and golden brown dog
Issued: 1941-1969

Description	U.S. $	Can. $	U.K. £
Spaniels, sleeping	100.00	150.00	65.00

HN 2591
Duck
Standing
Model No.:   395
Height: 2 ½", 6.4 cm
Size: Small
Colour: See below
Issued: 1. 1941-1968
               2. 1922-1996
Varieties: HN 806, 807

Colourways	U.S. $	Can. $	U.K. £
1. Green/white/brown	125.00	175.00	75.00
2. Flambé	125.00	175.00	85.00

HN 2592
Hare
Crouching - Style Three
Model No.:   1157
Height: 2 ¾", 7.0 cm
Colour: See below
Issued: 1. 1941-1968
               2. 1945-1996

Colourways	U.S $	Can. $	U.K. £
1. Light brown/white	150.00	225.00	100.00
2. Flambé	135.00	200.00	90.00

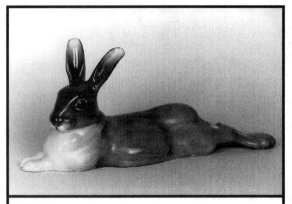

HN 2593
Hare
Lying, legs stretched behind - large

Model No.:	656		
Height:	3″ x 7 ½″, 7.6 x 19.1 cm		
Size:	Large		
Colour:	See below		
Issued:	1. 1941-1968		
	2. 1929-1962		
Varieties:	HN 979, 984, 985, 1071		

Colourways	U.S $	Can. $	U.K. £
1. Light brown/white	250.00	375.00	175.00
2. Flambé	450.00	675.00	300.00

HN 2594
Hare
Lying, legs stretched behind - small

Model No.:	656A		
Height:	1 ¾″ x 5 ¼″, 4.4 x 13.3 cm		
Size:	Small		
Colour:	See below		
Issued:	1. 1941-1985		
	2. 1929-1996		

Colourways	U.S $	Can. $	U.K. £
1. Light brown/white	125.00	175.00	75.00
2. Flambé	125.00	175.00	75.00

HN 2595
Lamb
Style Two

Model No.:	1117
Designer:	Peggy Davies
Height:	Unknown
Colour:	White
Issued:	Modelled 1941

Description	U.S $	Can. $	U.K. £
Lamb, style two		Extremely Rare	

HN 2596
Lamb
Style Three

Model No.:	1112
Designer:	Peggy Davies
Height:	Unknown
Colour:	White
Issued:	Modelled 1941

Description	U.S $	Can. $	U.K. £
Lamb, style three		Extremely Rare	

HN 2597
Lamb
Style Four

Model No.:	1115
Designer:	Peggy Davies
Height:	3 ¼", 8.3 cm
Colour:	Black lamb on white base
Issued:	Modelled 1941

Description	U.S $	Can. $	U.K. £
Lamb, style four		Extremely Rare	

HN 2598
Lamb
Style Five

Model No.:	1116
Designer:	Peggy Davies
Height:	Unknown
Colour:	White
Issued:	Modelled 1941

Description	U.S $	Can. $	U.K. £
Lamb, style five		Extremely Rare	

HN 2599
English Setter with Pheasant

Model No.:	1028
Designer:	Frederick Daws
Height:	8", 20.3 cm
Colour:	Red-brown
Issued:	1941
Varieties:	HN 2529

Description	U.S $	Can. $	U.K. £
English setter/pheasant		Extremely Rare	

HN 2600
Cocker Spaniel with Pheasant

Model No.:	714B
Designer:	Frederick Daws
Height:	3 ½", 8.9 cm
Size:	Small
Colour:	Black
Issued:	1941
Varieties:	HN 1029, 1062

Description	U.S $	Can. $	U.K. £
Cocker spaniel/pheasant		Only one known to exist.	

AMERICAN GREAT DANE

Colour: Light brown

	HN 2601	HN 2602	HN 2603
Model No.:	1171	1171A	1171B
Height:	8 ½", 21.6 cm	6 ½", 16.5 cm	4 ½", 11.4 cm
Size:	Large	Medium	Small
Issued:	1941-1955	1941-1960	1941-1960

Currency	Large	Medium	Small
U.S $	1,850.00	1,000.00	950.00
Can. $	2,750.00	1,500.00	1,400.00
U.K. £	1,250.00	650.00	625.00

HN 2604
Peacock Butterfly

Model No.:	1178	
Height:	2", 5.1 cm	
Colour:	Tan, black, yellow, blue, white and green	
Issued:	1941-by 1946	

Description	U.S $	Can. $	U.K. £
Peacock butterfly	1,500.00	2,250.00	1,000.00

HN 2605
Camberwell Beauty Butterfly

Model No.:	1181	
Height:	2", 5.1 cm	
Colour:	Purple, blue, white and green	
Issued:	1941-by 1946	

Description	U.S $	Can. $	U.K. £
Camberwell beauty	1,500.00	2,250.00	1,000.00

HN 2606
Swallowtail Butterfly

Model No.:	1175	
Height:	2 ¾", 7.0 cm	
Colour:	Yellow, black, blue, green and white	
Issued:	1941-by 1946	

Description	U.S $	Can. $	U.K. £
Swallowtail butterfly	1,500.00	2,250.00	1,000.00

HN 2607
Red Admiral Butterfly

Model No.:	1179	
Height:	2", 5.1 cm	
Colour:	Brown, black, red, yellow, white and green	
Issued:	1941-by 1946	

Description	U.S $	Can. $	U.K. £
Red admiral butterfly	1,500.00	2,250.00	1,000.00

HN 2608
Copper Butterfly

Model No.:	1177	
Height:	2", 5.1 cm	
Colour:	Unknown	
Issued:	1941-by 1946	

Description	U.S $	Can. $	U.K. £
Copper butterfly	1,500.00	2,250.00	1,000.00

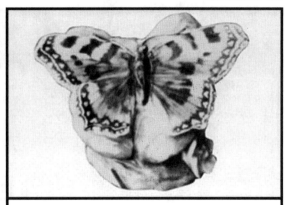

HN 2609
Tortoiseshell Butterfly

Model No.:	1180	
Height:	2", 5.1 cm	
Colour:	Unknown	
Issued:	1941-by 1946	

Description	U.S $	Can. $	U.K. £
Tortoiseshell butterfly	1,500.00	2,250.00	1,000.00

HN 2610
Pheasant Hen

Model No.:	1195	
Height:	6", 15.2 cm	
Colour:	Light brown with dark brown markings, green base	
Issued:	1942-1950	

Description	U.S $	Can. $	U.K. £
Pheasant hen	400.00	600.00	275.00

HN 2611
Chaffinch
Style Two

Model No.:	1200	
Height:	2", 5.1 cm	
Colour:	Brown feathers, blue, yellow and black markings, green base	
Issued:	c.1945-1950	

Description	U.S $	Can. $	U.K. £
Chaffinch	350.00	525.00	225.00

HN 2612
Baltimore Oriole
Style Three

Model No.:	1201
Height:	4", 10.1 cm
Colour:	Yellow with black head and wing tips, green base
Issued:	c.1945-1950

Description	U.S $	Can. $	U.K. £
Baltimore oriole	350.00	525.00	225.00

HN 2613
Golden-Crested Wren
Style Three

Model No.:	1202
Height:	2 ½", 6.4 cm
Colour:	Green with black markings, yellow and white breast, brown base
Issued:	c.1945-1950

Description	U.S $	Can. $	U.K. £
Golden-crested wren	350.00	525.00	225.00

HN 2614
Blue Bird

Model No.:	1203
Height:	5", 12.7 cm
Colour:	Blue with pink and white breast, green base
Issued:	c.1945-1950

Description	U.S $	Can. $	U.K. £
Blue bird	350.00	525.00	225.00

HN 2615
Cardinal
Style Three

Model No.:	1204
Height:	4 ½", 11.4 cm
Colour:	Red feathers with black markings, green base
Issued:	c.1945-1950

Description	U.S $	Can. $	U.K. £
Cardinal	350.00	525.00	225.00

HN 2616
Bullfinch
Style Three

Model No.:	1205		
Height:	4", 10.1 cm		
Colour:	Mauve and black feathers, pink breast, green base		
Issued:	c.1945-1950		

Description	U.S $	Can. $	U.K. £
Bullfinch	350.00	525.00	225.00

HN 2617
Robin
Style Two

Model No.:	1206		
Height:	2", 5.1 cm		
Colour:	Brown feathers, red breast, green base		
Issued:	c.1945-1950		

Description	U.S $	Can. $	U.K. £
Robin	350.00	525.00	225.00

Photograph
not available
at press time

HN 2618
Yellow-Throated Warbler
Style Three

Model No.:	1207		
Height:	4 ½", 11.4 cm		
Colour:	Blue feathers with black markings, yellow breast, green base		
Issued:	c.1945-1950		

Description	U.S $	Can. $	U.K. £
Yellow-throated warbler	350.00	525.00	225.00

HN 2619
Grouse

Model No.:	1161		
Height:	Unknown		
Colour:	Unknown		
Issued:	Unknown		

Description	U.S $	Can. $	U.K. £
Grouse		Extremely Rare	

HN 2620
English Setter - large

Model No.:	770
Designer:	Frederick Daws
Height:	7 ½″ x 12 ¼″, 19.1 x 31.1 cm
Colour:	White with liver highlights
Issued:	1. 1950-c.1960; 2. Unknown
Varieties:	English Setter Ch. 'Maesydd Mustard' HN 1049, Gordon Setter HN 1079, Irish Setter Ch. 'Pat O'Moy' HN 1054

Colourways	U.S $	Can. $	U.K. £
1. Natural	3,500.00	5,250.00	2,250.00
2. Flambé	1,200.00	1,800.00	800.00

HN 2621
English Setter - medium

Model No.:	770A
Designer:	Frederick Daws
Height:	5 ¼″, 13.3 cm
Colour:	Liver and white
Issued:	1950-c.1960
Varieties:	English Setter Ch. 'Maesydd Mustard' HN 1050, Gordon Setter HN 1080, Irish Setter Ch. 'Pat O'Moy' HN 1055
Derivative:	Bookend

Description	U.S $	Can. $	U.K. £
Medium	2,000.00	3,000.00	1,350.00

HN 2622
English Setter - small

Model No.:	770B
Designer:	Frederick Daws
Height:	3 ¾″, 9.5 cm
Size:	Small
Colour:	Liver and white
Issued:	1950-c.1960
Varieties:	English Setter Ch. 'Maesydd Mustard' HN 1051, Gordon Setter HN 1081, Irish Setter Ch. 'Pat O'Moy' HN 1056

Description	U.S $	Can. $	U.K. £
Small	1,500.00	2,250.00	1,000.00

HN 2623
Punch Peon, Chestnut Shire

Model No.:	1134
Designer:	W. M. Chance
Height:	7 ½″, 19.1 cm
Colour:	Brown with black mane and black and white markings on legs
Issued:	1950-1960
Varieties:	Also called 'Dapple Grey' HN 2578

Description	U.S $	Can. $	U.K. £
Punch Peon	900.00	1,450.00	600.00

HN 2624
Pointer
Style One

Model No.:	1312
Designer:	Peggy Davies
Height:	5 ½" x 11 ½", 14.0 cm x 29.2 cm
Colour:	White with dark brown markings, yellow and green leaves, brown tree stump
Issued:	1952-1985

Description	U.S $	Can. $	U.K. £
Pointer	450.00	675.00	300.00

HN 2625
French Poodle - large

Model No.:	1212
Designer:	Peggy Davies
Height:	9" x 10", 22.9 x 25.4 cm
Size:	Large
Colour:	White
Issued:	Modelled 1952

Description	U.S $	Can. $	U.K. £
Large		Only two known to exist.	

*

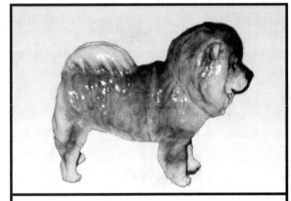

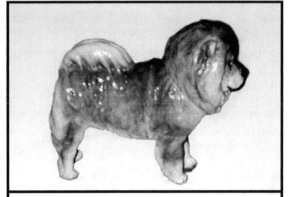

HN 2628
Chow Ch. 'T'Sioh of Kin-Shan'
Large

Model No.:	1209
Height:	Unknown
Size:	Large
Colour:	Golden brown
Issued:	Modelled 1952

Description	U.S $	Can. $	U.K. £
Large		Only one known to exist.	

HN 2629
Chow Ch. 'T'Sioh of Kin-Shan'
Medium

Model No.:	1209A
Height:	Unknown
Size:	Medium
Colour:	Golden brown
Issued:	Modelled 1952

Description	U.S $	Can. $	U.K. £
Medium		Not known to exist.	

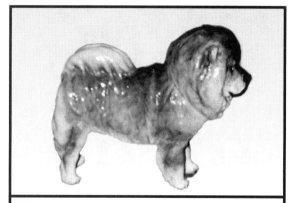

HN 2630
Chow Ch. 'T'Sioh of Kin-Shan'
Small

Model No.:	1209B		
Height:	Unknown		
Size:	Small		
Colour:	Golden brown		
Issued:	Modelled 1952		

Description	U.S $	Can. $	U.K. £
Small		Not known to exist.	

HN 2631
French Poodle - medium

Model No.:	1212A
Designer:	Peggy Davies
Height:	5 ¼", 13.3 cm
Size:	Medium
Colour:	White with pink, grey and black markings
Issued:	1952-1985

Description	U.S $	Can. $	U.K. £
Medium	150.00	225.00	100.00

HN 2632
Cock Pheasant

Model No.:	1063
Height:	6 ¾", 17.2 cm
Colour:	Red-brown feathers, dark blue markings, green-blue head, green-brown base (china)
Issued:	1952-1968
Varieties:	HN 2545
Series:	Prestige

Description	U.S $	Can. $	U.K. £
Cock pheasant	375.00	550.00	250.00

HN 2633
Peruvian Penguin - large

Model No.:	769
Designer:	Charles Noke
Height:	12", 30.1 cm (large)
Colour:	See below
Issued:	1. 1952-1973; 2. c.1946-1962
Varieties:	HN 1199
Series:	Prestige

Colourways	U.S $	Can. $	U.K. £
1. Black/white (china)	1,875.00	2,800.00	1,250.00
2. Flambé	2,250.00	3,350.00	1,500.00

Note: Naturalistic models are free standing. Flambé models incorporate a rock as the base.

HN 2634
Fox
Seated - Style Six

Model No.:	767	
Height:	10 ½", 26.7 cm	
Colour:	Golden brown with black highlights (china)	
Issued:	1952-1992	
Series:	Prestige	

Description	U.S $	Can. $	U.K. £
Fox, seated	1,100.00	1,600.00	750.00

HN 2635
Drake
Standing

Model No.:	307
Height:	13 ½", 34.3 cm
Size:	Large
Colour:	White with light brown shading (china)
Issued:	1952-1974
Series:	Prestige
Varieties:	HN 248, 249, 252, 1198

Description	U.S $	Can. $	U.K. £
White drake	1,500.00	2,250.00	1,000.00

HN 2636
Indian Runner Drake

Model No.:	1327
Designer:	Peggy Davies
Height:	18", 45.7 cm
Size:	Large
Colour:	White
Issued:	1952-c.1960

Description	U.S $	Can. $	U.K. £
Indian runner drake	1,500.00	2,250.00	1,000.00

HN 2637
Polar Bear and Cub on Base - Large

Model No.:	613
Designer:	Charles Noke
Height:	15", 38.1 cm
Colour:	See below
Issued:	1. 1952-c.1960
	2. 3. and 4. c.1929

Colourways	U.S $	Can. $	U.K. £
1. White/green	6,750.00	10,000.00	4,500.00
2. Flambé	6,750.00	10,000.00	4,500.00
3. Chang		Extremely Rare	
4. Sung		Extremely Rare	

HN 2638
Leopard on Rock

Model No.:	1036	
Designer:	Charles Noke	
Height:	9″ x 11 ½″, 22.9 x 29.2 cm	
Colour:	Golden brown with dark brown spots, charcoal rock (earthenware)	
Issued:	1952-1981	
Series:	Prestige	

Description	U.S $	Can. $	U.K. £
Leopard on rock	1,275.00	1,875.00	850.00

HN 2639
Tiger on a Rock
Style Five

Model No.:	1038	
Designer:	Charles Noke	
Height:	12″ x 10 ¼″, 30.5 x 26.0 cm	
Colour:	Golden brown with dark brown stripes, charcoal rock (earthenware)	
Issued:	1952-1992	
Series:	Prestige	

Description	U.S $	Can. $	U.K. £
Tiger on rock	1,150.00	1,700.00	750.00

HN 2640
Fighter Elephant - Large

Model No.:	626	
Designer:	Charles Noke	
Height:	12″ x 9″, 30.5 x 22.9 cm	
Colour:	See below	
Issued:	1. 1952-1992 2. and 3. c.1929	
Varieties:	HN 1120	
Series:	Prestige	

Colourways	U.S $	Can. $	U.K. £
1. Grey (earthenware)	1,150.00	1,700.00	750.00
2. Flambé	2,250.00	3,250.00	1,500.00
3. Sung	3,750.00	5,500.00	2,500.00

HN 2641
Lion on Rock
Style Two

Model No.:	1033	
Designer:	Charles Noke	
Height:	10 ½″, 26.7 cm	
Colour:	Golden brown lion, charcoal rock (earthenware)	
Issued:	1952-1992	
Series:	Prestige	

Description	U.S $	Can. $	U.K. £
Lion on rock	1,150.00	1,700.00	750.00

HN 2642
Red Squirrel in a Pine Tree
Prototype

Model No.:	1292
Designer:	Peggy Davies
Height:	8", 20.3 cm (length)
Colour:	Nut brown
Issued:	Modelled 1945

Description	U.S $	Can. $	U.K. £
Red squirrel		Prototype	

HN 2643
Boxer Ch. 'Warlord of Mazelaine'

Model No.:	1412A
Designer:	Peggy Davies
Height:	6 ½", 16.5 cm
Size:	Medium
Colour:	Golden brown coat with white bib
Issued:	1952-1985

Description	U.S $	Can. $	U.K. £
Boxer	150.00	225.00	100.00

HN 2644
Elephant
Trunk in salute - Style One

Model No.:	489B
Designer:	Charles Noke
Height:	4 ½", 11.4 cm (small)
Colour:	See below
Issued:	1. 1952-1985; 2. and 3. c.1926-1962
Varieties:	HN 891B, 941

Colourways	U.S $	Can. $	U.K. £
1. Grey/black (china)	185.00	275.00	125.00
2. Flambé	450.00	675.00	300.00
3. Sung	1,050.00	1,500.00	700.00

HN 2645
Doberman Pinscher Ch. 'Rancho Dobe's Storm'

Model No.:	1508
Designer:	Peggy Davies
Height:	6 ¼" x 6 ½", 15.9 x 16.5 cm
Size:	Medium
Colour:	See below
Issued:	1. 1955-1985
	2. c.1955

Colourways	U.S $	Can. $	U.K. £
1. Black/brown	200.00	300.00	135.00
2. Flambé		Extremely Rare	

HN 2646
Tiger, Stalking - Style Two - extra large

Model No.:	809
Designer:	Charles Noke
Height:	5 ¾" x 13 ¼", 14.6 x 33.5 cm (extra large)
Colour:	See below
Issued:	1. 1955-1992; 2. 1950-1996
Varieties:	HN 1082; Also Tiger on Alabaster Base HN 1126
Series:	Prestige

Colourways	U.S $	Can. $	U.K. £
1. Natural	900.00	1,350.00	600.00
2. Flambé	825.00	1,250.00	550.00

HN 2647
Drake, Standing - Medium

Model No.:	137
Height:	1. 5 ½", 14.0 cm
	2. 6 ½", 16.5 cm
Size:	Medium
Colour:	See below
Issued:	1. 1959-1962
	2. 1913-1996
Varieties:	HN 114, 115, 116, 956, 1191, 2555

Colourways	U.S $	Can. $	U.K. £
1. Green/grey/brown (china)	400.00	600.00	250.00
2. Flambé	200.00	300.00	125.00

HN 2648
Piglet
Style One

Model No.:	1279
Designer:	Peggy Davies
Height:	2", 5.1 cm
Colour:	Pink piglet on green grassy mound
Issued:	1959-1967

Description	U.S $	Can. $	U.K. £
Style one	150.00	225.00	95.00

HN 2649
Piglet
Style Two

Model No.:	1275
Designer:	Peggy Davies
Height:	2", 5.1 cm
Colour:	Pink piglet on green grassy mound
Issued:	1959-1967

Description	U.S $	Can. $	U.K. £
Style two	150.00	225.00	95.00

HN 2650
Piglet
Style Three

Model No.:	1282
Designer:	Peggy Davies
Height:	1", 2.5 cm
Colour:	Pink piglet on green grassy mound
Issued:	1959-1967

Description	U.S $	Can. $	U.K. £
Style three	150.00	225.00	95.00

HN 2651
Piglet
Style Four

Model No.:	1280
Designer:	Peggy Davies
Height:	1", 2.5 cm
Colour:	Pink piglet on green grassy mound
Issued:	1959-1967

Description	U.S $	Can. $	U.K. £
Style four	150.00	225.00	95.00

HN 2652
Piglet
Style Five

Model No.:	1281
Designer:	Peggy Davies
Height:	2", 5.1 cm
Colour:	Pink piglet on green grassy mound
Issued:	1959-1967

Description	U.S $	Can. $	U.K. £
Style five	150.00	225.00	95.00

HN 2653
Piglet
Style Six

Model No.:	1278
Designer:	Peggy Davies
Height:	2", 5.1 cm
Colour:	Pink piglet on green grassy mound
Issued:	1959-1967

Description	U.S $	Can. $	U.K. £
Style six	150.00	225.00	95.00

HN 2654
Character Dog with Slipper

Model No.:	1673
Designer:	Unknown
Height:	3", 7.6 cm
Colour:	White with black and brown patches, grey slipper
Issued:	1959-1985

Description	U.S $	Can. $	U.K. £
Dog with slipper	100.00	150.00	65.00

HN 2655
Siamese Cat
Seated - Style One

Model No.:	1672
Designer:	Joseph Ledger
Modeller:	Peggy Davies
Height:	5 ½", 14.0 cm
Colour:	Cream with black markings
Issued:	1960-1985
Series:	Chatcull Range

Description	U.S $	Can. $	U.K. £
Siamese cat, seated	125.00	175.00	85.00

HN 2656
Pine Marten

Model No.:	1689
Designer:	Joseph Ledger
Height:	4", 10.1 cm
Colour:	See below
Issued:	1. 1960-1969
	2. c.1960
Series:	Chatcull Range

Colourways	U.S $	Can. $	U.K. £
1. Natural colours	375.00	550.00	250.00
2. Flambé		Rare	

HN 2657
Langur Monkey

Model No.:	1703
Designer:	Joseph Ledger
Height:	4 ½", 11.4 cm
Colour:	Long-haired brown and white coat
Issued:	1960-1969
Series:	Chatcull Range

Description	U.S $	Can. $	U.K. £
Langur monkey	300.00	450.00	200.00

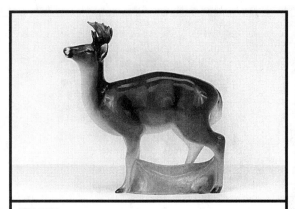

HN 2658
White -Tailed Deer

Model No.:	1707		
Designer:	Joseph Ledger		
Height:	6", 15.2 cm		
Colour:	Brown and grey		
Issued:	1960-1969		
Series:	Chatcull Range		

Description	U.S $	Can. $	U.K. £
White-tailed deer	300.00	450.00	200.00

HN 2659
Brown Bear
Style Two

Model No.:	1688		
Designer:	Joseph Ledger		
Height:	4", 10.1 cm		
Colour:	See below		
Issued:	1. 1960-1969		
	2. c.1960		
Series:	Chatcull Range		

Colourways	U.S $	Can. $	U.K. £
1. Brown/black	225.00	325.00	150.00
2. Mandarin		Very Rare	

HN 2660
Siamese Cat
Standing - Style One

Model No.:	1709		
Designer:	Joseph Ledger		
Modeller:	Peggy Davies		
Height:	5", 12.7 cm		
Colour:	Cream with black markings		
Issued:	1960-1985		
Series:	Chatcull Range		

Description	U.S $	Can. $	U.K. £
Siamese cat, standing	125.00	175.00	85.00

HN 2661
Mountain Sheep

Model No.:	1692		
Designer:	Joseph Ledger		
Height:	5", 12.7 cm		
Colour:	Brown with white highlights, green base		
Issued:	1960-1969		
Series:	Chatcull Range		

Description	U.S $	Can. $	U.K. £
Mountain sheep	300.00	450.00	200.00

HN 2662
Siamese Cat
Lying - Style One

Model No.:   1710
Designer: Joseph Ledger
Modeller: Peggy Davies
Height: 3 ¾", 9.5 cm
Colour: Cream with black markings
Issued: 1960-1985
Series: Chatcull Range

Description	U.S $	Can. $	U.K. £
Siamese cat, lying	125.00	175.00	85.00

HN 2663
River Hog

Model No.:   1704
Designer: Joseph Ledger
Height: 3 ½", 8.9 cm
Colour: Dark brown with light brown and white
               highlights
Issued: 1960-1969
Series: Chatcull Range

Description	U.S $	Can. $	U.K. £
River hog	250.00	375.00	175.00

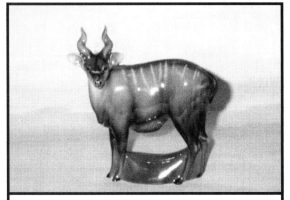

HN 2664
Nyala Antelope

Model No.:   1705
Designer: Joseph Ledger
Height: 5 ¾", 14.6 cm
Colour: Mushroom coloured coat with black
               and brown highlights
Issued: 1960-1969
Series: Chatcull Range

Description	U.S. $	Can. $	U.K. £
Nyala antelope	250.00	375.00	175.00

HN 2665
Llama
Style Two

Model No.:   1687
Designer: Joseph Ledger
Height: 6 ½", 16.5 cm
Colour: Brown with turquoise highlights
Issued: 1960-1969
Series: Chatcull Range

Description	U.S $	Can. $	U.K. £
Llama	300.00	450.00	200.00

HN 2666
Badger
Style One

Model No.:	1708
Designer:	Joseph Ledger
Height:	2 ¾", 7.0 cm
Colour:	See below
Issued:	1. 1960-1969
	2. c.1960
Series:	Chatcull Range

Colourways	U.S $	Can. $	U.K. £
1. Natural colours	250.00	375.00	175.00
2. Mandarin		Very Rare	

HN 2667
Labrador Ch. 'Bumblikite of Mansergh'

Model No.:	1946
Designer:	John Bromley
Height:	5 ¼", 13.3 cm
Size:	Medium
Colour:	Black
Issued:	1967-1985

Description	U.S $	Can. $	U.K. £
Labrador	200.00	300.00	125.00

HN 2668
Puffins

Model No.:	2289
Designer:	Robert Jefferson
Height:	9 ¾", 24.8 cm
Colour:	Dark grey and white birds with red, yellow and blue beaks
Issued:	1974 in a limited edition of 250
Series:	Jefferson Sculptures

Description	U.S $	Can. $	U.K. £
Puffins	750.00	1,100.00	500.00

HN 2669
Snowy Owl (male)

Model No.:	2264
Designer:	Robert Jefferson
Height:	16", 40.1 cm
Colour:	White with grey markings
Issued:	1976 in a limited edition of 150
Series:	Jefferson Sculptures

Description	U.S $	Can. $	U.K. £
Snowy owl (male)	750.00	1,100.00	500.00

HN 2670
Snowy Owl (female)

Model No.:	2389
Designer:	Robert Jefferson
Height:	9 ½", 24.0 cm
Colour:	White with grey markings
Issued:	1976 in a limited edition of 150
Series:	Jefferson Sculptures

Description	U.S $	Can. $	U.K. £
Snowy owl (female)	750.00	1,100.00	500.00

*

HN 3463
'Motherhood' Elephants

Model No.:	Unknown
Designer:	Adrian Hughes
Height:	8 ¾", 22.2 cm
Colour:	White
Issued:	1995-1998
Series:	Images of Nature
Varieties:	HN 3464

Colourways	U.S $	Can. $	U.K. £
White	200.00	300.00	125.00

HN 3464
'Motherhood' Elephants

Model No.:	Unknown
Designer:	Adrian Hughes
Height:	8 ¾", 22.2 cm
Colour:	Flambé
Issued:	1995-1997
Series:	Images of Fire
Varieties:	HN 3463

Colourways	U.S $	Can. $	U.K. £
Flambé	450.00	675.00	300.00

*

HN 3466
'Twilight' Barn Owls

Model No.:	Unknown
Designer:	Adrian Hughes
Height:	5 ¾", 14.6 cm
Colour:	White
Issued:	1996-1999
Series:	Images of Nature

Description	U.S $	Can. $	U.K. £
'Twilight'	75.00	125.00	50.00

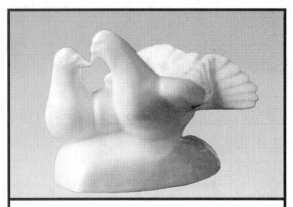

HN 3467
'Devotion' Doves

Designer:	Adrian Hughes		
Height:	2 ½", 6.3 cm		
Colour:	White		
Issued:	1996 to the present		
Series:	Images of Nature		

Description	U.S $	Can. $	U.K. £
'Devotion'	N/A	120.00	40.00

HN 3468
'First Born' Whales

Designer:	Adrian Hughes		
Height:	6", 15.2 cm		
Colour:	White		
Issued:	1997-2002		
Series:	Images of Nature		

Description	U.S $	Can. $	U.K. £
'First Born'	125.00	175.00	75.00

*

HN 3500
Black-Throated Loon

Model No.:	2268
Designer:	Robert Jefferson
Height:	9 ½" x 20", 24.0 x 50.8 cm
Colour:	Green head, black and white wings, white underbody
Issued:	1974 in a limited edition of 150
Series:	Jefferson Sculptures

Description	U.S $	Can. $	U.K. £
Black-throated loon	750.00	1,100.00	500.00

HN 3501
White-Winged Cross Bills

Model No.:	2208
Designer:	Robert Jefferson
Height:	8", 20.3 cm
Colour:	Red bird with white and brown wings, dull yellow bird with brown and white wings
Issued:	1974 in a limited edition of 250
Series:	Jefferson Sculptures

Description	U.S $	Can. $	U.K. £
White-winged cross bills	750.00	1,100.00	500.00

HN 3502
King Eider

Model No.:	2302
Designer:	Robert Jefferson
Height:	10", 25.4 cm
Colour:	Dark brown, grey head, red and yellow beak
Issued:	1974 in a limited edition of 150
Series:	Jefferson Sculptures

Description	U.S $	Can. $	U.K. £
King eider	750.00	1,100.00	500.00

HN 3503
Roseate Terns

Model No.:	2319
Designer:	Robert Jefferson
Height:	11", 27.9 cm
Colour:	Grey and white large bird, light brown chicks
Issued:	1974 in a limited edition of 150
Series:	Jefferson Sculptures

Description	U.S $	Can. $	U.K. £
Roseate terns	750.00	1,100.00	500.00

HN 3504
Golden-Crowned Kinglet

Model No.:	2406
Designer:	Robert Jefferson
Height:	8 ¼", 21.0 cm
Colour:	Brown branch and acorn, yellow, brown and red bird
Issued:	1974 in an unlimited number
Series:	Jefferson Sculptures

Description	U.S $	Can. $	U.K. £
Golden-crowned kinglet	400.00	600.00	250.00

HN 3505
Winter Wren

Model No.:	2405
Designer:	Robert Jefferson
Height:	5", 12.7 cm
Colour:	Brown with cream breast
Issued:	1974 in an unlimited number
Series:	Jefferson Sculptures

Description	U.S $	Can. $	U.K. £
Winter wren	400.00	600.00	250.00

HN 3506
Colorado Chipmunks

Model No.:	2404
Designer:	Robert Jefferson
Height:	13", 33.0 cm
Colour:	Brown with black patches
Issued:	1974 in a limited edition of 75
Series:	Jefferson Sculptures

Description	U.S $	Can. $	U.K. £
Colorado chipmunks	1,100.00	1,800.00	750.00

HN 3507
Harbour Seals

Model No.:	2434
Designer:	Robert Jefferson
Height:	8 ½", 21.6 cm
Colour:	Greys and browns
Issued:	1975 in a limited edition of 75
Series:	Jefferson Sculptures

Description	U.S $	Can. $	U.K. £
Harbour seals	750.00	1,100.00	500.00

HN 3508
Snowshoe Hares

Model No.:	2446
Designer:	Robert Jefferson
Height:	10 ¾", 27.3 cm
Colour:	Browns and white
Issued:	1975 in a limited edition of 75
Series:	Jefferson Sculptures

Description	U.S $	Can. $	U.K. £
Snowshoe hares	750.00	1,100.00	500.00

HN 3509
Downy Woodpecker

Model No.:	2469
Designer:	Robert Jefferson
Height:	7 ¼", 18.4 cm
Colour:	Black and white bird, green leaves, blue flower
Issued:	1975 in an unlimited number
Series:	Jefferson Sculptures

Description	U.S $	Can. $	U.K. £
Downy woodpecker	400.00	600.00	250.00

HN 3510
Eastern Bluebird Fledgling

Model No.:	2481
Designer:	Robert Jefferson
Height:	5 ¾", 14.6 cm
Colour:	Brown with light brown highlights, green leaves, purple flower, tan trowel
Issued:	1976 in a limited edition of 250
Series:	Jefferson Sculptures

Description	U.S $	Can. $	U.K. £
Bluebird fledgling	400.00	600.00	250.00

Photograph
not available
at press time

HN 3511
Chipping Sparrow

Model No.:	2466
Designer:	Robert Jefferson
Height:	7 ½", 19.1 cm
Colour:	Brown and yellow, red head
Issued:	1976 in a limited edition of 200
Series:	Jefferson Sculptures

Description	U.S $	Can. $	U.K. £
Chipping sparrow	400.00	600.00	250.00

HN 3512
Mallard (male)

Model No.:	2614
Designer:	Harry Sales from Lem Ward originals
Height:	4", 10.1 cm
Colour:	Light and dark brown, green head, yellow beak
Issued:	1979-1985
Series:	Wildlife Decoys

Description	U.S $	Can. $	U.K. £
Mallard (male)	150.00	225.00	100.00

HN 3513
Pintail (male)

Model No.:	Unknown
Designer:	Harry Sales from Lem Ward originals
Height:	4", 10.1 cm
Colour:	Light and dark brown with cream markings
Issued:	1979-1985
Series:	Wildlife Decoys

Description	U.S $	Can. $	U.K. £
Pintail (male)	150.00	225.00	100.00

HN 3514
Greater Scaup (male)

Model No.:	2620
Designer:	Harry Sales from Lem Ward originals
Height:	3 ¾", 9.5 cm
Colour:	Dark green with light green and beige, blue bill
Issued:	1979-1985
Series:	Wildlife Decoys

Description	U.S $	Can. $	U.K. £
Greater scaup (male)	150.00	225.00	100.00

HN 3515
Mallard (female)

Model No.:	2603
Designer:	Harry Sales from Lem Ward originals
Height:	4", 101. cm
Colour:	Dark brown, orange-brown
Issued:	1979-1985
Series:	Wildlife Decoys

Description	U.S $	Can. $	U.K. £
Mallard (female)	150.00	225.00	100.00

HN 3516
Pintail (female)

Model No.:	2612
Designer:	Harry Sales from Lem Ward originals
Height:	4", 10.1 cm
Colour:	Light brown, dark brown and cream
Issued:	1979-1985
Series:	Wildlife Decoys

Description	U.S $	Can. $	U.K. £
Pintail (female)	150.00	225.00	100.00

HN 3517
Greater Scaup (female)

Model No.:	2621
Designer:	Harry Sales from Lem Ward originals
Height:	4", 10.1 cm
Colour:	Dark brown, light brown, blue bill
Issued:	1979-1985
Series:	Wildlife Decoys

Description	U.S $	Can. $	U.K. £
Greater scaup (female)	150.00	225.00	100.00

HN 3518
Merganser (male)

Model No.:	Unknown
Designer:	Harry Sales from Lem Ward originals
Height:	4", 10.1 cm
Colour:	Charcoal, light brown and green
Issued:	1980-1985
Series:	Wildlife Decoys

Description	U.S $	Can. $	U.K. £
Merganser (male)	150.00	225.00	100.00

HN 3519
Merganser (female)

Model No.:	2643
Designer:	Harry Sales from Lem Ward originals
Height:	4", 10.1 cm
Colour:	Brown, light brown and black
Issued:	1980-1985
Series:	Wildlife Decoys

Description	U.S $	Can. $	U.K. £
Merganser (female)	150.00	225.00	100.00

HN 3520
Green Wing Teal (male)

Model No.:	2683
Designer:	Harry Sales from Lem Ward originals
Height:	4", 10.1 cm
Colour:	Brown, green and black
Issued:	1979-1986

Description	U.S. $	Can. $	U.K. £
Green wing teal (male)	150.00	225.00	100.00

HN 3521
Green Wing Teal (female)

Model No.:	2684
Designer:	Harry Sales from Lem Ward originals
Height:	4", 10.1 cm
Colour:	Beige, brown and green
Issued:	1979-1986

Description	U.S. $	Can. $	U.K. £
Green wing teal (female)	150.00	225.00	100.00

HN 3522
'The Leap' Dolphin

Model No.:	2949
Designer:	Adrian Hughes
Height:	9", 22.9 cm
Colour:	See below
Issued:	1. 1982-1999 2. 1983
Series:	Images of Nature

Colourways	U.S. $	Can. $	U.K. £
1. White	125.00	225.00	75.00
2. Flambé	675.00	1,000.00	450.00

Note: The flambé model was test marketed at selected Royal Doulton outlet stores in the U.K.

HN 3523
'Capricorn' Mountain Goat

Model No.:	2959
Designer:	Adrian Hughes
Height:	9 ¾", 24.8 cm
Colour:	See below
Issued:	1. 1982-1988
	2. 1983
Series:	Images of Nature

Colourways	U.S. $	Can. $	U.K. £
1. White	125.00	225.00	75.00
2. Flambé	1,100.00	1,700.00	750.00

HN 3524
'The Gift of Life' Mare and Foal

Model No.:	2923
Designer:	Russell Willis
Height:	8 ¼", 21.0 cm
Colour:	White
Issued:	1982-1996
Varieties	HN 3536 (flambé)
Series:	Images of Nature

Colourways	U.S. $	Can. $	U.K. £
White	500.00	750.00	300.00

HN 3525
'Courtship' Terns

Model No.:	2930
Designer:	Russell Willis
Height:	14 ¼", 36.2 cm
Colour:	White
Issued:	1982-2002
Varieties	HN 3535 (flambé)
Series:	Images of Nature

Colourways	U.S. $	Can. $	U.K. £
White	N/A	1,515.00	440.00

HN 3526
'Shadow Play' Cat

Model No.:	2936
Designer:	Russell Willis
Height:	10", 25.4 cm
Colour:	See below
Issued:	1. 1982-1999
	2. c.1983
Series:	Images of Nature

Colourways	U.S. $	Can. $	U.K. £
1. White	125.00	175.00	75.00
2. Flambé	1,250.00	1,750.00	750.00

HN 3527
'Going Home' Flying Geese

Model No.:	2925
Designer:	Adrian Hughes
Height:	6 ¼", 15.9 cm
Colour:	See below
Issued:	1982-2002
Series:	Images of Nature
Varieties:	HN 3546

Colourways	U.S. $	Can. $	U.K. £
1. White	75.00	125.00	50.00
2. Flambé	1,100.00	1,650.00	750.00

Note: Another style of prototype in flambé exists.

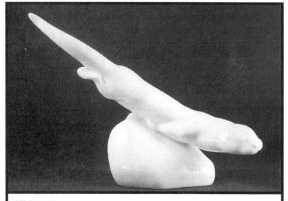

HN 3528
'Freedom' Otters

Model No.:	3058
Designer:	Robert Jefferson
Height:	8 ½", 21.6 cm
Colour:	White
Issued:	1983-1986
Series:	Images of Nature

Description	U.S. $	Can. $	U.K. £
White otters	225.00	325.00	150.00

HN 3529
'Bright Water' Otter

Model No.:	3058A
Designer:	Robert Jefferson
Height:	7 ½" x 11", 19.1 x 27.9 cm
Colour:	White
Issued:	1983-1986
Series:	Images of Nature

Description	U.S. $	Can. $	U.K. £
White otter	175.00	250.00	125.00

HN 3530
'Clear Water' Otter

Model No.:	3058B
Designer:	Robert Jefferson
Height:	8 ¼", 21.0 cm
Colour:	White
Issued:	1983-1986
Series:	Images of Nature

Description	U.S. $	Can. $	U.K. £
White otter	175.00	250.00	125.00

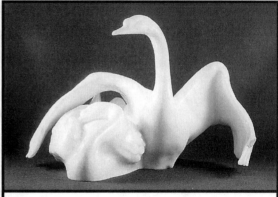

HN 3531
'Nestling Down' Swans

Model No.:	3198
Designer:	Adrian Hughes
Height:	8 ½" x 12", 21.6 x 30.5 cm
Colour:	White
Issued:	1985-1994
Series:	Images of Nature
Varieties:	HN 3538 (flambé)

Colourways	U.S. $	Can. $	U.K. £
White	350.00	500.00	225.00

HN 3532
'The Homecoming' Doves

Model No.:	3304
Designer:	Russell Willis
Height:	14 ¾", 37.5 cm
Colour:	White
Issued:	1987-1998
Series:	Images of Nature
Varieties:	HN 3539 (flambé)

Colourways	U.S. $	Can. $	U.K. £
White	400.00	600.00	275.00

HN 3533
'Patience' Heron

Model No.:	3467
Designer:	Peter Gee
Height:	12 ¼", 31.1 cm
Colour:	White
Issued:	1987-1995
Series:	Images of Nature

Description	U.S. $	Can. $	U.K. £
White heron	100.00	150.00	65.00

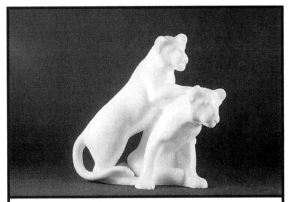

HN 3534
'Playful' Lion Cubs

Model No.:	3432
Designer:	Adrian Hughes
Height:	8", 20.3 cm
Colour:	White
Issued:	1987-1993
Series:	Images of Nature

Description	U.S. $	Can. $	U.K. £
White lion cubs	125.00	175.00	85.00

HN 3535
'Courtship' Terns

Model No.:	2930
Designer:	Russell Willis
Height:	15", 38.1 cm
Colour:	Flambé
Issued:	1987-1996
Series:	Images of Fire
Varieties:	HN 3525

Colourways	U.S. $	Can. $	U.K. £
Flambé	825.00	1,250.00	550.00

HN 3536
'The Gift of Life' Mare and Foal

Model No.:	2923
Designer:	Russell Willis
Height:	9", 22.9 cm
Colour:	Flambé
Issued:	1987-1996
Series:	Images of Fire
Varieties:	HN 3524

Colourways	U.S. $	Can. $	U.K. £
Flambé	900.00	1,350.00	600.00

*

HN 3538
'Nestling Down' Swans

Model No.:	3198
Designer:	Adrian Hughes
Height:	8 ½" x 12", 21.6 x 30.5 cm
Colour:	Flambé
Issued:	1988-1996
Series:	Images of Fire
Varieties:	HN 3531

Colourways	U.S. $	Can. $	U.K. £
Flambé	900.00	1,350.00	600.00

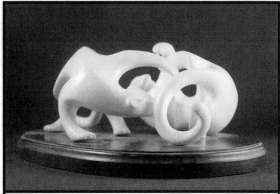

HN 3539
'The Homecoming' Doves

Model No.:	3304
Designer:	Russell Willis
Height:	14 ¾", 37.5 cm
Colour:	Flambé
Issued:	1989-1996
Series:	Images of Fire
Varieties:	HN 3532

Colourways	U.S. $	Can. $	U.K. £
Flambé	900.00	1,350.00	600.00

HN 3540
'Graceful' Panthers

Model No.:	3573
Designer:	John Ablitt
Height:	4 ½" x 11", 11.4 x 27.9 cm
Colour:	White
Issued:	1989-1992
Series:	Images of Nature

Description	U.S. $	Can. $	U.K. £
White panthers	225.00	325.00	150.00

HN 3541
Peregrine Falcon

Model No.:	3140
Designer:	Graham Tongue
Height:	11 ½", 29.2 cm
Colour:	Dark brown and cream
Issued:	1990 in a limited edition of 2,500
Series:	Artist's Signature Edition
Varieties:	DA 40

Description	U.S. $	Can. $	U.K. £
Peregrine falcon	175.00	250.00	125.00

HN 3542
'Serenity' Tropical Shoal of Fish

Model No.:	3660
Designer:	John Ablitt
Height:	11", 27.9 cm
Colour:	White
Issued:	1990-1995
Series:	Images of Nature

Description	U.S. $	Can. $	U.K. £
White fish	125.00	175.00	75.00

HN 3543
'Friendship' Borzoi Dog and Cat

Model No.:	3658		
Designer:	John Ablitt		
Height:	8 ¼", 21.0 cm		
Colour:	White		
Issued:	1990-1992		
Series:	Images of Nature		

Description	U.S. $	Can. $	U.K. £
White dog and cat	135.00	200.00	95.00

HN 3544
'Playtime' Cat with Kitten

Model No.:	3864		
Designer:	John R. Ablitt		
Height:	8", 20.3 cm		
Colour:	White		
Issued:	1990-1992		
Series:	Images of Nature		

Description	U.S. $	Can. $	U.K. £
White cat/kitten	135.00	200.00	95.00

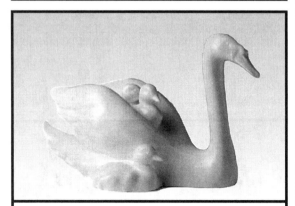

HN 3545
'Motherly Love' Swan and Two Cygnets

Model No.:	3901		
Designer:	Adrian Hughes		
Height:	6", 15.2 cm		
Colour:	White		
Issued:	1990-1999		
Series:	Images of Nature		

Description	U.S. $	Can. $	U.K. £
White swan/cygnets	125.00	175.00	75.00

HN 3546
'Going Home' Flying Geese

Model No.:	2925		
Designer:	Adrian Hughes		
Height:	6 ¼", 15.9 cm		
Colour:	White		
Issued:	1987 for Nabisco Foods Canada		

Colourways	U.S. $	Can. $	U.K. £
White	75.00	125.00	50.00

Note: A corporate commission of HN 3527

HN 3547
Pegasus

Model No.:	3187
Designer:	Alan Maslankowski
Height:	10", 25.4 cm
Colour:	White
Issued:	1990-1993

Description	U.S. $	Can. $	U.K. £
Pegasus	300.00	450.00	200.00

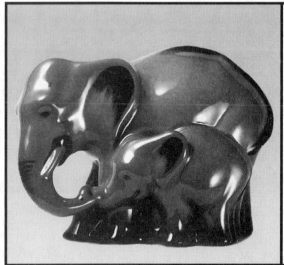

HN 3548
Elephant and Young

Model No.:	3789
Designer:	Eric Griffiths
Height:	3 ¼", 8.3 cm
Colour:	Flambé
Issued:	1990-1996
Series:	Images of Fire

Description	U.S. $	Can. $	U.K. £
Flambé elephants	250.00	375.00	175.00

HN 3549
Unicorn

Model No.:	3927
Designer:	Alan Maslankowski
Height:	10", 25.4 cm
Colour:	White unicorn, gold horn
Issued:	1991-1993

Description	U.S. $	Can. $	U.K. £
Unicorn	300.00	450.00	200.00

HN 3550
'Always and Forever' Doves

Model No.:	4188
Designer:	Adrian Hughes
Height:	4 ½", 11.4 cm
Colour:	White
Issued:	1993 to the present
Series:	Images of Nature

Description	U.S. $	Can. $	U.K. £
White doves	85.00	135.00	40.00

HN 3551
'New Arrival' Chicks

Model No.:	4300
Designer:	Alan Maslankowski
Height:	3", 7.6 cm
Colour:	White
Issued:	1994-1998
Series:	Images of Nature

Description	U.S. $	Can. $	U.K. £
White chicks	50.00	75.00	35.00

HN 3552
Dragon
Style Two

Model No.:	4315
Designer:	Robert Tabbenor
Height:	5 ¼", 13.3 cm
Colour:	Flambé
Issued:	1993-1995
Series:	RDICC

Description	U.S. $	Can. $	U.K. £
Flambé Dragon	250.00	375.00	175.00

*

HN 3893
'Playtime' Two Kittens

Designer:	Robert Tabbenor
Height:	4 ¾", 11.5 cm
Colour:	White
Issued:	1997-2000
Series:	Images of Nature

Description	U.S. $	Can. $	U.K. £
White kittens	45.00	65.00	30.00

HN 3894
'Sleepy Heads' Two Cats

Designer:	Robert Tabbenor
Height:	3 ½", 8.9 cm
Colour:	White
Issued:	1. 1998 to the present
	2. Unknown
Series:	Images of Nature

Description	U.S. $	Can. $	U.K. £
1. White	N/A	185.00	40.00
2. Flambé	600.00	900.00	400.00

HN 3895
'Night Watch' Owls

Designer:	Robert Tabbenor
Height:	6", 15.0 cm
Colour:	White
Issued:	1998-2002
Series:	Images of Nature

Description	U.S. $	Can. $	U.K. £
White owls	50.00	75.00	35.00

HN 3896
'Running Free' Rabbits

Designer:	Robert Tabbenor
Height:	8", 20.3 cm
Colour:	White
Issued:	1999-2001
Series:	Images of Nature

Description	U.S. $	Can. $	U.K. £
Hares	75.00	110.00	50.00

*

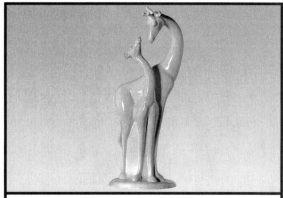

HN 3898
'Standing Tall' Giraffes

Designer:	Robert Tabbenor
Height:	13", 33.0 cm
Colour:	White
Issued:	1999 to the present
Series:	Images of Nature

Description	U.S. $	Can. $	U.K. £
Giraffes	N/A	315.00	99.00

*

HN 4087
'Soaring High' Eagle

Designer:	Alan Maslankowski
Height:	11", 27.9 cm
Colour:	White
Issued:	2000-2002
Series:	Images of Nature

Description	U.S. $	Can. $	U.K. £
Eagle	N/A	315.00	85.00

*

HN 4170
The Ox

Designer:	Robert Tabbenor
Height:	3", 7.5 cm
Colour:	White
Issued:	1999 in a limited edition of 2000
Series:	The Christmas Story

Description	U.S. $	Can. $	U.K. £
Ox	45.00	70.00	30.00

Note: Sold as part of the Christmas Story in a limited edition of 2,000 sets. Ten pieces comprise the set, all carrying the millennium backstamp. For other figures in the set see *Royal Doulton Figurines*.

HN 4171
The Ass

Designer: Robert Tabbenor
Height: 3 ¾", 9.4 cm
Colour: White
Issued: 1999 in a limited edition of 2,000
Series: The Christmas Story

Description	U.S. $	Can. $	U.K. £
Ass	45.00	70.00	30.00

Note: Sold as part of the Christmas Story in a limited edition of 2,000 sets. Ten pieces comprise the set, all carrying the millennium backstamp. For other pieces in the set see *Royal Doulton Figurines*.

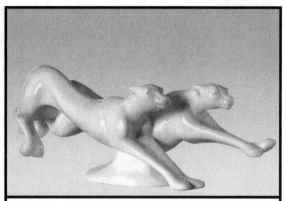

HN 4172
'Running Wild' Cheetahs

Designer: Robert Tabbenor
Height: 4", 10.1 cm
Colour: White
Issued: 2000-2002
Series: Images of Nature

Description	U.S. $	Can. $	U.K. £
Cheetahs	N/A	315.00	85.00

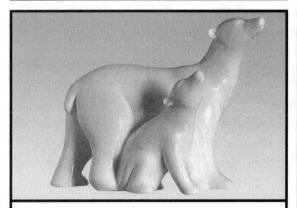

HN 4173
'Dedication' Polar Bears

Designer: Robert Tabbenor
Height: 6", 15.2 cm
Colour: White
Issued: 2000 to the present
Series: Images of Nature

Description	U.S. $	Can. $	U.K. £
Polar Bears	N/A	280.00	75.00

*

HN 4176
'Pride' Lions

Designer: Robert Tabbenor
Height: 4 ½" x 10", 11.4 x 25.4 cm
Colour: White
Issued: 2001-2002
Series: 1. Images of Nature
      2. WWF Charity Figures

Description	U.S. $	Can. $	U.K. £
Lions	N/A	N/A	85.00

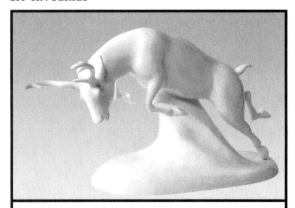

HN 4177
'Majestic' The Stag

Designer:	Robert Tabbenor
Height:	5 ¼" x 11 ¾", 13.3 x 29.4 cm
Colour:	White
Issued:	2001-2002
Series:	Images of Nature

Description	U.S. $	Can. $	U.K. £
Stag	175.00	315.00	99.00

HN 4178
Polar Bear and Cub

Designer:	Robert Tabbenor after Charles Noke
Height:	9 ½", 24.0 cm
Colour:	White
Issued:	2001 in a limited edition of 200
Series:	The Noke Collection

Description	U.S. $	Can. $	U.K. £
Polar bear and cub	1,595.00	2,400.00	895.00

Note: HN 4178 is based on the original model designed by Charles Noke in the 1920s. *

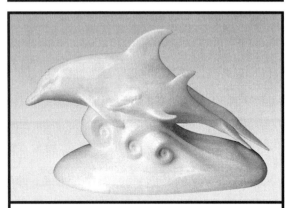

HN 4181
'Crest of A Wave' Dolphins

Designer:	Robert Tabbenor
Height:	6 ¼", 15.9 cm
Colour:	White
Issued:	2002-2002
Series:	1. Images of Nature
	2. WWF Charity Figure
	3. Image of the year

Description	U.S. $	Can. $	U.K. £
Dolphins	N/A	250.00	95.00

HN 4182
'Playfulness' Otters

Designer:	Robert Tabbenor
Length:	4", 10.1 cm
Colour:	White
Issued:	2002 to the present
Series:	Images of Nature

Description	U.S. $	Can. $	U.K. £
Seals??	N/A	210.00	65.00

*

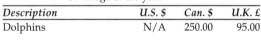

HN 4184
A New Life'

Designer:	Robert Tabbemor
Height:	7 ¼", 18.4 cm
Colour:	White
Issued:	2003 to the present
Series:	Images of Nature

Description	U.S. $	Can. $	U.K. £
Horses		Not available at press time	

HN 4359
'Tumbling Waters' Otters

Designer:	Alan Maslankowski
Height:	14 ½", 36.8 cm
Colour:	White
Issued:	2001 in a limited edition of 750
Series:	Images of Nature

Description	U.S. $	Can. $	U.K. £
Otters	N/A	2,000.00	525.00

*

HN 4440
'Endless Love' Swans

Designer:	Alan Maslankowski
Height:	5 ¼" x 13 ½", 13.3 x 34.3 cm
Colour:	White
Issued:	2002 to the present
Series:	Images of Nature

Description	U.S. $	Can. $	U.K. £
Swans	135.00	245.00	75.00

HN 4441
'Contentment' Cat

Designer:	Alam Maslankow ski
Height:	6 ¾", 17.2 cm
Colour:	White
Issued:	2002 to the present
Series:	Images of Nature

Description	U.S. $	Can. $	U.K. £
Cat	N/A	150.00	45.00

K SERIES

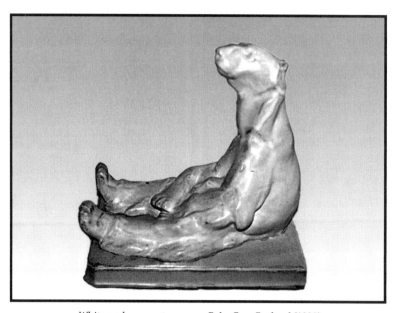

White and green stoneware *Polar Bear Bookend* (1938)

K1
Bulldog
Seated - Style Five

Model No.:	762
Designer:	Unknown
Height:	2 ½", 6.3 cm
Colour:	Tan with dark brown patches over eye and back
Issued:	1931-1977

Description	U.S. $	Can. $	U.K. £
Bulldog, seated	100.00	150.00	65.00

K2
Bulldog Puppy

Model No.:	763
Designer:	Unknown
Height:	2", 5.1 cm
Colour:	Tan with dark brown patches over eye and back
Issued:	1931-1977
Varieties:	Two variations are known. The patch can be on either the left or right side of face.

Description	U.S. $	Can. $	U.K. £
Bulldog puppy	90.00	135.00	60.00

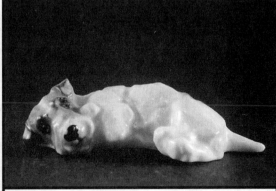

K3
Sealyham
Begging

Model No.:	760
Designer:	Unknown
Height:	2 ¾", 7.0 cm
Colour:	White with light brown patches over the eyes and ears
Issued:	1931-1977

Description	U.S. $	Can. $	U.K. £
Sealyham, begging	100.00	150.00	65.00

K4
Sealyham
Lying - Style Two

Model No.:	765
Designer:	Unknown
Height:	1 ½" x 3 ¼", 3.8 x 8.3 cm
Colour:	White with light brown patches over eyes and ears
Issued:	1931-1959

Description	U.S. $	Can. $	U.K. £
Sealyham, lying	300.00	450.00	200.00

K5
Airedale Terrier
Lying

Model No.:	757
Designer:	Unknown
Height:	1 ¼" x 2 ¼", 3.1 x 5.7 cm
Colour:	Dark brown coat, light brown head and underbody
Issued:	1931-1959

Description	U.S. $	Can. $	U.K. £
Airedale terrier	300.00	450.00	175.00

K6
Pekinese
Seated

Model No.:	758
Designer:	Unknown
Height:	2", 5.1 cm
Colour:	Golden brown with black markings on face and ears
Issued:	1931-1977

Description	U.S. $	Can. $	U.K. £
Pekinese	85.00	125.00	60.00

K7
Foxhound
Seated - Style Two

Model No.:	764
Designer:	Unknown
Height:	2 ½", 6.4 cm
Colour:	White with dark brown and black patches over ears, eyes and back
Issued:	1931-1977
Derivative:	On ashtray

Description	U.S. $	Can. $	U.K. £
Foxhound	125.00	175.00	85.00

K8
Fox Terrier
Seated - Style Three

Model No.:	759
Designer:	Unknown
Height:	2 ½", 6.4 cm
Colour:	White with black and brown patches over ears, eyes and back
Issued:	1931-1977

Description	U.S. $	Can. $	U.K. £
Fox terrier	125.00	175.00	85.00

K9A
Cocker Spaniel
Seated - Style One

Model No.:	755
Designer:	Unknown
Height:	2 ½″, 6.4 cm
Colour:	Golden brown with black highlights
Issued:	1931-1977
Varieties:	K9B

Colourways	U.S. $	Can. $	U.K. £
Golden brown	85.00	125.00	55.00

K9B
Cocker Spaniel
Seated - Style One

Model No.:	755
Designer:	Unknown
Height:	2 ½″, 6.4 cm
Colour:	Black and brown
Issued:	1931-1977
Varieties:	K9A

Colourways	U.S. $	Can. $	U.K. £
Black and brown		Rare	

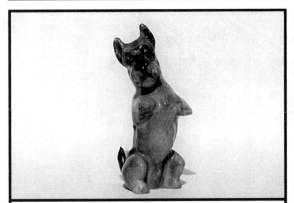

K10
Scottish Terrier
Begging - Style Two

Model No.:	761
Designer:	Unknown
Height:	2 ¾″, 7.0 cm
Colour:	Grey with black highlights
Issued:	1931-1977

Description	U.S. $	Can. $	U.K. £
Scottish terrier, begging	125.00	175.00	85.00

K11
Cairn Terrier
Seated

Model No.:	766
Designer:	Unknown
Height:	2 ½″, 6.4 cm
Colour:	Grey with black highlights
Issued:	1931-1977

Description	U.S. $	Can. $	U.K. £
Cairn terrier	125.00	175.00	85.00

K12
'Lucky' Black Cat

Model No.:	400
Designer:	Charles Noke
Height:	2 ¾", 7.0 cm
Colour:	Black with white face
Issued:	1932-1975
Varieties:	Also called 'Ooloo' HN 818, 819, 827, 828, 829, HN 971 on ashtray

Description	U.S. $	Can. $	U.K. £
'Lucky'	125.00	175.00	75.00

K13
Alsatian
Seated - Style One

Model No.:	787
Designer:	Unknown
Height:	3", 7.6 cm
Colour:	Dark brown body, light brown underbody
Issued:	1931-1977

Description	U.S. $	Can. $	U.K. £
Alsatian	125.00	175.00	85.00

K14
Bull Terrier
Lying

Model No.:	1093
Designer:	Unknown
Height:	1 ¼" x 2 ¾", 3.2 x 7.0 cm
Colour:	White
Issued:	1940-1959

Description	U.S. $	Can. $	U.K. £
Bull terrier	375.00	550.00	250.00

K15
Chow (Shibu Ino)

Model No.:	1095
Designer:	Unknown
Height:	2 ½", 6.3 cm
Colour:	Golden brown
Issued:	1940-1977

Description	U.S. $	Can. $	U.K. £
Chow	150.00	225.00	100.00

K16
Welsh Corgi

Model No.:	1094	
Designer:	Unknown	
Height:	2 ½" x 2 ¼", 6.3 x 5.7 cm	
Colour:	Golden brown	
Issued:	1940-1977	

Description	U.S. $	Can. $	U.K. £
Welsh corgi	150.00	225.00	100.00

K17
Dachshund
Seated

Model No.:	1096	
Designer:	Unknown	
Height:	1 ¾" x 2 ¾", 4.4 x 7.0 cm	
Colour:	Golden brown with dark brown markings	
Issued:	1940-1977	

Description	U.S. $	Can. $	U.K. £
Dachshund	100.00	150.00	65.00

K18
Scottish Terrier
Seated - Style Three

Model No.:	1092	
Designer:	Unknown	
Height:	2 ¼" x 2 ¾", 5.7 x 7.0 cm	
Colour:	Black with grey highlights	
Issued:	1940-1977	

Description	U.S. $	Can. $	U.K. £
Scottish terrier, seated	125.00	175.00	85.00

K19
St. Bernard
Lying

Model No.:	1097	
Designer:	Unknown	
Height:	1 ½" x 2 ½", 3.8 x 6.3 cm	
Colour:	Brown and cream, black highlights	
Issued:	1940-1977	

Description	U.S. $	Can. $	U.K. £
St. Bernard	100.00	150.00	65.00

K20
Penguin with Chick Under Wing

Model No.:	1084
Designer:	Peggy Davies
Height:	2 ¼", 5.7 cm
Colour:	Black and white
Issued:	1940-1968

Description	U.S. $	Can. $	U.K. £
Penguin with chick	225.00	325.00	150.00

K21
Penguin
Style Four

Model No.:	1099
Designer:	Peggy Davies
Height:	2", 5.1 cm
Colour:	Black and white
Issued:	1940-1968

Description	U.S. $	Can. $	U.K. £
Style four	225.00	325.00	150.00

K22
Penguin
Style Five

Model No.:	1098
Designer:	Peggy Davies
Height:	1 ¾", 5.1 cm
Colour:	Grey and white with black tips
Issued:	1940-1968

Description	U.S. $	Can. $	U.K. £
Style five	225.00	325.00	150.00

K23
Penguin
Style Six

Model No.:	1101
Designer:	Peggy Davies
Height:	1 ½", 3.8 cm
Colour:	Grey, white and black, green patches under eyes
Issued:	1940-1968

Description	U.S. $	Can. $	U.K. £
Style six	225.00	325.00	150.00

K24
Penguin
Style Seven

Model No.:	1100	
Designer:	Peggy Davies	
Height:	2″, 5.1 cm	
Colour:	Black and white	
Issued:	1940-1968	

Description	U.S. $	Can. $	U.K. £
Style seven	225.00	325.00	150.00

K25
Penguin
Style Eight

Model No.:	1083	
Designer:	Peggy Davies	
Height:	2 ¼″, 5.7 cm	
Colour:	Grey, white and black	
Issued:	1940-1968	

Description	U.S. $	Can. $	U.K. £
Style eight	225.00	325.00	150.00

K26
Mallard Duck

Model No.:	1133	
Designer:	Unknown	
Height:	1 ½″, 3.8 cm	
Colour:	Yellow with brown spots on green grass	
Issued:	1940-1946	

Description	U.S. $	Can. $	U.K. £
Mallard duck	650.00	1,000.00	400.00

K27
Yellow-Throated Warbler
Style One

Model No.:	1128	
Designer:	Unknown	
Height:	2″, 5.1 cm	
Colour:	Blue feathers with black markings, yellow breast, green base and leaves, pink and white flowers	
Issued:	1940-1946	

Description	U.S. $	Can. $	U.K. £
Yellow-throated warbler	900.00	1,250.00	600.00

K28
Cardinal
Style One

Model No.:	1127
Designer:	Unknown
Height:	2 ¾″, 7.0 cm
Colour:	Red feathers with black markings, green leaves and base, white flowers
Issued:	1940-1946

Description	U.S. $	Can. $	U.K. £
Cardinal	900.00	1,250.00	600.00

K29
Baltimore Oriole
Style Four

Model No.:	1130
Designer:	Unknown
Height:	2 ¾″, 7.0 cm
Colour:	Orange with black head and wings, white flowers, green leaves, beige base
Issued:	1940-1946

Description	U.S. $	Can. $	U.K. £
Baltimore oriole	900.00	1,250.00	600.00

K30
Bluebird with Lupins
Style One

Model No.:	1129
Designer:	Unknown
Height:	2 ½″, 6.4 cm
Colour:	Blue feathers with pink highlights, green leaves, pink-green base
Issued:	1940-1946

Description	U.S. $	Can. $	U.K. £
Bluebird	900.00	1,250.00	600.00

K31
Bullfinch
Style One

Model No.:	1126
Designer:	Unknown
Height:	2 ¼″, 5.7 cm
Colour:	Blue feathers with black head and wing tips, red breast, pink flowers, green leaves and base
Issued:	1940-1946

Description	U.S. $	Can. $	U.K. £
Bullfinch	900.00	1,250.00	600.00

K32
Budgerigar
Style One

Model No.:	1144		
Designer:	Unknown		
Height:	Unknown		
Colour:	Unknown		
Issued:	1940-1946		

Description	U.S. $	Can. $	U.K. £
Budgerigar		Extremely Rare	

K33
Golden-Crested Wren
Style One

Model No.:	1135		
Designer:	Unknown		
Height:	Unknown		
Colour:	Unknown		
Issued:	1940-1946		

Description	U.S. $	Can. $	U.K. £
Golden-crested wren		Extremely Rare	

K34
Magpie

Model No.:	1151		
Designer:	Unknown		
Height:	Unknown		
Colour:	Unknown		
Issued:	1940-1946		

Description	U.S. $	Can. $	U.K. £
Magpie		Extremely Rare	

K35
Jay

Model No.:	1146		
Designer:	Unknown		
Height:	2 ¼", 5.7 cm		
Colour:	Brown and white with blue wing		
Issued:	1940-1946		

Description	U.S. $	Can. $	U.K. £
Jay	900.00	1,250.00	600.00

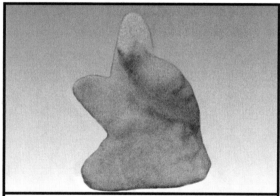

K36
Goldfinch
Style One

Model No.:	1145	
Designer:	Unknown	
Height:	Unknown	
Colour:	Unknown	
Issued:	1940-1946	

Description	U.S. $	Can. $	U.K. £
Goldfinch		Extremely Rare	

K37
Hare
Crouching - Style Two

Model No.:	1148	
Designer:	Unknown	
Height:	1 ½", 3.8 cm	
Colour:	Brown and white, with black highlights	
Issued:	1940-1977	

Description	U.S. $	Can. $	U.K. £
Hare, crouching	100.00	150.00	65.00

K38
Hare
Seated, ears down

Model No.:	1150	
Designer:	Unknown	
Height:	2 ½", 6.4 cm	
Colour:	Dark brown and white	
Issued:	1940-1977	

Description	U.S. $	Can. $	U.K. £
Hare, ears down	100.00	150.00	65.00

K39
Hare
Seated, ears up

Model No.:	1149	
Designer:	Unknown	
Height:	2 ¼", 5.7 cm	
Colour:	Light brown and white	
Issued:	1940-1977	

Description	U.S. $	Can. $	U.K. £
Hare, ears up	100.00	150.00	65.00

D SERIES

D 5772A
Owl Wall Pocket

Model No.:	Unknown
Designer:	Unknown
Height:	7 ½", 19.0 cm
Colour:	Brown owl, green oak leaves, cream wall pocket
Issued:	1937

Description	U.S. $	Can. $	U.K. £
Owl wall pocket	375.00	525.00	250.00

D 5772B
Crow Wall Pocket

Model No.:	Unknown
Designer:	Unknown
Height:	7 ¼", 18.4 cm
Colour:	Black crow, green oak leaves, cream wall pocket
Issued:	1937

Description	U.S. $	Can. $	U.K. £
Crow wall pocket	375.00	525.00	250.00

D 5913
Bulldog Draped in Union Jack

Model No.:	Unknown
Designer:	Charles Noke
Height:	Large — 6", 15.2 cm
	Medium — 4", 10.1 cm
	Small — 2 ¼", 5.7 cm
Colour:	1. Cream dog with black collar, red, white and blue Union Jack
	2. White
Issued:	Large — 1941-1961
	Medium — 1941-1961
	Small — 1941

Description	U.S. $	Can. $	U.K. £
Large	1,000.00	1,500.00	650.00
Medium	300.00	450.00	200.00
Small	200.00	300.00	125.00

Note: 1. All-white models exist of the medium and large sizes. An all-white model of the small size is not known.
Large, white, sold at Phillips 6/99 for £1,200.
Medium, white, sold at Phillips 6/99 for £950.
2. A Khaki dog with Union Jack sold at Phillips 6/99 for £1,125.

Bulldog Draped in Union Jack with Derby Hat

Model No.:	Unknown
Designer:	Charles Noke
Colour:	Cream dog, beige hat with brown band, blue spotted bow tie, brown cigar, red, white and blue Union Jack

D 6178

Height:	7 ½", 19.1 cm
Size:	Large
Issued:	1941

D 6179

Height:	5", 12.7 cm
Size:	Medium
Issued:	1941

D 6180

Height:	3", 7.6 cm
Size:	Small
Issued:	1941

Description	U.S. $	Can. $	U.K. £
Large	2,750.00	4,000.00	1,750.00
Medium	2,000.00	3,000.00	1,350.00
Small	1,250.00	1,875.00	850.00

Bulldog Draped in Union Jack With Trinity Cap

Model No.:	Unknown
Designer:	Charles Noke
Colour:	Cream dog, navy cap, red, white and blue Union Jack

D 6181

Height:	7", 17.8 cm
Size:	Large
Issued:	1941

D 6182

Height:	5", 12.7 cm
Size:	Medium
Issued:	1941

D 6183

Height:	2 ¾", 6.9 cm
Size:	Small
Issued:	1941

Description	U.S. $	Can. $	U.K. £
Large	3,500.00	5,250.00	2,250.00
Medium	2,500.00	3,750.00	1,650.00
Small	2,000.00	3,000.00	1,350.00

6193
Bulldog Wearing Sailor Suit and Hat

Model No.:	Unknown
Designer:	Charles Noke
Height:	Large — 6″, 15.2 cm
	Medium — 4 ¾″, 12.1 cm
	Small — 2 ¾″, 6.9 cm
Colour:	Cream dog, navy and white sailor's suit and hat
Issued:	1941

Description	U.S. $	Can. $	U.K. £
Large		Very Rare	
Medium	4,000.00	6,000.00	2,500.00
Small		Very Rare	

D 6448
Huntsman Fox

Model No.:	Unknown
Designer:	Unknown
Height:	4 ½″, 11.4 cm
Colour:	Brown fox wearing a maroon jacket, white jodhpurs, black hat and boots
Issued:	1956-1981

Description	U.S. $	Can. $	U.K. £
Huntsman fox	150.00	225.00	100.00

D 6449
Christmas Turkey

Model No.:	Unknown
Designer:	Graham Tongue
Height:	6 ¼″, 15.9 cm
Colour:	White feathers, red head
Issued:	1990-1990
Varieties:	DA 161

Description	U.S. $	Can. $	U.K. £
Christmas turkey	75.00	125.00	50.00

Note: Commissioned by Sir Bernard Matthews, Norfolk. A turkey was given to each member of his staff.

ROYAL ADDERLEY
(BIRD STUDIES)

American Blue Bird

Height:	3 ¾", 9.5 cm
Colour:	Blue bird with orange breast, brown nest and white eggs
Issued:	1979-1983

Finish	U.S. $	Can. $	U.K. £
Gloss	135.00	200.00	95.00

Baltimore Oriole
Style Five

Height:	4 ½", 11.4 cm
Colour:	Orange feathers, black head, black and yellow wings and tail feathers
Issued:	1979-1983

Finish	U.S. $	Can. $	U.K. £
Gloss	135.00	200.00	95.00

Black-Headed Gouldian Finch

Height:	4", 10.1 cm
Colour:	Black head, pink and yellow breast, green feathers, white and black tail feathers, blue and pink flowers
Issued:	1979-1982
Varieties:	Also called 'Red-Headed Gouldian Finch'

Finish	U.S. $	Can. $	U.K. £
Gloss	135.00	200.00	95.00

Blue Gnatcatcher

Height:	4", 10.1 cm
Colour:	Blue and pink feathers with black markings, yellow breast
Issued:	1979-1982

Finish	U.S. $	Can. $	U.K. £
Gloss	135.00	200.00	95.00

Blue Jay
Style One

Height:	4 ¾", 12.1 cm
Colour:	Blue feathers with black markings, white throat, pink flower
Issued:	1979-1983

Finish	U.S. $	Can. $	U.K. £
Gloss	135.00	200.00	95.00

Blue Tit
Style One

Height:	3 ¾", 9.5 cm
Colour:	Yellow feathers, blue head and wings with black and white markings, pink flower
Issued:	1979-1983
Varieties:	Also called 'Chicadee, Style One'

Finish	U.S. $	Can. $	U.K. £
Gloss	135.00	200.00	95.00

Blue Tit
Style Two

Height:	3 ¼", 9.5 cm
Colour:	Yellow feathers, blue head and wings with black and white markings, pink flower
Issued:	1979-1983
Varieties:	Also called 'Chicadee, Style Two'

Finish	U.S. $	Can. $	U.K. £
Gloss	135.00	200.00	95.00

Blue Tit and Young

Height:	4 ¾", 12.1 cm
Colour:	Yellow breasts, brown and green feathers, blue heads with white markings
Issued:	1979-1983

Finish	U.S. $	Can. $	U.K. £
Gloss	200.00	300.00	135.00

Blue Tits (two)
Style One

Height:	5 ¼", 13.3 cm
Colour:	Yellow breasts, light blue heads and wings with white markings, pink flowers
Issued:	1979-1983
Varieties:	Also called 'Great Tits' and 'Hudsonian Chicadees'

Finish	U.S. $	Can. $	U.K. £
Gloss	175.00	250.00	125.00

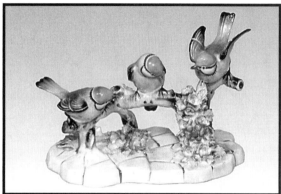

Blue Tits (three)
Style Two

Height:	4 ¾", 12.1 cm
Colour:	Yellow breasts, light blue heads and wings with white markings, pink flowers
Issued:	1979-1983
Varieties:	Also called 'Chicadees'

Finish	U.S. $	Can. $	U.K. £
Gloss	200.00	300.00	135.00

Budgerigar
Style Two - large

Height:	5 ¼", 13.3 cm
Size:	Large
Colour:	Yellow head and tail feathers, green breast, green wings with black markings, blue tail feathers
Issued:	1979-1983

Finish	U.S. $	Can. $	U.K. £
Gloss	135.00	200.00	95.00
Matt	135.00	200.00	95.00

Budgerigar
Style Two - medium

Height:	4 ¾", 12.1 cm
Size:	Medium
Colour:	White head, white wings with black markings, blue breast and tail feathers, yellow and pink flowers
Issued:	1979-1983

Finish	U.S. $	Can. $	U.K. £
Gloss	135.00	200.00	95.00
Matt	135.00	200.00	95.00

Budgerigars

Height:	4 ½", 11.4 cm
Colour:	Yellow and green feathers with black markings, blue and white feathers with black markings
Issued:	1979-1983

Finish	U.S. $	Can. $	U.K. £
Gloss	175.00	250.00	125.00
Matt	175.00	250.00	125.00

Canary - orange

Height:	5 ¼", 13.3 cm
Colour:	Orange with black tail feathers, black and red head, red flowers
Issued:	1979-1983
Varieties:	Also called 'Canary, yellow'

Finish	U.S. $	Can. $	U.K. £
Gloss	135.00	200.00	95.00

Canary - yellow

Height:	5 ¼", 13.3 cm
Colour:	Yellow with black and red markings, white breast
Issued:	1979-1983
Varieties:	Also called 'Canary, orange'

Finish	U.S. $	Can. $	U.K. £
Gloss	135.00	200.00	95.00
Matt	135.00	200.00	95.00

NOTES ON PRICING

• Animal figures are not as plentiful as pretty ladies or character figures and caution in pricing must prevail.

• In the pricing tables N/A (not available) indicates that the animal figure was not available in that particular market.

• Italicized prices are an indication only and form a starting point for discussion on the final price, which may be lower or higher depending on supply and demand.

• Rarity classification provides a range for the collector to work with.

Rarity Class	Rare	Very Rare	Extremely Rare
U.S. $	1,100./1,500.	1,500./2,250.	2,250./3,250.
Can. $	1,650./2,200.	2,250./3,250.	3,250./4,500.
U.K. £	750./1,000.	1,000./1,500.	1,500./2,250.

• Always remember that when dealing with rare animal figures you need two willing parties, a buyer and a seller. One without the other will not work and only when they agree do you have a market price.

Cardinal (female)
Style Four

Colour:	Yellow face and breast, red head and wings
Issued:	1979-1983
Varieties:	Also called 'Cardinal, male,' 'Red-Crested Cardinal' and 'Virginia Cardinal'

Large

Height:	4 ½", 11.4 cm

Medium

Height:	4", 10.1 cm

Small

Height:	3 ½", 8.9 cm

Currency	Large	Medium	Small
U.S. $	225.00	175.00	135.00
Can. $	350.00	250.00	200.00
U.K. £	150.00	125.00	95.00

Cardinal (male)
Style Five

Colour:	Red feathers with yellow highlights, yellow tail feathers, pink flower
Issued:	1979-1983
Varieties:	Also called 'Cardinal, female,' 'Red-Crested Cardinal' and 'Virginia Cardinal'

Large

Height:	5", 12.7 cm

Medium

Height:	4 ½", 11.4 cm

Small

Height:	3 ½", 8.9 cm

Currency	Large	Medium	Small
U.S. $	225.00	175.00	135.00
Can. $	350.00	250.00	200.00
U.K. £	150.00	125.00	95.00

Cardinals (Two)

Height:	5 ¼", 13.3 cm		
Colour:	Red and yellow, purple flowers		
Issued:	1979-1983		

Finish	U.S. $	Can. $	U.K. £
Gloss	175.00	250.00	125.00

Chaffinch
Style Three

Height:	4 ¼", 10.8 cm		
Colour:	Yellow and pink breast, black head, white, yellow and pink wings with black markings, pink and yellow flowers		
Issued:	1979-1983		
Varieties:	Also called 'Coppersmith Barbet'		

Finish	U.S. $	Can. $	U.K. £
Gloss	135.00	200.00	95.00

Chicadee
Style One - head up

Height:	3 ¾", 9.5 cm		
Colour:	Dark blue head, white breast, brown feathers with black markings, pink flowers		
Issued:	1979-1983		
Varieties:	Also called 'Blue Tit, Style One'		

Finish	U.S. $	Can. $	U.K. £
Gloss	135.00	200.00	95.00

Chicadee
Style Two - head down

Height:	3 ½', 8.9 cm		
Colour:	Dark blue head, white breast, brown feathers with black markings, pink flowers		
Issued:	1979-1983		
Varieties:	Also called 'Blue Tit, Style Two'		

Finish	U.S. $	Can. $	U.K. £
Gloss	135.00	200.00	95.00

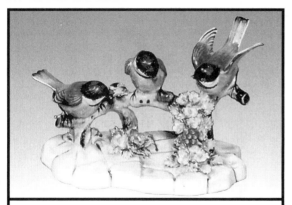

Chicadees

Height:	4 ¾", 12.1 cm			
Colour:	Dark blue head, white breast, brown feathers with white markings, pink and yellow flowers			
Issued:	1979-1983			
Varieties:	Also called 'Blue Tits, Style Two'			

Finish	U.S. $	Can. $	U.K. £
Gloss	200.00	300.00	135.00

Coppersmith Barbet

Height:	4 ½", 11.4 cm			
Colour:	Red and black head, yellow breast with black markings, pink flowers			
Issued:	1979-1983			
Varieties:	Also called 'Chaffinch, Style Three'			

Finish	U.S. $	Can. $	U.K. £
Gloss	135.00	200.00	95.00

Photograph
not available
at press time

English Robin
Style Two

Height:	4 ½", 11.4 cm
Colour:	Red breast, brown feathers, red flowers
Issued:	1979-1983
Varieties:	Also called 'Pekin Robin'

Finish	U.S. $	Can. $	U.K. £
Gloss	135.00	200.00	95.00
Matt	135.00	200.00	95.00

Goldfinch
Style Two

Height:	3 ¾", 9.5 cm
Colour:	Unknown
Issued:	1979-1983

Finish	U.S. $	Can. $	U.K. £
Gloss	135.00	200.00	95.00

Great Tits

Height:	5 ¼", 13.3 cm
Colour:	Dark blue heads, yellow feathers, blue wings and tail feathers with black and white markings, pink flowers
Issued:	1979-1983
Varieties:	Also called 'Blue Tits, Style One' and 'Hudsonian Chicadees'

Finish	U.S. $	Can. $	U.K. £
Gloss	175.00	250.00	125.00

Hudsonian Chicadees

Height:	5 ¼", 13.3 cm
Colour:	Red heads, yellow breasts, black and yellow wings and tail feathers, pink flowers
Issued:	1979-1983
Varieties:	Also called 'Blue Tits, Style One' and 'Great Tits'

Finish	U.S. $	Can. $	U.K. £
Gloss	175.00	250.00	125.00

Photograph
not available
at press time

Hummingbird

Height:	3 ¾", 9.5 cm
Colour:	Blue and green feathers with black markings, black beak, pink flowers
Issued:	1979-1983

Finish	U.S. $	Can. $	U.K. £
Gloss	135.00	200.00	95.00

Mallard Landing

Height:	3 ½", 8.9 cm
Colour:	Unknown
Issued:	1979-1983

Finish	U.S. $	Can. $	U.K. £
Gloss	135.00	200.00	95.00

Painted Bunting

Height:	3", 7.6 cm
Colour:	Blue head, red breast, green wings with black markings, maroon tail feathers, pink flowers
Issued:	1979-1983

Finish	U.S. $	Can. $	U.K. £
Gloss	135.00	200.00	95.00
Matt	135.00	200.00	95.00

Parakeet

Height:	5", 12.7 cm
Colour:	Green, red and blue bird, pink flowers
Issued:	1979-1982

Finish	U.S. $	Can. $	U.K. £
Gloss	135.00	200.00	95.00

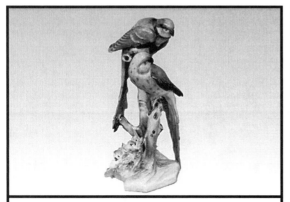

Parakeets

Height:	6", 15.2 cm
Colour:	Blue, green and red bird, green and yellow bird, pink flowers
Issued:	1979-1982

Finish	U.S. $	Can. $	U.K. £
Gloss	175.00	250.00	125.00

Pekin Robin

Height:	4 ½", 11.5 cm
Colour:	Red breast, brown head and back, yellow underbody, red flowers
Issued:	1979-1982
Varieties:	Also called 'English Robin, Style Two'

Finish	U.S. $	Can. $	U.K. £
Gloss	135.00	200.00	95.00

Red Crested Cardinal

Colour:	Red head, grey-white body, grey wings and tail feathers with black markings
Issued:	1979-1983
Varieties:	Also called 'Cardinal, female,' 'Cardinal, male' and 'Virginia Cardinal'

Medium

Height:	4", 10.1 cm

Small

Height:	3 1/3", 8.9 cm

Currency	Medium	Small
U.S. $	135.00	200.00
Can. $	200.00	250.00
U.K. £	95.00	125.00

Red-Headed Gouldian Finch

Height:	4", 10.1 cm
Colour:	Red and black head, green wings with black markings, pink and yellow breast
Issued:	1979-1983
Varieties:	Also called 'Black-Headed Gouldian Finch'

Finish	U.S. $	Can. $	U.K. £
Gloss	135.00	200.00	95.00

Robin with Can

Height:	4", 10.1 cm
Colour:	Brown, red, green and pink bird, white and yellow can
Issued:	1979-1983

Finish	U.S. $	Can. $	U.K. £
Gloss	250.00	375.00	125.00
Matt	250.00	375.00	125.00

Tanager

Height:	4", 10.1 cm		
Colour:	Red head, yellow and black feathers		
Issued:	1979-1983		

Finish	U.S. $	Can. $	U.K. £
Gloss	135.00	200.00	95.00

Warbler Tall

Height:	6 ½", 16.5 cm		
Colour:	Blue and yellow feathers with black markings, orange and yellow bird with black markings, purple flowers		
Issued:	1979-1983		

Finish	U.S. $	Can. $	U.K. £
Gloss	175.00	250.00	125.00

Virginia Cardinal

Colour:	Red with black markings, lilac flowers
Issued:	1979-1982
Varieties:	Also called 'Cardinal, female,' 'Cardinal, male' and 'Red-Crested Cardinal'

Large

Height:	5", 12.7 cm

Medium

Height:	4 ½", 11.4 cm

Small

Height:	3 ½", 8.9 cm

Currency	Large	Medium	Small
U.S. $	225.00	175.00	135.00
Can. $	350.00	250.00	200.00
U.K. £	150.00	125.00	95.00

DA SERIES

Spirit of the Wild (DA 183)

DA 1
Barn Owl (Tyto Alba)
Style Two

Model No.:	Unknown
Designer:	Graham Tongue
Height:	11″, 27.9 cm
Colour:	Golden feathers with dark brown markings
Issued:	1989-1996
Series:	Wildlife Collection / Connoisseur

Description	U.S. $	Can. $	U.K. £
Barn owl	875.00	1,300.00	600.00

DA 2
Robin on Branch

Model No.:	Unknown
Designer:	Graham Tongue
Height:	6 ¼″, 15.9 cm
Colour:	Red breast, red-brown feathers with black highlights
Issued:	1989-1992
Series:	Garden Birds

Description	U.S. $	Can. $	U.K. £
Robin on branch	125.00	175.00	75.00

DA 3
Suspended Blue Tit

Model No.:	Unknown
Designer:	Martyn C. R. Alcock
Height:	5″, 12.7 cm
Colour:	Yellow breast, blue feathers with black markings
Issued:	1989-1992
Series:	Garden Birds

Description	U.S. $	Can. $	U.K. £
Blue tit	125.00	175.00	75.00

DA 4
Wren
Style Two

Model No.:	Unknown
Designer:	Martyn C. R. Alcock
Height:	5 ¼″, 13.3 cm
Colour:	Light brown feathers with dark brown markings
Issued:	1989-1992
Series:	Garden Birds

Description	U.S. $	Can. $	U.K. £
Wren	125.00	175.00	75.00

DA 5
Chaffinch
Style Four

Model No.:	Unknown
Designer:	Warren Platt
Height:	6", 15.2 cm
Colour:	Reddish-brown with yellow and black highlights
Issued:	1989-1992
Series:	Garden Birds

Description	U.S. $	Can. $	U.K. £
Chaffinch	125.00	175.00	75.00

DA 6
Hare
Standing - Style Two

Model No.:	Unknown
Designer:	Warren Platt
Height:	8 ½", 21.6 cm
Colour:	Golden brown hare with white highlights
Issued:	1989-1992
Series:	Wildlife Collection

Description	U.S. $	Can. $	U.K. £
Hare	150.00	225.00	100.00

DA 7
Otter

Model No.:	Unknown
Designer:	Amanda Hughes-Lubeck
Height:	9", 22.9 cm
Colour:	Black and white
Issued:	1989-1992
Series:	Wildlife Collection

Description	U.S. $	Can. $	U.K. £
Otter	175.00	250.00	125.00

DA 8
Badger
Style Two

Model No.:	Unknown
Designer:	Amanda Hughes-Lubeck
Height:	5 ½", 14.0 cm
Colour:	Black with black and white striped face
Issued:	1989-1992
Series:	Wildlife Collection

Description	U.S. $	Can. $	U.K. £
Badger	150.00	225.00	100.00

DA 9
Fox
Standing

Model No.:	Unknown
Designer:	Warren Platt
Height:	7 ½", 19.1 cm
Colour:	Brown fox with dark brown highlights, white neck and tail end
Issued:	1989-1992
Series:	Wildlife Collection

Description	U.S. $	Can. $	U.K. £
Fox, standing	175.00	250.00	125.00

DA 10
Fox with Cub

Model No.:	Unknown
Designer:	Warren Platt
Height:	6 ½", 16.5 cm
Colour:	Brown
Issued:	1989-1992
Series:	Wildlife Collection

Description	U.S. $	Can. $	U.K. £
Fox with cub	125.00	175.00	75.00

DA 11
Wood Mice

Model No.:	Unknown
Designer:	Amanda Hughes-Lubeck
Height:	7 ½", 19.1 cm
Colour:	Brown mice, cream mushroom
Issued:	1989-1992
Series:	Wildlife Collection

Description	U.S. $	Can. $	U.K. £
Wood mice	135.00	200.00	90.00

DA 12
Robin on Apple

Model No.:	Unknown
Designer:	Graham Tongue
Height:	6 ¼", 15.9 cm
Colour:	Red breast, red-brown feathers with black markings, yellow apple
Issued:	1989-1992
Series:	Garden Birds

Description	U.S. $	Can. $	U.K. £
Robin	125.00	175.00	75.00

DA 13
Blue Tit with Matches

Model No.:	Unknown
Designer:	Martyn C. R. Alcock
Height:	6 ¾", 17.2 cm
Colour:	Blue and yellow bird, brown and cream box of matches
Issued:	1989-1992
Series:	Garden Birds

Description	U.S. $	Can. $	U.K. £
Blue tit	135.00	200.00	90.00

DA 14
Arab Colt 'Xayal'

Beswick No.:	1265
Designer:	Arthur Gredington
Height:	7 ¼", 18.4 cm
Colour:	Dark brown (matt)
Issued:	1989-1990
Series:	Connoisseur Horses
Varieties:	DA 50

Description	U.S. $	Can. $	U.K. £
'Xayal'	175.00	275.00	125.00

DA 15
'Arkle'
Style One

Beswick No.:	2065
Designer:	Arthur Gredington
Height:	12", 30.5 cm
Colour:	Bay (matt)
Issued:	1989-1999
Series:	Connoisseur Horses

Description	U.S. $	Can. $	U.K. £
'Arkle'	250.00	375.00	175.00

DA 16
'Nijinsky'

Beswick No.:	2345
Designer:	Albert Hallam
Height:	11", 27.9 cm
Colour:	Bay (matt)
Issued:	1989-1999
Series:	Connoisseur Horses

Description	U.S. $	Can. $	U.K. £
'Nijinsky'	250.00	375.00	175.00

DA 17
'Black Beauty' and Foal

Beswick No.:	2466/2536
Designer:	Graham Tongue
Height:	8", 20.3 cm
Colour:	Black (gloss or matt)
Issued:	1. gloss — 1989-1990
	2. Matt — 1989-1999
Series:	Connoisseur Horses

Description	U.S. $	Can. $	U.K. £
1. gloss	225.00	325.00	150.00
2. Matt	175.00	250.00	125.00

Note: gloss model available only from catalogue firm.

DA 18
'Red Rum'
Style One

Beswick No.:	2510
Designer:	Graham Tongue
Height:	12 ½", 31.7 cm
Colour:	Bay (matt)
Issued:	1989-1999
Series:	Connoisseur Horses

Description	U.S. $	Can. $	U.K. £
Style one	250.00	375.00	175.00

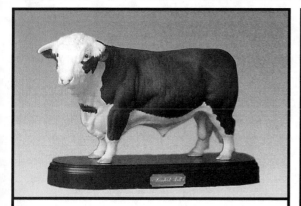

DA 19
Hereford Bull

Beswick No:	A2542
Designer:	Graham Tongue
Height:	7 ½" x 11", 19.1 x 27.9 cm
Colour:	Brown and cream (matt)
Issued:	1989-1996
Series:	Connoisseur Cattle

Description	U.S. $	Can. $	U.K. £
Hereford bull	250.00	375.00	175.00

DA 20
'Grundy'

Beswick No.:	2558
Designer:	Graham Tongue
Height:	11 ¼", 28.9 cm
Colour:	Chestnut (matt)
Issued:	1989-1997
Series:	Connoisseur Horses

Description	U.S. $	Can. $	U.K. £
'Grundy'	250.00	375.00	175.00

DA 21
Polled Hereford Bull

Beswick No.: A2574
Designer: Graham Tongue
Height: 7 ½", 19.1 cm
Colour: Brown and white (matt)
Issued: 1989-1996
Series: Connoisseur Cattle

Description	U.S. $	Can. $	U.K. £
Polled hereford bull	225.00	350.00	150.00

DA 22
Lifeguard

Beswick No.: 2562
Designer: Graham Tongue
Height: 14 ½", 36.8 cm
Colour: Black horse, Guardsman wears scarlet silver, white and black uniform (matt)
Issued: 1989-1996
Series: Connoisseur Horses
Varieties: Also called 'Blues and Royals' DA 25

Description	U.S. $	Can. $	U.K. £
Life guard	550.00	825.00	400.00

DA 23
Friesian Bull

Beswick No.: A2580
Designer: Graham Tongue
Height: 7" x 11 ½", 17.8 x 29.2 cm
Colour: Black and white (matt)
Issued: 1989-1997
Series: Connoisseur Cattle

Description	U.S. $	Can. $	U.K. £
Friesian bull	225.00	350.00	150.00

DA 24
Collie
Standing

Beswick No.: 2581
Designer: Graham Tongue
Height: 8 ¼", 21.0 cm
Colour: Golden brown and white (matt)
Issued: 1989-1994
Series: Connoisseur Dogs

Description	U.S. $	Can. $	U.K. £
Collie	150.00	225.00	100.00

DA 25
Blues and Royals

Beswick No.: 2582
Designer: Graham Tongue
Height: 14 ½", 36.8 cm
Colour: Black horse, Guardsman wears blue, silver, white and red uniform (matt)
Issued: 1989-1996
Series: Connoisseur Horses
Varieties: Also called 'Lifeguard' DA 22

Description	U.S. $	Can. $	U.K. £
Blues and Royals	600.00	900.00	425.00

DA 26
Alsatian
Standing - Style One

Beswick No.: 2587
Designer: Graham Tongue
Height: 9", 22.9 cm
Colour: Dark and sandy brown (matt)
Issued: 1989-1994
Series: Connoisseur Dogs

Description	U.S. $	Can. $	U.K. £
Alsatian	150.00	225.00	100.00

DA 27
Charolais Bull

Beswick No.: A2600
Designer: Graham Tongue
Height: 7 ½" x 12", 19.1 x 30.5 cm
Colour: Light golden brown
Issued: 1989-1996
Series: Connoisseur Cattle

Description	U.S. $	Can. $	U.K. £
Charolais bull	250.00	375.00	175.00

DA 28
Morgan Horse

Beswick No.: 2605
Designer: Graham Tongue
Height: 11 ½", 29.2 cm
Colour: Black (matt)
Issued: 1989-1996
Series: Connoisseur Horses

Description	U.S. $	Can. $	U.K. £
Morgan horse	300.00	450.00	200.00

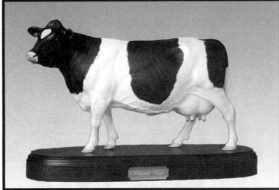

DA 29
Friesian Cow

Beswick No.: A2607
Designer: Graham Tongue
Height: 7 ½", 19.1 cm
Colour: Black and white (matt)
Issued: 1989-1997
Series: Connoisseur Cattle

Description	U.S. $	Can. $	U.K. £
Friesian cow	225.00	350.00	150.00

DA 30
Friesian Cow and Calf

Beswick No.: A2607/2690
Designer: Graham Tongue
Height: 7 ½", 19.1 cm
Colour: Black and white (matt)
Issued: 1989-1997
Series: Connoisseur Cattle

Description	U.S. $	Can. $	U.K. £
Friesian cow/calf	250.00	375.00	175.00

DA 31
'The Minstrel'

Beswick No.: 2608
Designer: Graham Tongue
Height: 13 ¼", 33.5 cm
Colour: Chestnut (matt)
Issued: 1989-1997
Series: Connoisseur Horses

Description	U.S. $	Can. $	U.K. £
'The Minstrel'	250.00	375.00	175.00

DA 32
Majestic Stag
Beswick No.: 2629
Designer: Graham Tongue
Height: 13 ½", 34.3 cm
Colour: Golden brown (matt)
Issued: 1989-1996
Series: Connoisseur

Description	U.S. $	Can. $	U.K. £
Majestic stag	300.00	450.00	200.00

DA 33
Charolais Cow and Calf
Beswick No.: A2648/2652
Designer: Graham Tongue
Height: 7 ¼", 18.4 cm
Colour: Cream (matt)
Issued: 1989-1996
Series: Connoisseur Cattle

Description	U.S. $	Can. $	U.K. £
Charolais cow/calf	250.00	375.00	175.00

DA 34
Hereford Cow and Calf
Beswick No.: A2667\2669
Designer: Graham Tongue
Height: 7", 17.8 cm
Colour: Brown and white (matt)
Issued: 1989-1996
Series: Connoisseur Cattle

Description	U.S. $	Can. $	U.K. £
Hereford cow/calf	250.00	375.00	175.00

DA 35A
'Champion'

Beswick No.:	2671
Designer:	Graham Tongue
Height:	11 ¼", 28.9 cm
Colour:	Chestnut (matt)
Issued:	1989-1996
Series:	Connoisseur Horses
Varieties:	Also called 'Moonlight' DA 35B, 'Sunburst' DA 36

Description	U.S. $	Can. $	U.K. £
'Champion'	250.00	375.00	175.00

DA 35B
'Moonlight'

Beswick No.:	2671
Designer:	Graham Tongue
Height:	11 ¼", 28.9 cm
Colour:	Grey (matt)
Issued:	1989-1996
Series:	Connoisseur Horses
Varieties:	Also called 'Champion' DA 35A, 'Sunburst' DA 36

Description	U.S. $	Can. $	U.K. £
'Moonlight'	200.00	300.00	150.00

DA 36
'Sunburst' Palomino Horse

Beswick No.:	2671
Designer:	Graham Tongue
Height:	11 ¼", 28.9 cm
Colour:	Light brown, white mane and tail (matt)
Issued:	1989-1995
Series:	Connoisseur Horses
Varieties:	Also called 'Champion' DA 35A, 'Moonlight' DA 35B

Description	U.S. $	Can. $	U.K. £
'Sunburst'	250.00	375.00	175.00

DA 37
'Troy'

Beswick No.:	2674
Designer:	Graham Tongue
Height:	11 ¾", 29.8 cm
Colour:	Bay (matt)
Issued:	1989-1997
Series:	Connoisseur Horses

Description	U.S. $	Can. $	U.K. £
'Troy'	250.00	375.00	175.00

DA 38
'Open Ground' (Pheasant)

Beswick No.: 2760
Designer: Graham Tongue
Height: 11 ½", 29.2 cm
Colour: Golden brown with black and red head (matt)
Issued: 1989-1994
Series: Connoisseur

Description	U.S. $	Can. $	U.K. £
Pheasant	300.00	450.00	200.00

DA 39
'The Watering Hole'(Leopard)

Model No.: Unknown
Designer: Graham Tongue
Height: 6 ½", 16.5 cm
Colour: Pale brown with dark brown spots
Issued: 1989-1994
Series: Connoisseur

Description	U.S. $	Can. $	U.K. £
Leopard	275.00	400.00	175.00

DA 40
Peregrine Falcon

Model No.: 3140
Designer: Graham Tongue
Height: 11", 27.9 cm
Colour: Browns and creams
Issued: 1989-1996
Series: Connoisseur
Varieties: HN 3541

Description	U.S. $	Can. $	U.K. £
Peregrine falcon	175.00	250.00	125.00

DA 41
Prancing Horse (rearing horse)

Beswick No.: 1014
Designer: Arthur Gredington
Height: 10 ¼", 26.0 cm
Colour: 1. Black (gloss and matt)
         2. Brown (gloss)
Issued: 1. 1994-1994
         2. 1989-1990

Colourways	U.S. $	Can. $	U.K. £
1. Black (gloss)	250.00	375.00	175.00
2. Black (matt)	250.00	375.00	175.00
3. Brown (gloss)	150.00	225.00	100.00

DA 42
'Bois Roussel' Race Horse

Beswick No.: 701
Designer: Arthur Gredington
Height: 8", 20.3 cm
Colour: See below (gloss and matt)
Issued: 1. Brown — 1989-1999
         2. Dapple grey — 1989-1995

Colourways	U.S. $	Can. $	U.K. £
1. Brown (gloss)	75.00	100.00	50.00
2. Brown (matt)	80.00	125.00	55.00
3. Dapple grey (gloss)	120.00	175.00	80.00

DA 43
Shire Mare

Beswick No.: 818
Designer: Arthur Gredington
Height: 8 ½", 21.6 cm
Colour: Brown with white feet (gloss and matt)
Issued: 1A. gloss — 1989-1999
         1B. Matt — 1989-1996

Colourways	U.S. $	Can. $	U.K. £
1. Brown (gloss)	75.00	100.00	50.00
2. Brown (matt)	115.00	165.00	75.00

DA 44
Horse
Stocky, jogging mare

Beswick No.: 855
Designer: Arthur Gredington
Height: 6", 15.2 cm
Issued: 1. Black - 1998
         2. Brown - 1989-1999

Description	U.S. $	Can. $	U.K. £
1. Black	75.00	115.00	50.00
2. Brown	75.00	115.00	50.00

Note: The black colourway was exclusive to Index Catalogue.

DA 45
Trotting Horse (cantering shire)

Beswick No.: 975
Designer: Arthur Gredington
Height: 8 ¾", 22.2 cm
Colour: Brown (gloss)
Issued: 1989-1999
Varieties: Flambé prototype

Description	U.S. $	Can. $	U.K. £
Cantering shire	85.00	125.00	60.00

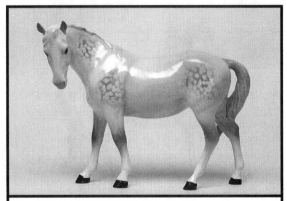

DA 46
Mare (facing left)

Beswick No.: 976
Designer: Arthur Gredington
Height: 6 ¾", 17.2 cm
Colour: See below (gloss and matt)
Issued: 1989 -1997

Colourways	U.S. $	Can. $	U.K. £
1. Brown (gloss)	65.00	95.00	45.00
2. Brown (matt)	75.00	115.00	50.00
3. Dapple grey (gloss)	100.00	150.00	70.00

DA 47
Shetland Pony (Woolly Shetland Mare)
Style One

Beswick No.: 1033
Designer: Arthur Gredington
Height: 5 ¾", 14.6 cm
Colour: Brown (gloss)
Issued: 1989-1999

Description	U.S. $	Can. $	U.K. £
Shetland pony	50.00	75.00	35.00

DA 48
Horse (Swish Tail)

Beswick No: 1182
Designer: Arthur Gredington
Height: 8 ¾", 22.2 cm
Colour: Brown (gloss and matt)
Issued: 1. Brown (gloss) — 1989-1999
2. Brown (matt) — 1989-1997

Colourways	U.S. $	Can. $	U.K. £
1. Brown (gloss)	75.00	125.00	50.00
2. Brown (matt)	75.00	125.00	50.00

DA 49
Palomino Horse (prancing Arab type)

Beswick No.: 1261
Designer: Arthur Gredington
Height: 6 ¾", 17.2 cm
Colour: See below (gloss and matt)
Issued: 1. Brown (gloss), Dapple grey - 1989-1999
2. Brown (matt), Palomino - 1989-1998

Colourways	U.S. $	Can. $	U.K. £
1. Brown (gloss)	75.00	110.00	50.00
2. Brown (matt)	75.00	110.00	50.00
3. Dapple grey (gloss)	75.00	110.00	50.00
4. Palomino (gloss)	70.00	110.00	50.00

DA 50
Arab Horse 'Xayal'

Beswick No.: 1265
Designer: Arthur Gredington
Height: 6 ¼", 15.9 cm
Colour: See below (gloss)
Issued: 1. Brown — 1989-1996
2. Dapple grey, Palomino — 1989-1997
Varieties: DA 14

Colourways	U.S. $	Can. $	U.K. £
1. Brown	80.00	125.00	50.00
2. Dapple grey	115.00	165.00	75.00
3. Palomino	115.00	165.00	75.00

DA 51
Horse (head tucked, leg up)

Beswick No.: 1549
Designer: Pal Zalmen
Height: 7 ½", 19.1 cm
Colour: Brown (gloss)
Issued: 1989-1999

Description	U.S. $	Can. $	U.K. £
Head tucked, leg up	80.00	120.00	55.00

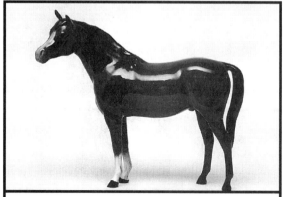

DA 52
Arab Horse

Beswick No.: 1771
Designer: Arthur Gredington
Height: 7 ½", 19.1 cm
Colour: Brown (gloss and matt)
Issued: 1989-1997

Description	U.S. $	Can. $	U.K. £
1. gloss	95.00	145.00	65.00
2. Matt	90.00	135.00	60.00

DA 53
Thoroughbred Horse

Beswick No.: 1772A
Designer: Arthur Gredington
Height: 8", 20.3 cm
Colour: See below (gloss)
Issued: 1. Brown — 1989-1999
　　　　 2. Dapple grey — 1989-1998
Varieties: Also called 'Appaloosa' DA 68

Colourways	U.S. $	Can. $	U.K. £
1. Brown	80.00	125.00	55.00
2. Dapple grey	120.00	185.00	80.00

DA 54
Mare (facing right, head down)

Beswick No.: 1812
Designer: Arthur Gredington
Height: 5 ¾", 14.6 cm
Colour: Brown (gloss)
Issued: 1989-1989

Description	U.S. $	Can. $	U.K. £
Mare (facing right)	75.00	110.00	50.00

DA 55
Mare (small, facing right, head up)

Beswick No.: 1991
Designer: Arthur Gredington
Height: 5 ½", 14.0 cm
Colour: See below (gloss and matt)
Issued: 1. Brown (gloss) — 1989-1999
　　　　 2. Other colours — 1989-1995

Colourways	U.S. $	Can. $	U.K. £
1. Brown (gloss)	50.00	75.00	35.00
2. Brown (matt)	50.00	75.00	35.00
3. Dapple grey (gloss)	65.00	100.00	45.00
4. Palomino (gloss)	65.00	100.00	45.00

DA 56
Horse (small thoroughbred stallion)

Beswick No.: 1992
Designer: Arthur Gredington
Height: 5 ½", 14.0 cm
Colour: See below (gloss and matt)
Issued: 1. Brown — 1989-1999
　　　　 2. Dapple grey — 1989-1998

Colourways	U.S. $	Can. $	U.K. £
1. Brown (gloss)	50.00	75.00	35.00
2. Brown (matt)	50.00	75.00	35.00
3. Dapple grey (gloss)	65.00	95.00	45.00

DA 57A
Spirit of the Wind (not on plinth)
Beswick No.: 2688
Designer: Graham Tongue
Height: 8", 20.3 cm
Colour: Brown (gloss and matt)
Issued: 1989-1996
Series: Spirited Horses

Colourways	U.S. $	Can. $	U.K. £
1. Brown (gloss)	100.00	150.00	75.00
2. Brown (matt)	100.00	150.00	75.00

DA 57B
Spirit of the Wind (on plinth)
Beswick No.: 2688
Designer: Graham Tongue
Height: 9", 22.9 cm
Colour: See below (gloss and matt)
Issued: 1. Black — 1989-1990
             2. Other colours — 1989-1999
Series: Spirited Horses

Colourways	U.S. $	Can. $	U.K. £
1. Black (matt)	100.00	150.00	75.00
2. Brown (gloss)	100.00	150.00	75.00
3. Brown (matt)	100.00	150.00	75.00
4. White (matt)	80.00	120.00	55.00

DA 58A
Spirit of Freedom (not on plinth)
Beswick No.: 2689
Designer: Graham Tongue
Height: 7", 17.8 cm
Colour: Brown (gloss and matt)
Issued: 1989-1997
Series: Spirited Horses

Colourways	U.S. $	Can. $	U.K. £
1. Brown (gloss)	90.00	135.00	60.00
2. Brown (matt)	90.00	135.00	60.00

DA 58B
Spirit of Freedom (on plinth)
Beswick No.: 2689
Designer: Graham Tongue
Height: 8", 20.3 cm
Colour: See below (gloss and matt)
Issued: 1. Black — 1989-1993
             2. Other colours — 1989-1999
Series: Spirited Horses

Colourways	U.S. $	Can. $	U.K. £
1. Black (matt)	100.00	150.00	75.00
2. Brown (gloss)	100.00	150.00	75.00
3. Brown (matt)	100.00	150.00	75.00
4. White (matt)	80.00	120.00	55.00

DA 59A
Spirit of Youth (not on plinth)
Beswick No.: 2703
Designer: Graham Tongue
Height: 7", 17.8 cm
Colour: Brown (gloss and matt)
Issued: 1989-1996
Series: Spirited Horses

Colourways	U.S. $	Can. $	U.K. £
1. Brown (gloss)	90.00	135.00	60.00
2. Brown (matt)	90.00	135.00	60.00

DA 59B
Spirit of Youth (on wooden plinth)
Beswick No.: 2703
Designer: Graham Tongue
Height: 8", 20.3 cm
Colour: See below (matt)
Issued: See below
Series: Spirited Horses

Colourways	U.S. $	Can. $	U.K. £
1. Black (matt) 1989-1993	100.00	150.00	75.00
2. Brown (gloss) 1989-1999	100.00	150.00	75.00
3. Brown (matt) 1989-1996	100.00	150.00	75.00
4. White (matt) 1989-1995	80.00	120.00	55.00

DA 60A
Spirit of Fire (not on plinth)
Beswick No.: 2829
Designer: Graham Tongue
Height: 8", 20.3 cm
Colour: See below (gloss and matt)
Issued: 1989-1994
Varieties: Spirited Horses

Colourways	U.S. $	Can. $	U.K. £
1. Brown (gloss)	90.00	135.00	60.00
2. Brown (matt)	90.00	135.00	60.00

DA 60B
Spirit of Fire (on plinth)
Beswick No.: 2829
Designer: Graham Tongue
Height: 9", 22.9 cm
Colour: See below (matt)
Issued: See below
Series: Spirited Horses

Colourways	U.S. $	Can. $	U.K. £
1. Black (matt) 1989-1994	90.00	135.00	60.00
2. Brown (matt) 1989-1994	100.00	150.00	75.00
3. White (matt) 1989-1993	80.00	120.00	55.00

DA 61A
Spirit of Earth (not on plinth)

Beswick No.:	2914
Designer:	Graham Tongue
Height:	7 ½", 19.1 cm
Colour:	Brown (gloss and matt)
Issued:	1989-1993

Colourways	U.S. $	Can. $	U.K. £
1. Brown (gloss)	110.00	165.00	75.00
2. Brown (matt)	100.00	150.00	70.00

DA 61B
Spirit of Earth (on plinth)

Beswick No.:	2914
Designer:	Graham Tongue
Height:	8 ½", 21.6 cm
Colour:	See below (matt)
Issued:	1989-1993
Series:	Spirited Horses

Colourways	U.S. $	Can. $	U.K. £
1. Black	110.00	165.00	75.00
2. Brown	120.00	175.00	85.00
3. White	100.00	150.00	70.00

DA 62A
Shire Horse (not on plinth)
Style One

Beswick No.:	2578
Designer:	Alan Maslankowski
Height:	8 ¼", 21.0 cm
Colour:	Brown (matt)
Issued:	1989 -1997
Series:	Connoisseur Horses

Colourways	U.S. $	Can. $	U.K. £
Brown	225.00	325.00	150.00

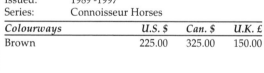

DA 62B
Shire Horse (on wooden plinth)
Style One

Beswick No.:	2578
Designer:	Alan Maslankowski
Height:	8 ¾", 22.2 cm
Colour:	Brown (matt)
Issued:	1994-1996
Series:	Connoisseur Horses

Colourways	U.S. $	Can. $	U.K. £
Brown	225.00	325.00	150.00

DA 63A
Spirit of Peace (not on plinth)

Beswick No.: 2916
Designer: Graham Tongue
Height: 4 ¾", 12.1 cm
Colour: Brown (matt)
Issued: 1989-1997

Colourways	U.S. $	Can. $	U.K. £
Brown	90.00	135.00	60.00

DA 63B
Spirit of Peace (on wooden plinth)

Beswick No.: 2916
Designer: Graham Tongue
Height: 5 ¾", 14.6 cm
Colour: See below (matt)
Issued: 1989 -1997
Series: Spirited Horses

Colourways	U.S. $	Can. $	U.K. £
1. Brown	115.00	165.00	80.00
2. White	90.00	135.00	60.00

DA 64A
Spirit of Affection (not on plinth)

Beswick No.: H2689/2536
Designer: Graham Tongue
Height: 7", 17.8 cm
Colour: White (matt)
Issued: 1989-1996
Series: Spirited Horses

Colourways	U.S. $	Can. $	U.K. £
White	125.00	200.00	90.00

DA 64B
Spirit of Affection (on wooden plinth)

Beswick No.: H2689/2536
Designer: Graham Tongue
Height: 8", 20.3 cm
Colour: See below (matt)
Issued: 1. Brown —1989-1996
 2. White — 1989-1999
Series: Spirited Horses

Colourways	U.S. $	Can. $	U.K. £
1. Brown	150.00	225.00	100.00
2. White	125.00	200.00	90.00

DA 65
'Black Beauty'
Beswick No.: 2466
Designer: Graham Tongue
Height: 7", 17.8 cm
Colour: Black (matt)
Issued: 1989-1999

Description	U.S. $	Can. $	U.K. £
'Black Beauty'	80.00	120.00	55.00

DA 66
'Black Beauty' as a Foal
Beswick No.: 2536
Designer: Graham Tongue
Height: 5 ¾", 14.6 cm
Colour: Black (matt)
Issued: 1989-1999

Description	U.S. $	Can. $	U.K. £
'Black Beauty' as Foal	50.00	75.00	35.00

DA 67
Pinto Pony
Beswick No.: 1373
Designer: Arthur Gredington
Height: 6 ½", 16.5 cm
Colour: See below (gloss and matt)
Issued: 1989-1990

Colourways	U.S. $	Can. $	U.K. £
1. Piebald (gloss)	125.00	200.00	80.00
2. Piebald (matt)	125.00	200.00	80.00
3. Skewbald (gloss)	125.00	200.00	80.00
4. Skewbald (matt)	125.00	200.00	80.00

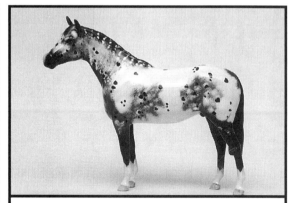

DA 68
Appaloosa
Beswick No.: 1772B
Designer: Arthur Gredington
Height: 8", 20.3 cm
Colour: Black and white (gloss)
Issued: 1989-1996
Varieties: Also called 'Thoroughbred Horse' DA 53

Colourways	U.S. $	Can. $	U.K. £
Black and white	100.00	150.00	70.00

DA 69A
Springtime (not on plinth)

Beswick No.: 2837
Designer: Graham Tongue
Height: 4 ½", 11.4 cm
Colour: Brown (gloss)
Issued: 1989-1999
Series: Spirited Foals

Colourways	U.S. $	Can. $	U.K. £
Brown	45.00	65.00	30.00

Note: Beswick model illustrated.

DA 69B
Springtime (on wooden plinth)

Beswick No.: 2837
Designer: Graham Tongue
Height: 5 ½", 14.0 cm
Colour: See below (matt)
Issued: 1989-1999
Series: Spirited Foals

Colourways	U.S. $	Can. $	U.K. £
1. Brown	45.00	65.00	30.00
2. White	45.00	65.00	30.00

DA 70A
Young Spirit (not on plinth)

Beswick No.: 2839
Designer: Graham Tongue
Height: 3 ½", 8.9 cm
Colour: Brown (gloss)
Issued: 1989-1993
Series: Spirited Foals

Colourways	U.S. $	Can. $	U.K. £
Brown	45.00	65.00	30.00

DA 70B
Young Spirit (on wooden plinth)

Beswick No.: 2839
Designer: Graham Tongue
Height: 4 ¼", 10.7 cm
Colour: See below (matt)
Issued: 1. Black — 1989-1996
         2. Brown and white — 1989-1995
Series: Spirited Foals

Colourways	U.S. $	Can. $	U.K. £
1. Black	45.00	65.00	30.00
2. Brown	50.00	75.00	35.00
3. White	45.00	65.00	30.00

DA 71A
Sunlight (not on plinth)

Beswick No.:	2875
Designer:	Graham Tongue
Height:	3 ½", 8.9 cm
Colour:	Brown (gloss)
Issued:	1989-1996
Series:	Spirited Foals

Colourways	U.S. $	Can. $	U.K. £
Brown	45.00	65.00	30.00

DA 71B
Sunlight (on wooden plinth)

Beswick No.:	2875
Designer:	Graham Tongue
Height:	4 ¼", 10.7 cm
Colour:	See below (matt)
Issued:	1989-1996
Series:	Spirited Foals

Colourways		U.S. $	Can. $	U.K. £
1.	Black	45.00	65.00	30.00
2.	Brown	60.00	90.00	40.00
3.	White	35.00	55.00	25.00

DA 72A
Adventure (not on plinth)

Beswick No.:	2876
Designer:	Graham Tongue
Height:	4 ½", 11.4 cm
Colour:	Brown (gloss)
Issued:	1989-1997
Series:	Spirited Foals

Colourways	U.S. $	Can. $	U.K. £
Brown	45.00	65.00	30.00

DA 72B
Adventure (on plinth)

Beswick No.:	2876
Designer:	Graham Tongue
Height:	5 ½", 14.0 cm
Colour:	See below (matt)
Issued:	1989-1997
Series:	Spirited Foals

Colourways		U.S. $	Can. $	U.K. £
1.	Brown	50.00	75.00	35.00
2.	White	45.00	65.00	30.00

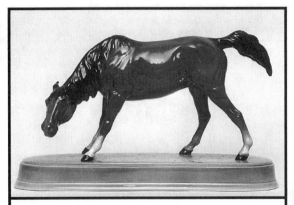

DA 73
Spirit of Nature (on wooden plinth)
Beswick No.: 2935
Designer: Graham Tongue
Height: 6 ¼", 15.9 cm
Colour: Brown (matt)
Issued: 1989-1996
Series: Spirited Horses

Colourways	U.S. $	Can. $	U.K. £
Brown	110.00	165.00	75.00

Note: Beswick model illustrated.

DA 74
Foal (small, stretched, facing right)
Beswick No: 815
Designer: Arthur Gredington
Height: 3 ¼", 8.3 cm
Colour: See below
Issued: 1. Brown (gloss) — 1989-1999
              2. Brown (matt) — 1989-1996
              3. Dapple grey — 1989-1995

Colourways	U.S. $	Can. $	U.K. £
1. Brown (gloss)	35.00	55.00	25.00
2. Brown (matt)	35.00	55.00	25.00
3. Dapple grey (gloss)	45.00	65.00	30.00

DA 75
Foal (lying)
Beswick No: 915
Designer: Arthur Gredington
Height: 3 ¼", 8.3 cm
Colour: See below (gloss and matt)
Issued: 1. Brown (gloss) — 1989-1999
              2. Brown (matt) — 1989-1996
              3. Dapple grey — 1989-1995

Colourways	U.S. $	Can. $	U.K. £
1. Brown (gloss)	30.00	45.00	20.00
2. Brown (matt)	35.00	55.00	25.00
3. Dapple grey (gloss)	45.00	65.00	30.00

DA 76
Foal (grazing)
Beswick No.: 946
Designer: Arthur Gredington
Height: 3 ¼", 8.3 cm
Colour: See below (gloss and matt)
Issued: 1. Brown (gloss) — 1989-1999
              2. Other colours — 1989-1996

Colourways	U.S. $	Can. $	U.K. £
1. Brown (gloss)	30.00	45.00	20.00
2. Brown (matt)	35.00	50.00	25.00
3. Dapple grey (gloss)	50.00	75.00	35.00
4. Palomino (gloss)	45.00	70.00	30.00

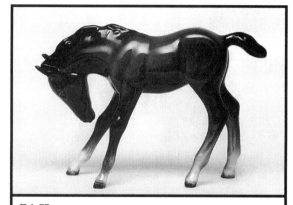

DA 77
Foal (large, head down)
Beswick No.: 947
Designer: Arthur Gredington
Height: 4 ½", 11.4 cm
Colour: Brown (gloss and matt)
Issued: 1. Brown (gloss) —1989-1999
             2. Brown (matt) — 1989-1996

Colourways	U.S. $	Can. $	U.K. £
1. Brown (gloss)	45.00	65.00	30.00
2. Brown (matt)	45.00	65.00	30.00

DA 78
Foal (small, stretched, facing left)
Beswick No.: 997
Designer: Arthur Gredington
Height: 3 ¼", 8.3 cm
Colour: See below

Colourways	U.S. $	Can. $	U.K. £
1. Black (gloss) 1995-1997	50.00	75.00	35.00
2. Brown (gloss) 1989-1999	30.00	45.00	20.00
3. Brown (matt) 1989-1996	45.00	70.00	30.00
4. Grey (gloss) 1989-1997	50.00	75.00	35.00

DA 79
Shetland Foal
Beswick No.: 1034
Designer: Arthur Gredington
Height: 3 ¾", 9.5 cm
Colour: Brown (gloss and matt)
Issued: 1. Brown (gloss) — 1989-1999
             2. Brown (matt) — 1989-1996

Colourways	U.S. $	Can. $	U.K. £
1. Brown (gloss)	30.00	45.00	20.00
2. Brown (matt)	45.00	65.00	30.00

DA 80
Foal (Arab type)
Beswick No.: 1407
Designer: Arthur Gredington
Height: 4 ½", 11.4 cm
Colour: 1. Brown, Dapple grey (gloss) - 1989-1999
             2. Brown (matt) - 1989-1996
             3. Palomino (gloss) - 1989-1995

Colourways	U.S. $	Can. $	U.K. £
1. Brown (gloss)	30.00	45.00	20.00
2. Brown (matt)	45.00	70.00	30.00
3. Dapple grey (gloss)	65.00	95.00	45.00
4. Palomino (gloss)	50.00	75.00	35.00

DA 81
Foal (larger, thoroughbred type)

Beswick No.:	1813
Designer:	Arthur Gredington
Height:	4 ½", 11.4 cm
Colour:	Brown (gloss and matt)
Issued:	1. Brown (gloss) — 1989-1999
	2. Brown (matt) — 1989-1995

Colourways	U.S. $	Can. $	U.K. £
1. Brown (gloss)	40.00	60.00	25.00
2. Brown (matt)	40.00	60.00	25.00

DA 82
Foal (smaller thoroughbred type, facing left)

Beswick No.:	1816
Designer:	Arthur Gredington
Height:	3 ½", 8.9 cm
Colour:	See below
Issued:	1. Brown (gloss) — 1989-1999
	2. Brown (matt) — 1989-1996
	3. Palomino (gloss) — 1989-1996

Colourways	U.S. $	Can. $	U.K. £
1. Brown (gloss)	30.00	45.00	20.00
2. Brown (matt)	30.00	45.00	20.00
3. Palomino (gloss)	45.00	70.00	30.00

DA 83
Siamese Cat
Seated - Style Two

Beswick No.:	2139
Designer:	Mr. Garbet
Height:	13 ¾", 34.9 cm
Colour:	Cream and black (gloss)
Issued:	1989-1996
Series:	Fireside Models

Description	U.S. $	Can. $	U.K. £
Siamese cat	125.00	175.00	90.00

DA 84
Old English Sheepdog
Seated

Beswick No.:	2232
Designer:	Albert Hallam
Height:	11 ½", 29.2 cm
Colour:	Grey and white (gloss)
Issued:	1989-1994
Series:	Fireside Models

Description	U.S. $	Can. $	U.K. £
Old English sheepdog	225.00	325.00	150.00

DA 85
Dalmatian

Beswick No.:	2271
Designer:	Graham Tongue
Height:	13 ¾", 34.9 cm
Colour:	White with black spots (gloss)
Issued:	1989-1996
Series:	Fireside Models

Description	U.S. $	Can. $	U.K. £
Dalmatian	250.00	375.00	175.00

DA 86
Labrador (seated)

Beswick No.:	2314
Designer:	Graham Tongue
Height:	13 ¼", 33.6 cm
Colour:	See below (gloss)
Issued:	1989-1996
Series:	Fireside Models
Varieties:	'Black Labrador' HN 86B

Colourways	U.S. $	Can. $	U.K. £
1. Black	200.00	300.00	125.00
2. Golden	200.00	300.00	125.00

DA 87
Yorkshire Terrier
Seated - Style One

Beswick No.:	2377
Designer:	Graham Tongue
Height:	10 ¼", 26.0 cm
Colour:	Dark and light brown (gloss)
Issued:	1989-1994
Series:	Fireside Models

Description	U.S. $	Can. $	U.K. £
Yorkshire terrier	250.00	375.00	175.00

DA 88
Alsatian
Seated - Style Two

Beswick No.:	2410
Designer:	Graham Tongue
Height:	14", 35.5 cm
Colour:	Dark and sandy brown (gloss)
Issued:	1989-1996
Series:	Fireside Models

Description	U.S. $	Can. $	U.K. £
Alsatian	225.00	325.00	150.00

DOGS

K1
BULLDOG

K2
BULLDOG PUPPY

HN2599
ENGLISH SETTER WITH PHEASANT

K19
ST. BERNARD

HN1062
COCKER SPANIEL WITH PHEASANT

HN1064 COCKER SPANIEL
WITH HARE

K11
CAIRN TERRIER

K6
PEKINESE

K9A
COCKER SPANIEL

DOGS

HN1050
ENGLISH SETTER CH. 'MAESYDD MUSTARD'

HN1055
IRISH SETTER CH. 'PAT O'MOY'

HN2558
WELSH CORGI CH. 'SPRING ROBIN'

HN1031
SEALYHAM CH. 'SCOTIA STYLIST'

HN1015
SCOTTISH TERRIER CH. 'ALBOURNE ARTHUR'

HN1139
DACHSHUND

DOGS

HN1065
GREYHOUND

HN2561
GREAT DANE CH. 'REBELLER OF OUBOROUGH'

HN1069 SMOOTH-HAIRED TERRIER
CH. 'CHOSEN DON OF NOTTS'

HN1113
DALMATIAN CH. 'GOWORTH VICTOR'

HN921 ALSATIAN, SEATED,
WITHOUT COLLAR

HN105
COLLIE

HN924
FOX TERRIER

GLAZES

**ENGLISH ST. BERNARD
FLAMBÉ**

**DACHSHUND, STANDING
FLAMBÉ**

**POLAR BEAR AND CUB ON BASE
SUNG**

GLAZES

POLAR BEAR AND CUB ON BASE
FLAMBÉ

TIGER, SEATED
SUNG

FOX, SEATED
SUNG

ELEPHANT, TRUNK IN SALUTE
FLAMBÉ

GLAZES

EAGLE ON ROCK
COLOURWAY OF HN139

COMIC BEAR
FLAMBÉ (LEFT); BLUE (RIGHT)

FOXES, CURLED
HOLBIEN

PIG BOWL
BROWN/CREAM (TOP); BLUE (BOTTOM)

GLAZES

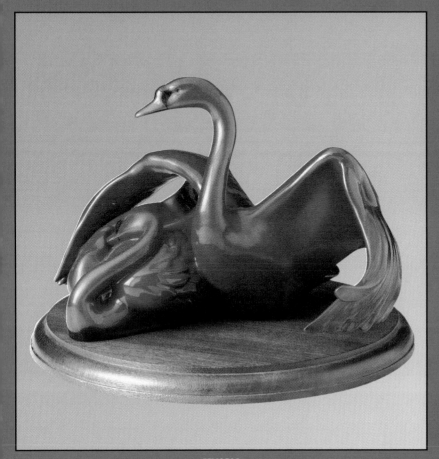

**PERUVIAN PENGUIN
ON ROCK, FLAMBÉ**

**EMPEROR PENGUIN
FLAMBÉ**

**HN3538
'NESTLING DOWN' SWANS, FLAMBÉ**

**MONKEY, HAND TO EAR
FLAMBÉ**

**TWO CUDDLING ORANG-OUTANS
FLAMBÉ**

GLAZES

LEAPING SALMON
FLAMBÉ

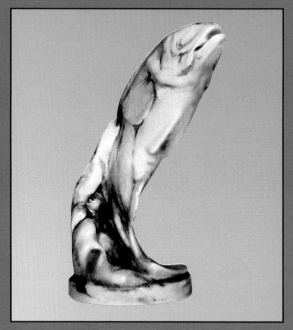

LEAPING SALMON
JADE

CAT, SEATED
FLAMBÉ

BULLDOG, SEATED
SUNG

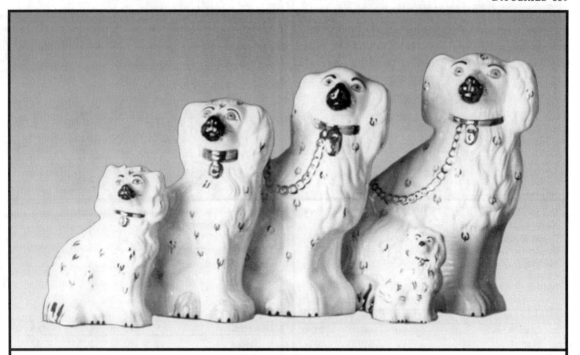

OLD ENGLISH DOGS (left and right facing pairs)

Designer: Unknown
Colour: White and gold (gloss)
Series: Traditional Staffordshire dogs

	DA 89 - 90	DA 91 - 92	DA 93 - 94	DA 95 - 96	DA 97 - 98
Beswick No.:	M1378 / 3	M1378 / 4	M1378 / 5	M1378 / 6	M1378 / 7
Height:	10", 25.4 cm	9", 22.9 cm	7 ½", 19.1 cm	5 ½", 14.0 cm	3 ½", 8.9 cm
Issued:	1989-1997	1989-1999	1989-1997	1989-1999	1989-1999
Currency	*DA 89 - 90*	*DA91 - 92*	*DA 93 - 94*	*DA 95 - 96*	*DA 97 - 98*
U.S. $	100.00	75.00	60.00	45.00	30.00
Can. $	150.00	110.00	85.00	65.00	40.00
U.K. £	60.00	50.00	35.00	30.00	20.00

DA 99
Rottweiler

Beswick No.: 3056
Designer: Alan Maslankowski
Height: 5 ¼", 13.3 cm
Colour: Brown and black (gloss and matt)
Issued: 1. gloss —1990-1999
2. Matt — 1990-1996

Description	U.S. $	Can. $	U.K. £
1. Gloss	60.00	90.00	40.00
2. Matt	60.00	90.00	40.00

DA 100
Old English Sheepdog
Standing

Beswick No.: 3058
Designer: Warren Platt
Height: 5 ½", 14.0 cm
Colour: Grey and white
Issued: 1. gloss — 1990-1999
2. Matt — 1990-1995

Description	U.S. $	Can. $	U.K. £
1. Gloss	65.00	95.00	45.00
2. Matt	90.00	135.00	60.00

DA 101
Staffordshire Bull Terrier - Style Two

Beswick No.: 3060
Designer: Alan Maslankowski
Height: 4", 10.1 cm
Colour: 1. Brindle — 1990-1996
2. White/tan (gloss) — 1990-1995
3. White/tan (matt) —1990-1997

Colourways	U.S. $	Can. $	U.K. £
1. Brindle (gloss)	95.00	140.00	65.00
2. Brindle (matt)	95.00	140.00	65.00
3. White/tan (gloss)	95.00	140.00	65.00
4. White/tan (matt)	95.00	140.00	65.00

DA 102
Afghan Hound

Beswick No.: 3070
Designer: Alan Maslankowski
Height: 5 ½", 14.0 cm
Colour: Light brown and cream (gloss and matt)
Issued: 1990-1996

Description	U.S. $	Can. $	U.K. £
1. Gloss	90.00	125.00	60.00
2. Matt	90.00	125.00	60.00

DA 103
Alsatian
Standing - Style Two
Beswick No.: 3073
Designer: Alan Maslankowski
Height: 5 ¾", 14.6 cm
Colour: Dark and light brown
Issued: 1. gloss — 1990-1999
2. Matt — 1990-1996

Description	U.S. $	Can. $	U.K. £
1. Gloss	60.00	90.00	40.00
2. Matt	75.00	110.00	50.00

DA 104
Boxer
Beswick No.: 3081
Designer: Alan Maslankowski
Height: 5 ½", 14.0 cm
Colour: Golden brown and white
Issued: 1. gloss — 1990-1999
2. Matt — 1990-1995

Description	U.S. $	Can. $	U.K. £
1. Gloss	60.00	90.00	40.00
2. Matt	75.00	100.00	50.00

DA 105
Doberman
Beswick No.: 3121
Designer: Alan Maslankowski
Height: 5 ¼", 13.3 cm
Colour: Dark brown
Issued: 1990-1996

Description	U.S. $	Can. $	U.K. £
1. Gloss	80.00	125.00	55.00
2. Matt	80.00	125.00	55.00

DA 106
Rough Collie
Beswick No.: 3129
Designer: Warren Platt
Height: 5 ½", 14.0 cm
Colour: Golden brown and white
Issued: 1. gloss —1990-1995
2. Matt —1990-1996

Description	U.S. $	Can. $	U.K. £
1. Gloss	90.00	135.00	60.00
2. Matt	90.00	135.00	60.00

DA 107
Springer Spaniel
Beswick No.: 3135
Designer: Amanda Hughes-Lubeck
Height: 5", 12.7 cm
Colour: Dark brown and white
Issued: 1. Gloss — 1990-1999
               2. Matt — 1990-1996

Description	U.S. $	Can. $	U.K. £
1. Gloss	60.00	90.00	40.00
2. Matt	80.00	120.00	55.00

DA 108
The Spaniel (on ceramic plinth)
Beswick No.: 2980
Designer: Alan Maslankowski
Height: 8 ¼", 21.0 cm
Colour: See below (matt)
Issued: 1990-1995
Series: Spirited Dogs

Colourways	U.S. $	Can. $	U.K. £
1. Black/white	175.00	250.00	100.00
2. Golden	175.00	250.00	100.00
3. Liver/white	175.00	250.00	100.00

DA 109
The Setter (on ceramic plinth)
Beswick No.: 2986
Designer: Graham Tongue
Height: 8 ½", 21.6 cm
Colour: See below (matt)
Issued: 1990-1995
Series: Spirited Dogs

Description	U.S. $	Can. $	U.K. £
1. English Setter	175.00	250.00	125.00
2. Gordon Setter	175.00	250.00	125.00
3. Red Setter	175.00	250.00	125.00

DA 110
The Pointer (on ceramic plinth)
Style Two
Beswick No.: 3011
Designer: Graham Tongue
Height: 8 ½", 21.6 cm
Colour: White with dark brown patches (matt)
Issued: 1990-1995
Series: Spirited Dogs

Description	U.S. $	Can. $	U.K. £
Pointer	125.00	200.00	90.00

DA 111
The Labrador (on ceramic plinth)
Standing - Style One

Beswick No.: 3062A
Designer: Alan Maslankowski
Height: 7 ½", 19.1 cm
Colour: See below (matt)
Issued: 1990-1995
Series: Spirited Dogs

Colourways	U.S. $	Can. $	U.K. £
1. Black	125.00	200.00	85.00
2. Golden	125.00	200.00	85.00

DA 112
The Retriever (on ceramic plinth)

Beswick No.: 3066
Designer: Graham Tongue
Height: 7 ½", 19.1 cm
Colour: Golden brown (matt)
Issued: 1990-1995
Series: Spirited Dogs

Colourways	U.S. $	Can. $	U.K. £
Golden brown	150.00	225.00	100.00

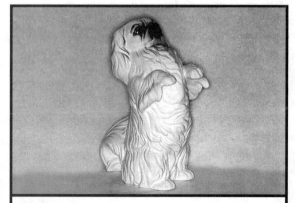

DA 113
Pekinese
Begging

Beswick No.: 2982
Designer: Alan Maslankowski
Height: 5 ½", 14.0 cm
Colour: Cream (gloss and matt)
Issued: 1990-1995
Series: Good Companions

Description	U.S. $	Can. $	U.K. £
1. Gloss	60.00	90.00	40.00
2. Matt	60.00	90.00	40.00

DA 114
Norfolk Terrier

Beswick No.: 2984
Designer: Alan Maslankowski
Height: 4", 10.1 cm
Colour: Dark brown (gloss and matt)
Issued: 1990-1995
Series: Good Companions

Description	U.S. $	Can. $	U.K. £
1. Gloss	60.00	90.00	40.00
2. Matt	60.00	90.00	40.00

DA 115
Poodle on Blue Cushion

Beswick No.: 2985
Designer: Alan Maslankowski
Height: 5", 12.7 cm
Colour: White poodle, blue cushion (gloss
               and matt)
Issued: 1990-1995
Series: Good Companions

Description	U.S. $	Can. $	U.K. £
1. Gloss	90.00	135.00	65.00
2. Matt	90.00	135.00	65.00

DA 116
**Dachshund
Standing - Style Four**

Beswick No.: 3013
Designer: Alan Maslankowski
Height: 4 ½", 11.4 cm
Colour: See below (gloss and matt)
Issued: 1990-1995
Series: Good Companions

Colourways	U.S. $	Can. $	U.K. £
1. Black/tan (gloss)	50.00	75.00	35.00
2. Black/tan (matt)	50.00	75.00	35.00
3. Tan (gloss)	50.00	75.00	35.00

DA 117
Shetland Sheepdog

Beswick No.: 3080
Designer: Alan Maslankowski
Height: 5", 12.7 cm
Colour: Golden brown and white (gloss or matt)
Issued: 1990-1995
Series: Good Companions

Description	U.S. $	Can. $	U.K. £
1. Gloss	60.00	90.00	40.00
2. Matt	60.00	90.00	40.00

DA 118
**Cairn Terrier
Standing**

Beswick No.: 3082
Designer: Warren Platt
Height: 4 ½", 11.4 cm
Colour: Light brown (gloss and matt)
Issued: 1990-1995
Series: Good Companions

Description	U.S. $	Can. $	U.K. £
1. Gloss	60.00	90.00	40.00
2. Matt	60.00	90.00	40.00

DA 119
Yorkshire Terrier
Seated - Style Two

Beswick No.: 3083
Designer: Warren Platt
Height: 5", 12.7 cm
Colour: Light brown and cream (gloss or matt)
Issued: 1990-1995
Series: Good Companions

Description	U.S. $	Can. $	U.K. £
1. Gloss	55.00	85.00	40.00
2. Matt	55.00	85.00	40.00

DA 120
West Highland Terrier
Style Two

Beswick No.: 3149
Designer: Martyn C. R. Alcock
Height: 5", 12.7 cm
Colour: White (gloss or matt)
Issued: 1990-1995
Series: Good Companions

Description	U.S. $	Can. $	U.K. £
1. Gloss	60.00	90.00	40.00
2. Matt	60.00	90.00	40.00

DA 121
Cavalier King Charles Spaniel - Style Two

Beswick No.: 3155
Designer: Warren Platt
Height: 5", 12.7 cm
Colour: See below (gloss or matt)
Issued: 1990-1995
Series: Good Companions

Colourways	U.S. $	Can. $	U.K. £
1. Black/tan/white (gloss)	60.00	90.00	40.00
2. Black/tan/white (matt)	60.00	90.00	40.00
3. Tan/white (gloss)	60.00	90.00	40.00

DA 122
Siamese Kittens

Beswick No.: 1296
Designer: Miss Granoska
Height: 2 ¾", 7.0 cm
Colour: Cream and black (gloss)
Issued: 1990-1999

Colourways	U.S. $	Can. $	U.K. £
Cream / black	30.00	45.00	20.00

Note: Flambé prototype exists.

DA 123
Kitten

Beswick No.:	1436
Designer:	Colin Melbourne
Height:	3 ¼", 8.3 cm
Colour:	See below (gloss)
Issued:	1990-1999

Colourways	U.S. $	Can. $	U.K. £
1. Ginger	25.00	35.00	15.00
2. Grey	25.00	35.00	15.00
3. White	25.00	35.00	15.00

DA 124
Siamese Cat
Lying - Style Two

Beswick No.:	1558B
Designer:	Pal Zalmen
Remodelled:	Albert Hallam
Length:	7 ¼", 18.4 cm
Colour:	Cream and black (gloss)
Issued:	1990-1999

Description	U.S. $	Can. $	U.K. £
Gloss	35.00	50.00	25.00

DA 125
Siamese Cat
Lying - Style Three

Beswick No.:	1559B
Designer:	Pal Zalmen
Remodelled:	Albert Hallam
Height:	7 ¼", 18.4 cm (length)
Colour:	Cream and black (gloss)
Issued:	1990-1999

Colourways	U.S. $	Can. $	U.K. £
Cream / black	35.00	50.00	25.00

DA 126
Persian Cat
Seated - Style Two

Beswick No.:	1867
Designer:	Albert Hallam
Height:	6 ¼", 15.9 cm
Colour:	See below (gloss)
Issued:	See below

Colourways	U.S. $	Can. $	U.K. £
1. Ginger 1990-1996	80.00	120.00	55.00
2. Grey 1990-1999	80.00	120.00	55.00
3. White 1990-1996	80.00	120.00	55.00

DA 127
Siamese Cat
Seated - Style Three
Beswick No.: 1882
Designer: Albert Hallam
Height: 9", 22.9 cm
Size: Large
Colour: Cream and black (gloss)
Issued: 1990-1999

Description	U.S. $	Can. $	U.K. £
Gloss	80.00	120.00	55.00

DA 128
Persian Kitten
Style Two
Beswick No.: 1886
Designer: Albert Hallam
Height: 4", 10.1 cm
Colour: See below (gloss)
Issued: 1990-1999

Colourways	U.S. $	Can. $	U.K. £
1. Ginger	25.00	35.00	15.00
2. Grey	25.00	35.00	15.00
3. White	25.00	35.00	15.00

DA 129
Siamese Cat
Seated - Style Four
Beswick No.: 1887
Designer: Albert Hallam
Height: 4", 10.1 cm
Size: Small
Colour: Cream and black (gloss)
Issued: 1990-1999

Description	U.S. $	Can. $	U.K. £
Gloss	25.00	35.00	15.00

DA 130
Siamese Cat
Standing - Style Two
Beswick No.: 1897
Designer: Albert Hallam
Height: 6 ½", 16.5 cm
Colour: Cream and black (gloss)
Issued: 1990-1997

Description	U.S. $	Can. $	U.K. £
Gloss	45.00	65.00	30.00

DA 131
Black Cat

Beswick No.:	1897
Designer:	Albert Hallam
Height:	6 ½″, 16.5 cm
Colour:	Black (gloss)
Issued:	1990-1994

Description	U.S. $	Can. $	U.K. £
Gloss	85.00	125.00	60.00

DA 132
Persian Cat
Standing

Beswick No.:	1898
Designer:	Albert Hallam
Height:	5″, 12.7 cm
Colour:	See below (gloss)
Issued:	1990-1994

Colourways	U.S. $	Can. $	U.K. £
1. Ginger	45.00	65.00	30.00
2. Grey	45.00	65.00	30.00
3. White	45.00	65.00	30.00

*

DA 134
Desert Orchid
Style One

Model No.:	Unknown
Designer:	Graham Tongue
Height:	12″ x 14″, 30.5 x 35.5 cm
Colour:	Light grey
Issued:	1990 in a limited edition of 7,500

Description	U.S. $	Can. $	U.K. £
1. Ceramic base	550.00	800.00	400.00
2. Wooden base	550.00	800.00	400.00

*

DA 137
The Barn Owl
Style Three

Model No.:	Unknown
Designer:	Amanda Hughes-Lubeck
Height:	7 ½″, 19.1 cm
Colour:	Browns and cream
Issued:	1990-1992
Series:	Wildlife Collection

Description	U.S. $	Can. $	U.K. £
Barn owl	150.00	225.00	100.00

DA 138
Kingfisher (on plinth)
Style Three

Model No.:	Unknown	
Designer:	Warren Platt	
Height:	8 ¾", 22.2 cm	
Colour	Blue and orange-red, cream and brown	
Issued:	1990-1992	
Series:	Nature Sculptures	

Description	U.S. $	Can. $	U.K. £
Kingfisher	150.00	225.00	90.00

DA 139
Osprey (on plinth)

Model No.:	Unknown
Designer:	Unknown
Height:	7 ¾", 19.7 cm
Colour:	Browns and white
Issued:	1990-1992
Series:	Wildlife Collection

Description	U.S. $	Can. $	U.K. £
Osprey	150.00	225.00	100.00

*

DA 141
Cocker Spaniel
Seated - Style Two

Model No.:	Unknown	
Designer:	Martyn C. R. Alcock	
Height:	4 ¼", 10.8 cm	
Colour:	See below (gloss and matt)	
Issued:	1. Golden — 1990-1995	
	2. Liver/white — 1990-1997	

Colourways	U.S. $	Can. $	U.K. £
1. Golden	75.00	115.00	50.00
2. Liver/white	75.00	115.00	50.00

DA 142
Golden Retriever

Model No.:	D 142
Designer:	Amanda Hughes-Lubeck
Height:	5", 12.7 cm
Colour:	Golden brown (gloss and matt)
Issued:	1. gloss — 1990-1999
	2. Matt — 1990-1997

Description	U.S. $	Can. $	U.K. £
1. Gloss	65.00	100.00	45.00
2. Matt	65.00	100.00	45.00

DA 143
Border Collie

Designer:	Amanda Hughes-Lubeck
Height:	4", 10.1 cm
Colour:	See below (gloss and matt)
Issued:	1. Black/white (gloss) — 1990-1999
	2. Black/white (matt) — 1990-1995
	3. Tan/black/white — 1990-1995

Colourways	U.S. $	Can. $	U.K. £
1. Black/white (gloss)	75.00	115.00	50.00
2. Black/white (matt)	75.00	115.00	50.00
3. Tan/black/white	75.00	115.00	50.00

DA 144
Kestrel (on plinth)
Style One

Model No.:	Unknown
Designer:	Graham Tongue
Height:	12 ¼", 31.1 cm
Colour:	Golden brown bird with black markings, pink bone china flowers
Issued:	1991 in a limited edition of 950
Series:	Artist's Signature Edition/Wildlife

Description	U.S. $	Can. $	U.K. £
Kestral	875.00	1,300.00	600.00

DA 145
Labrador, Standing - Style Two

Model No.:	D 145
Designer:	Warren Platt
Height:	5", 12.7 cm
Colour:	See below (gloss and matt)
Issued:	1. Black —1990-1999
	2. Chocolate — 1990-1996
	3. Golden — 1990-1999

Colourways	U.S. $	Can. $	U.K. £
1. Black	65.00	100.00	45.00
2. Chocolate	75.00	115.00	50.00
3. Golden	65.00	100.00	45.00

DA 148
Cat
Walking

Designer:	Alan Maslankowski
Height:	5 ½", 14.0 cm
Colour:	See below (gloss)
Issued:	1. Black with white — 1992-1995
	2. Ginger — 1997, special edition of 1,000
	3. White with black— 1992-1997

Colourways	U.S. $	Can. $	U.K. £
1. Black with white	55.00	80.00	35.00
2. Ginger	75.00	115.00	50.00
3. White with black	55.00	80.00	35.00

DA 149
Cat
Stalking

Model No.:	Unknown
Designer:	Alan Maslankowski
Height:	5 ½", 14.0 cm
Colour:	See below
Issued:	1. Grey — 1992-1998
	2. White — 1992-1999

Colourways	U.S. $	Can. $	U.K. £
1. Grey	40.00	60.00	20.00
2. White	40.00	60.00	20.00

DA 150
Panda

Designer:	Warren Platt
Height:	5 ½", 14.0 cm
Colour:	White
Issued:	Black and white panda, green-brown base
Issued:	1. 1991 in a limited edition of 2,500
	2. 1991-1992
Series:	1. Artist's Signature Edition
	2. Endangered Species

Description	U.S. $	Can. $	U.K. £
1. Artist's Edition	125.00	175.00	85.00
2. Endangered Species	125.00	175.00	85.00
*			

DA 154A
Spirit of Life (on wooden plinth)

Model No.:	Unknown
Designer:	Amanda Hughes-Lubeck
Height:	7 ½", 19.1 cm
Colour:	White (matt)
Issued:	1991-1997
Varieties:	DA 154B 'The Winner'
Series:	Spirited Horses

Description	U.S. $	Can. $	U.K. £
Spirit of Life	100.00	150.00	75.00

DA 154B
The Winner (on wooden plinth) - Style Two

Model No.:	Unknown
Designer:	Amanda Hughes-Lubeck
Height:	7 ½", 19.1 cm
Colour:	Brown with black mane and tail (gloss and matt)
Issued:	1991-1997
Varieties:	DA 154A 'The Spirit of Life'
Series:	Connoisseur Horses

Description	U.S. $	Can. $	U.K. £
1. Gloss	175.00	275.00	125.00
2. Matt	150.00	225.00	100.00

DA 155
Polar Bear (standing)
Style Two

Designer:	Amanda Hughes-Lubeck
Height:	4 ¾", 12.1 cm
Colour:	White, grey base
Issued:	1. 1991 in a limited edition of 2,500
	2. 1991-1992
Series:	1. Artist's Signature Edition
	2. Endangered Species

Description	U.S. $	Can. $	U.K. £
1. Artist's Edition	90.00	135.00	60.00
2. Endangered Species	90.00	135.00	60.00

DA 156
The Tawny Owl

Designer:	Graham Tongue
Height:	9 ¾", 24.8 cm
Colour:	Light and golden brown
Issued:	1. 1991 in a limited edition of 2,500
	2. 1991-1994
Series:	1. Artist's Signature Edition
	2. Connoisseur Birds

Description	U.S. $	Can. $	U.K. £
1. Artist's Edition	225.00	325.00	150.00
2. Connoisseur Birds	225.00	325.00	150.00

*

DA 158
The Christmas Robin (on plinth)

Model No.:	Unknown
Designer:	Graham Tongue
Height:	5 ¼", 13.3 cm
Colour:	Red breast, brown feathers, green holly on snowy bough
Issued:	1990-1992

Description	U.S. $	Can. $	U.K. £
Christmas Robin	75.00	115.00	50.00

DA 159
African Elephant
Style Three

Designer:	Martyn C. R. Alcock
Height:	6", 15.2 cm
Colour:	Grey
Issued:	1. 1991 in a limited edition of 2,500
	2. 1991-1992
Series:	1. Artist's Signature Edition
	2. Endangered Species

Description	U.S. $	Can. $	U.K. £
1. Artist's Edition	125.00	175.00	85.00
2. Endangered Species	125.00	175.00	85.00

DA 161
Christmas Turkey

Model No.:	Unknown
Designer:	Graham Tongue
Height:	6 ¼″, 15.9 cm
Colour:	White feathers, red head
Issued:	1990-1990
Varieties:	D 6449

Description	U.S. $	Can. $	U.K. £
Christmas turkey	90.00	135.00	60.00

DA 163A
Quarter Horse (not on plinth)

Model No.:	Unknown
Designer:	Graham Tongue
Height:	7 ½″, 19.1 cm
Colour:	Brown (gloss)
Issued:	1991-1997
Series:	Nature Sculptures

Colourways	U.S. $	Can. $	U.K. £
Brown	125.00	175.00	85.00

DA 163B
Quarter Horse (on wooden plinth)

Model No.:	Unknown
Designer:	Graham Tongue
Height:	8 ½″, 21.6 cm
Colour:	Bay (matt)
Issued:	1991-1997
Series:	Connoisseur Horses

Colourways	U.S. $	Can. $	U.K. £
Bay	150.00	225.00	100.00

DA 164
Welsh Mountain Pony
Style One

Model No.:	Unknown
Designer:	Amanda Hughes-Lubeck
Height:	6 ¼″, 15.9 cm
Colour:	Dapple grey (gloss)
Issued:	1991-1997

Description	U.S. $	Can. $	U.K. £
Welsh mountain pony	100.00	150.00	65.00

DA 165
Poodle

Model No.:	Unknown
Designer:	Warren Platt
Height:	5 ½", 14.0 cm
Colour:	1. Black
	2. White
Issued:	1993-1993

Colourways	U.S. $	Can. $	U.K. £
1. Black	150.00	225.00	100.00
2. White	150.00	225.00	100.00

*

DA 168
Labrador and Pup

Model No.:	Unknown
Designer:	Warren Platt
Length:	7", 17.8 cm
Colour:	Golden brown (gloss)
Issued:	1992-1996
Series:	Dogs and Puppies

Description	U.S. $	Can. $	U.K. £
Labrador and pup	65.00	100.00	45.00

*

DA 172
Leaping Trout (on wooden plinth)

Model No.:	Unknown
Designer:	Graham Tongue
Height:	11", 27.9 cm
Colour:	Brown and cream trout on blue-grey
	base, yellow flowers, green reeds
Issued:	1994-1994
Series:	Connoisseur

Description	U.S. $	Can. $	U.K. £
Leaping trout	350.00	525.00	250.00

DA 173
Retriever and Pup

Model No.:	Unknown
Designer:	Warren Platt
Length:	6", 15.2 cm
Colour:	Golden brown (gloss)
Issued:	1992-1997
Series:	Dogs and Puppies

Description	U.S. $	Can. $	U.K. £
Retriever and pup	65.00	100.00	45.00

DA 174
Spaniel and Pup

Model No.: Unknown
Designer: Warren Platt
Height: 5 ½", 14.0 cm (length)
Colour: 1. Golden (gloss)
2. Liver and white (gloss)
Issued: 1992-1997
Series: Dogs and Puppies

Colourways	U.S. $	Can. $	U.K. £
1. Golden	65.00	100.00	45.00
2. Liver and white	65.00	100.00	45.00

*

DA 176
Sheepdog and Pup

Model No.: Unknown
Designer: Warren Platt
Height: 4 ½", 11.4 cm
Colour: Grey and white (gloss)
Issued: 1992-1997
Series: Dogs and Puppies

Description	U.S. $	Can. $	U.K. £
Sheepdog and pup	65.00	100.00	45.00

*

DA 179
Black Bess

Model No.: Unknown
Designer: Graham Tongue
Height: 7 ¾", 19.7 cm
Colour: Black (matt)
Issued: 1992-1997
Series: Connoisseur Horses

Description	U.S. $	Can. $	U.K. £
Black Bess	175.00	250.00	125.00

*

DA 182
First Born (on wooden plinth)

Model No.: A 182
Designer: Amanda Hughes-Lubeck
Height: 7", 17.8 cm
Colour: Chestnut mare and foal (matt)
Issued: 1992-1999
Series: Connoisseur Horses

Description	U.S. $	Can. $	U.K. £
First Born	175.00	275.00	125.00

Note: This model is a combination of DA 180 and DA 181.

DA 183
Spirit of the Wild (on wooden plinth)

Model No.:	A 183
Designer:	Warren Platt
Height:	12", 30.5 cm
Colour:	See below (matt)
Issued:	1993-1999
Series:	Spirited Horses

Colourways	U.S. $	Can. $	U.K. £
1. Black	140.00	210.00	95.00
2. Brown	140.00	210.00	95.00
3. White	130.00	200.00	90.00

DA 184
Desert Orchid (on wooden plinth)
Style Two

Model No.:	A 184
Designer:	Warren Platt
Height:	7 ¾", 19.7 cm
Colour:	Light grey (matt)
Issued:	1994-1999
Series:	Connoisseur Horses

Description	U.S. $	Can. $	U.K. £
Desert Orchid	175.00	275.00	125.00

DA 185
Shetland Pony
Style Two

Model No.:	H 185
Designer:	Amanda Hughes-Lubeck
Height:	5 ¼", 13.3 cm
Colour:	Dapple grey (gloss)
Issued:	1992-1999

Description	U.S. $	Can. $	U.K. £
Shetland pony	70.00	100.00	50.00

*

DA 188
Mr. Frisk (on plinth)
Style One

Model No.:	Unknown
Designer:	Graham Tongue
Height:	12 ¼" x 14", 31.1 x 35.5 cm
Colour:	Chestnut (matt)
Issued:	1992 in a limited edition of 7,500
Series:	Connoisseur Horses

Description	U.S. $	Can. $	U.K. £
Mr. Frisk	600.00	900.00	400.00

DA 189
Vietnamese Pot-Bellied Pig

Model No.:	G 189
Designer:	Amanda Hughes-Lubeck
Length:	6", 15.2 cm
Colour:	Dark brown (gloss)
Issued:	1992-1999
Series:	Connoisseur

Description	U.S. $	Can. $	U.K. £
Vietnamese pot-bellied pig	45.00	65.00	30.00

DA 190
Mr. Frisk (on wooden plinth)
Style Two

Model No.:	Unknown
Designer:	Warren Platt
Height:	7 ½", 19.1 cm
Colour:	Chestnut (matt)
Issued:	1992-1997
Series:	Connoisseur Horses

Description	U.S. $	Can. $	U.K. £
Mr. Frisk	175.00	250.00	125.00

*

DA 193A
Horse of the Year 1992

Model No.:	A 193
Designer:	Amanda Hughes-Lubeck
Height:	8 ¼", 21.0 cm
Colour:	Chestnut (matt)
Issued:	1992-1992
Varieties:	Also called 'My First Horse' DA 193B

Description	U.S. $	Can. $	U.K. £
Horse of the Year	90.00	150.00	60.00

DA 193B
My First Horse (on wooden plinth)

Model No.:	A 193
Designer:	Amanda Hughes-Lubeck
Height:	8 ¼", 21.0 cm
Colour:	Chestnut (gloss)
Issued:	1994-1999
Varieties:	Also called 'Horse of the Year 1992' DA 193A

Description	U.S. $	Can. $	U.K. £
My First Horse	90.00	150.00	60.00

DA 194
Cat
Seated - Style Three

Model No.:	K194
Designer:	Martyn C. R. Alcock
Height:	3 ¾", 9.5 cm
Colour:	See below (gloss)
Issued:	1. Black/white — 1992-1999
	2. Ginger — 1992-1997

Colourways	U.S. $	Can. $	U.K. £
1. Black with white	30.00	45.00	20.00
2. Ginger	30.00	45.00	20.00

DA 195
Cat with Bandaged Paw

Model No.:	Unknown
Designer:	Martyn C. R. Alcock
Height:	3 ½", 8.9 cm
Colour:	1. Grey
	2. Ginger
Issued:	1. 1992-1999
	2. 1998

Description	U.S. $	Can. $	U.K. £
1. Grey	40.00	60.00	25.00
2. Ginger	30.00	45.00	20.00

Note: Ginger colourway exclusive to Index Catalogue.

DA 196
Give Me A Home, Dog

Model No.:	Unknown
Designer:	Martyn C. R. Alcock
Height:	5 ¾", 14.6 cm
Colour:	Brown and white (gloss)
Issued:	1994-1997

Description	U.S. $	Can. $	U.K. £
Give me a home, dog	65.00	100.00	45.00

*

DA 205
Kestrel
Style Two

Model No.:	Unknown
Designer:	Graham Tongue
Height:	10", 24.5 cm
Colour:	Light and dark brown (matt)
Issued:	1992 in a limited editon of 2,500
Series:	Artist's Signature Edition

Description	U.S. $	Can. $	U.K. £
Kestrel	200.00	300.00	125.00

*

DA 213
Vietnamese Pot-Bellied Piglet

Model No.:	G 213		
Designer:	Warren Platt		
Length:	3", 7.6 cm		
Colour:	Grey (gloss)		
Issued:	1993-1999		

Description	U.S. $	Can. $	U.K. £
Pot-bellied piglet	20.00	30.00	15.00

DA 214
Mick the Miller (Greyhound) (on wooden base)

Model No.:	Unknown		
Designer:	Graham Tongue		
Height:	9 ½", 24.1 cm		
Colour:	Pale brown and white (gloss)		
Issued:	1993 in a limited edition of 7,500		

Description	U.S. $	Can. $	U.K. £
Greyhound	125.00	175.00	85.00

DA 215
Tamworth Pig

Model No.:	G 215		
Designer:	Amanda Hughes-Lubeck		
Height:	6", 15.2 cm		
Colour:	Brown (gloss)		
Issued:	1994-1999		

Description	U.S. $	Can. $	U.K. £
Tamworth pig	45.00	65.00	30.00

*

DA 218
'Red Rum'
Style Two

Model No.:	Unknown		
Designer:	Graham Tongue		
Height:	12", 30.5 cm		
Colour:	Bay (matt)		
Issued:	1993 in a limited edition of 7,500		

Description	U.S. $	Can. $	U.K. £
1. Ceramic Base	600.00	900.00	400.00
2. Wooden plinth	600.00	900.00	400.00

*

DA 222
Bulldog
Seated - Style Six

Designer:	Warren Platt
Height:	5″, 12.7 cm
Colour:	1. Fawn and white
	2. White, tan patches over ears
Issued:	1. 1996 in a special edition of 1,000
	2. 1993-1999

Colourways	U.S. $	Can. $	U.K. £
1. Fawn/white	100.00	150.00	65.00
2. White/tan patches	45.00	65.00	30.00

DA 223
Nigerian Pot-Bellied Pygmy Goat

Model No.:	G 223
Designer:	Amanda Hughes-Lubeck
Height:	5 ¼″, 14.0 cm
Colour:	White with black patches (gloss)
Issued:	1993-1999

Description	U.S. $	Can. $	U.K. £
Pygmy goat	45.00	65.00	30.00

DA 224
Cancara - running

Model No.:	Unknown
Designer:	Warren Platt
Height:	7 ½″, 19.1 cm
Colour:	Black (matt)
Issued:	1995-1997
Series:	Connoisseur

Description	U.S. $	Can. $	U.K. £
Cancara	250.00	350.00	175.00

DA 225
Spirit of Love, Horses (on wooden plinth)

Model No.:	Unknown
Designer:	Alan Maslankowski
Height:	6 ½″, 16.5 cm
Colour:	Bay (matt)
Issued:	1994-1997
Series:	Spirited Horses

Description	U.S. $	Can. $	U.K. £
Spirit of Love	150.00	250.00	100.00

DA 226
'Red Rum'
Style Three

Model No.:	A 226
Designer:	Amanda Hughes-Lubeck
Height:	9", 22.9 cm
Colour:	Brown (matt)
Issued:	1995-1999

Description	U.S. $	Can. $	U.K. £
'Red Rum'	175.00	275.00	125.00

DA 227
'Arkle'
Style Two

Model No.:	Unknown
Designer:	Graham Tongue
Height:	12", 30.5 cm
Colour:	Bay (matt)
Issued:	1994 in a limited edition of 5,000

Description	U.S. $	Can. $	U.K. £
'Arkle'	600.00	900.00	400.00

DA 228
British Bulldog

Model No.:	Unknown
Designer:	Denise Andrews
Modeller:	Amanda Hughes-Lubeck
Height:	4 ½" x 5 ½", 11.3 x 14.0 cm
Colour:	1. Tan dog, white hat and jacket
	2. White dog, black hat and jacket
Issued:	Tan — 1994 in a limited edition of 1,000
	White — 1994 in a limited edition of 1,000

Colourways	U.S. $	Can. $	U.K. £
1. Tan dog	150.00	200.00	100.00
2. White dog	150.00	200.00	100.00

DA 229
Quiet Please, 'Cats'

Model No.:	K229
Designer:	Warren Platt
Height:	1 ¾", 4.4 cm
Colour:	See below
Issued:	1. 1998
	2. 1995-1999
Series:	Cute Cats

Colourways	U.S. $	Can. $	U.K. £
1. Ginger/white	30.00	45.00	20.00
2. Grey/white	30.00	45.00	20.00

Note: Ginger/white colourway exclusive to Index Catalogue.

DA 230
Gloucester Old Spot Pig

Model No.:	G230		
Designer:	Amanda Hughes-Lubeck		
Height:	3", 7.6 cm		
Colour:	Pink with black markings (gloss)		
Issued:	1995-1999		

Description	U.S. $	Can. $	U.K. £
Pig	45.00	65.00	30.00

DA 231
Dinnertime

Model No.:	Unknown
Designer:	Warren Platt
Height:	2 ½", 6.3 cm
Colour:	See below
Issued:	1. 1995-1999
	2. 1998
Series:	Cute Cats

Colourways	U.S. $	Can. $	U.K. £
1. Black/white	30.00	45.00	20.00
2. Ginger	30.00	45.00	20.00

Note: Ginger colourway exclusive to Index Catalogue.

DA 232
New Toy

Model No.:	Unknown
Designer:	Amanda Hughes-Lubeck
Height:	2 ½", 6.3 cm
Colour:	Cream and white cat (gloss)
Issued:	1995-1999
Series:	Cute Cats

Description	U.S. $	Can. $	U.K. £
New toy	30.00	45.00	20.00

DA 233
In the News

Model No.:	Unknown
Designer:	Amanda Hughes-Lubeck
Height:	2 ½", 6.3 cm
Colour:	Cream and black striped cat (gloss)
Issued:	1995-1999
Series:	Cute Cats

Description	U.S. $	Can. $	U.K. £
In the news	30.00	45.00	20.00

DA 234
Cancara - rearing

Beswick No.:	3426		
Designer:	Graham Tongue		
Height:	16 ½", 41.9 cm		
Colour:	Black (matt)		
Issued:	1995-1999		
Series:	Connoisseur		

Description	U.S. $	Can. $	U.K. £
Cancara	425.00	650.00	300.00

Note: Previously released with a Beswick backstamp to commemorate the centenary in 1994.   *

DA 236
The Flight of the Trakehner

Model No.:	Unknown
Designer:	Graham Tongue
Height:	15", 38.1 cm
Colour:	Brown (matt)
Issued:	1996 in a limited edition of 1,500

Description	U.S. $	Can. $	U.K. £
Trakehner	750.00	1,100.00	500.00

DA 237
'Peakstone Lady Margaret' (Shire horse)

Model No.:	Unknown
Designer:	Warren Platt
Height:	13", 33.0 cm
Colour:	Black, white feet, yellow ribbon, red rosette (matt)
Issued:	1996-1998

Description	U.S. $	Can. $	U.K. £
Shire horse	600.00	900.00	400.00

DA 238
Shire Horse
Style Two

Model No.:	Unknown
Designer:	Amanda Hughes-Lubeck
Height:	7", 17.8 cm
Colour:	Bay (matt)
Issued:	1996-1997

Description	U.S. $	Can. $	U.K. £
Shire horse	250.00	300.00	125.00

DA 239
Spirit of Tomorrow

Model No.:	Unknown
Designer:	Warren Platt
Height:	8", 20.3 cm
Colour:	1. Brown (matt)
	2. White (matt)
Issued:	1. 1996-1996
	2. 1996-1997

Colourways	U.S. $	Can. $	U.K. £
1. Brown	100.00	150.00	65.00
2. White	100.00	150.00	65.00

*

DA 243
The Lipizzaner

Model No.:	Unknown
Designer:	Shane Ridge
Height:	11", 28.0 cm
Colour:	Light grey (matt)
Issued:	1996 in a limited edition of 1,500
Series:	Connoisseur

Description	U.S. $	Can. $	U.K. £
Lipizzaner	600.00	900.00	400.00

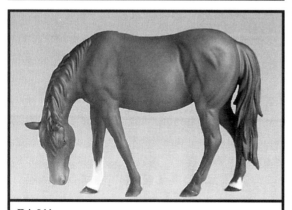

DA 244
New Forest Pony

Model No.:	A 244
Designer:	Shane Ridge
Height:	6", 15.0 cm
Colour:	Brown (matt)
Issued:	1997-1999

Description	U.S. $	Can. $	U.K. £
New Forest pony	80.00	125.00	55.00

DA 245
Milton

Model No.:	Unknown
Designer:	Martyn Alcock
Height:	12 ¼", 31.0 cm
Colour:	White (matt)
Issued:	1997 in a limited edition of 1,000
Series:	Connoisseur

Description	U.S. $	Can. $	U.K. £
Milton	600.00	900.00	400.00

*

DA 247
Welsh Mountain Pony
Style Two

Model No.:	A 247
Designer:	Graham Tongue
Height:	8 ¼", 21.0 cm
Colour:	White with navy and red blanket
Issued:	1998-1999
Series:	Connoisseur

Description	U.S. $	Can. $	U.K. £
Welsh Mountain Pony	175.00	275.00	125.00

DA 248
The Bulldog Pups

Model No.:	Unknown
Designer:	Shane Ridge
Height:	3 ½", 8.9 cm
Colour:	Cream and light brown pups (gloss)
Issued:	1997 in a limited edition of 1,000

Description	U.S. $	Can. $	U.K. £
Bulldog pups	75.00	100.00	50.00

*

DA 250
Lammtarra

Model No.:	A 250
Designer:	Warren Platt
Height:	7 ¾", 19.5 cm
Colour:	Chestnut (matt)
Issued:	1999-1999
Series:	Connoisseur

Description	U.S. $	Can. $	U.K. £
Lammtarra	175.00	250.00	125.00

*

DA 259
Palomino

Model No.:	A 259
Designer:	Shane Ridge
Height:	6 ¾", 17 cm
Colour:	Palomino (gloss)
Issued:	1999-1999

Description	U.S. $	Can. $	U.K. £
Palomino	100.00	150.00	70.00

DA 260
Hunter

Model No.:	A 260
Designer:	Graham Tongue
Height:	8", 20.3 cm
Colour:	Grey (gloss)
Issued:	1999-1999

Description	U.S. $	Can. $	U.K. £
Hunter	100.00	150.00	70.00

DA 261
Hackney Pony

Model No.:	A 261
Designer:	Martyn C. R. Alcock
Height:	6 ¾", 17.2 cm
Colour:	Brown (gloss)
Issued:	1999-1999

Description	U.S. $	Can. $	U.K. £
Hackney Pony	75.00	115.00	50.00

ART IS LIFE

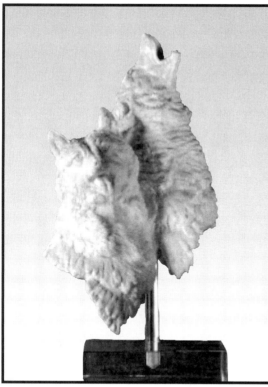

AIL 3
Wolves

Designer: Alan Maslankowski
Height: 11 ¾", 29.5 cm
Colour: White matt
Issued: 2000 in a limited edition of 1,500
Series: Art Is Life

Glaze	U.S. $	Can. $	U.K. £
Wolves	N/I	N/I	185.00

AIL 4
Horses

Designer: Alan Maslankowski
Height: 14", 35.5 cm
Colour: White matt
Issued: 2000 in a limited edition of 1,500
Series: Art Is Life

Glaze	U.S. $	Can. $	U.K. £
Horses	N/I	N/I	175.00

AIL 5
Eagle

Designer:	Alan Maslankowski
Height:	16 ¼", 41.5 cm
Colour:	White matt
Issued:	2000 in a limited edition of 1,500
Series:	Art Is Life

Glaze	U.S. $	Can. $	U.K. £
Eagle	N/I	550.00	175.00

*

AIL 11
Lions

Designer:	Alan Maslankowski
Height:	7 ¼", 18.4 cm
Colour:	White matt
Issued:	2001 in a limited edition of 950
Series:	Art Is Life

Glaze	U.S. $	Can. $	U.K. £
Lions	N/I	575.00	195.00

AIL 12
Bear

Designer: Alan Maslankowski
Height: 12", 30.5 cm
Colour: White matt
Issued: 2001 in a limited edition of 950
Series: Art Is Life

Glaze	U.S. $	Can. $	U.K. £
Bear	N/I	575.00	185.00

GLAZES

CHANG
CHINESE JADE
FLAMBÉ
MANDARIN
SUNG
TITANIAN
TREACLE

Bison
Style Two

Model No.:	1799
Designer:	Joseph Ledger
Height:	5 ½", 14.0 cm
Size:	Medium
Glaze:	Flambé
Issued:	c.1960

Glaze	U.S. $	Can. $	U.K. £
Flambé		Very Rare	

Bison
Style Three

Model No.:	1847
Height:	3", 7.6 cm
Size:	Small
Glaze:	Flambé
Issued:	c.1963

Glaze	U.S. $	Can. $	U.K. £
Flambé		Very Rare	

Borzoi

Model No.:	261
Height:	Unknown
Glaze:	Flambé
Issued:	c.1924

Glaze	U.S. $	Can. $	U.K. £
Flambé		Very Rare	

Bull
Style One

Model No.:	612
Height:	7" x 10 ¾", 17.8 x 27.3 cm
Glaze:	See below
Issued:	c.1928

Glaze	U.S. $	Can. $	U.K. £
1. Chinese Jade	3,750.00	5,500.00	2,500.00
2. Flambé	3,750.00	5,500.00	2,500.00
2. Sung	3,750.00	5,500.00	2,500.00

Bull
Style Two

Model No.:	Unknown
Designer:	Eric Griffiths
Height:	10 ½", 26.7 cm
Glaze:	Flambé
Issued:	c.1927

Glaze	U.S. $	Can. $	U.K. £
Flambé		Prototype	

Bulldog
Seated - Style One

Model No.:	38
Height:	4", 10.1 cm
Glaze:	Flambé
Issued:	1912-1936

Glaze	U.S. $	Can. $	U.K. £
Flambé	1,500.00	2,250.00	1,000.00

Bulldog
Seated - Style Two

Model No.:	120
Height:	3", 7.6 cm
Glaze:	Flambé
Issued:	c.1913

Glaze	U.S. $	Can. $	U.K. £
Flambé	1,500.00	2,250.00	1,000.00

Note: A tan and white colourway was sold by
Bonhams, London, October 2002, for £2,000.00

Butterfly

Model No.:	142A
Height:	2″ x 4 ½", 5.1 x 11.4 cm
Glaze:	Flambé
Issued:	c.1912

Glaze	U.S. $	Can. $	U.K. £
Flambé		Rare	

Cat
Seated - Style Two

Model No.:	2269
Designer:	Alan Maslankowski
Height:	11 ½", 29.2 cm
Glaze:	Flambé
Issued:	1977-1996

Glaze	U.S. $	Can. $	U.K. £
Flambé	675.00	1,000.00	450.00

Chicks (three)

Model No.:	1163
Designer:	Charles Noke
Height:	2 ¼" x 3 ½", 5.7 x 8.9 cm
Glaze:	Flambé
Issued:	c.1908

Glaze	U.S. $	Can. $	U.K. £
Flambé	450.00	675.00	300.00

Cockatoos

Model No.:	630
Designer:	Charles Noke
Height:	4 ½", 11.4 cm
Glaze:	Chinese Jade
Issued:	c.1929

Glaze	U.S. $	Can. $	U.K. £
Chinese Jade	750.00	1,100.00	500.00

Cockerel Bowl

Model No.:	Unknown
Height:	3 ¼", 8.3 cm
Glaze:	Flambé with sterling silver rim
Issued:	Unknown
Varieties:	Cockerel Crouching HN 178, 180, 267

Glaze	U.S. $	Can. $	U.K. £
Flambé		Rare	

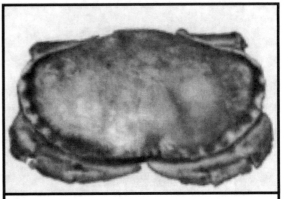

Cormorant on a Rock

Model No.:	22
Designer:	Harry Simeon
Height:	6", 15.0 cm
Glaze:	Flambé
Issued:	c.1930

Glaze	U.S. $	Can. $	U.K. £
Flambé		Very Rare	

Crab

Model No.:	42
Height:	2" x 4 ½", 5.1 x 11.4 cm
Glaze:	See below
Issued:	c.1936

Glaze		U.S. $	Can. $	U.K. £
1.	Crystalline		Very rare	
2.	Flambé		Very rare	

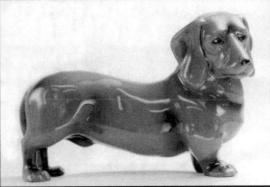

Dachshund, Begging

Model No.:	41
Height:	4", 10.1 cm
Glaze:	Flambé
Issued:	c.1912

Glaze	U.S. $	Can. $	U.K. £
Flambé		Very Rare	

Dachshund
Standing - Style One

Model No.:	36A
Height:	4 ½" x 6 ½", 11.4 x 16.5 cm
Glaze:	Flambé
Issued:	c.1912

Glaze	U.S. $	Can. $	U.K. £
Flambé	2,250.00	3,400.00	1,500.00

Dog of Fo

Model No.:	2957
Designer:	William K. Harper
Height:	5 ¼", 13.3 cm
Glaze:	Flambé
Issued:	1982-1982
Series:	RDICC

Glaze	U.S. $	Can. $	U.K. £
Flambé	300.00	450.00	200.00

Dragon
Style One

Model No.:	2085
Designer:	John Bromley
Height:	7 ½", 19.0 cm
Glaze:	Flambé
Issued:	1973-1996

Glaze	U.S. $	Can. $	U.K. £
Flambé	675.00	1,000.00	450.00

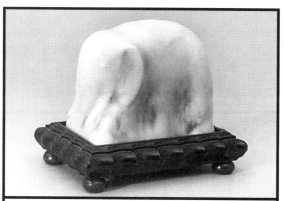

Elephant
Stylized

Model No.:	633
Height:	3", 7.6 cm
Glaze:	Chinese Jade
Issued:	c.1929

Glaze	U.S. $	Can. $	U.K. £
Chinese Jade		Extremely Rare	

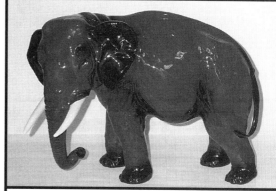

Elephant
Trunk down, curled - medium

Model No.:	Unknown
Designer:	Charles Noke
Height:	6 ½", 16.5 cm
Size:	Medium
Glaze:	Flambé
Issued:	Unknown

Glaze	U.S. $	Can. $	U.K. £
Flambé	750.00	1,000.00	500.00

Elephant
Trunk stretching

Model No.:	Unknown
Designer:	Charles Noke
Height:	12" x 18", 30.5 x 45.7 cm
Glaze:	See below
Issued:	c.1930

Glaze	U.S. $	Can. $	U.K. £
1. Flambé	6,000.00	9,000.00	4,000.00
2. Sung	7,500.00	11,000.00	5,000.00

Fighter Elephant - small

Model No.:	624
Designer:	Charles Noke
Height:	4", 10.1 cm
Size:	Small
Glaze:	See below
Issued:	c.1929

Glaze	U.S. $	Can. $	U.K. £
1. Chinese Jade	1,500.00	2,250.00	1,000.00
2. Flambé	1,500.00	2,250.00	1,000.00

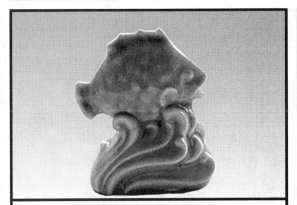

Fish

Model No.:	625
Designer:	Charles Noke
Height:	3 ½" x 5 ½", 8.9 x 14.0 cm
Glaze:	Chinese Jade
Issued:	c.1929

Glaze	U.S. $	Can. $	U.K. £
Chinese Jad		Very Rare	

Fish (shoal of fish)

Model No.:	632
Height:	6 ½", 16.5 cm
Glaze:	See below
Issued:	c.1929
Derivative:	Lamp, Model No. L23

Glaze	U.S. $	Can. $	U.K. £
1. Chinese Jade		Very Rare	
2. Flambé		Very Rare	

Fox
Seated - Style Two - medium

Model No.:	14A
Height:	5 ½", 14.0 cm
Size:	Medium
Glaze:	Flambé
Issued:	c.1912

Glaze	U.S. $	Can. $	U.K. £
Flambé	750.00	1,100.00	500.00

Photograph not
available
at press time

Fox Bowl

Model No.:	20
Height:	2 ½" x 12 ½", 6.4 x 31.7 cm
Glaze:	Flambé
Issued:	c.1912-1936

Glaze	U.S. $	Can. $	U.K. £
Flambé	1,800.00	2,750.00	1,200.00

Frog
Style One - large

Model No.:	1162
Height:	Unknown
Size:	Large
Glaze:	Flambé
Issued:	c.1908-1936

Glaze	U.S. $	Can. $	U.K. £
Flambé		Rare	

Frog
Style One - medium

Model No.:	1162A
Height:	Unknown
Size:	Medium
Glaze:	Flambé
Issued:	c.1908-1936

Glaze	U.S. $	Can. $	U.K. £
Flambé		Rare	

Frog
Style One - small

Model No.:	1162B
Height:	1 ¼" x 3 ½", 4.4 x 8.9 cm
Size:	Small
Glaze:	Flambé
Issued:	1908-1936

Glaze	U.S. $	Can. $	U.K. £
Flambé		Rare	

Photograph not
available
at press time

Hare
Standing - Style One
Model No.:	86
Height:	5 ¾", 14.6 cm
Glaze:	Flambé
Issued:	c.1912-14936

Glaze	U.S. $	Can. $	U.K. £
Flambé			Rare

Hebei Goat (BA 36)
Designer:	Alan Maslankowski
Height:	10 ¼", 26.0 cm
Glaze:	Flambé
Issued:	2002 in a limited edition of 250
Series:	Burslem Artware

Glaze	U.S. $	Can. $	U.K. £
Flambé	1,645.00	2,800.00	650.00

Photograph not
available
at press time

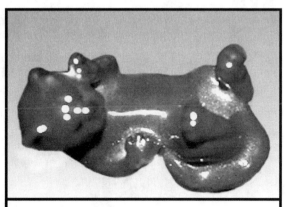

Horse
Model No.:	882
Height:	Unknown
Glaze:	Chinese Jade
Issued:	c.1934
Derivitive:	Lamp

Glaze	U.S. $	Can. $	U.K. £
Chinese Jade		Extremely Rare	

Kitten Lying on Back
Model No.:	17
Size:	1 ½" x 2", 3.8 x 5.0 cm
Glaze:	Flambé
Issued:	Unknown

Glaze	U.S. $	Can. $	U.K. £
Flambé		Very Rare	

Leaping Salmon

Model No.:	666
Designer:	Charles Noke
Height:	12 ¼," 31.1 cm
Glaze:	See below
Issued:	1. Chinese Jade — c.1930
	2. Flambé — c.1940-1950

Glaze	U.S. $	Can. $	U.K. £
1. Chinese Jade	Very Rare		
2. Flambé	900.00	1,350.00	600.00
3. Natural	1,800.00	2,700.00	1,200.00

Lion
Lying

Model No.:	64
Height:	2 ½" x 7", 6.4 x 17.8 cm
Glaze:	Flambé
Issued:	c.1918-1936

Glaze	U.S. $	Can. $	U.K. £
Flambé	Very Rare		

Llama
Style One

Model No.:	827
Height:	6", 15.2 cm
Glaze:	See below
Issued:	c.1933
Derivitive:	Lamp

Glaze	U.S. $	Can. $	U.K. £
1. Chinese Jade	Very Rare		
2. Flambé	Very Rare		

Lop-Eared Rabbit - Small

Model No.:	1165
Height:	2 ½", 6.4 cm
Glaze:	Flambé
Issued:	1913-1996
Varieties:	HN 1091A on fluted ashtray
	HN 1091B on plain ashtray

Glaze	U.S. $	Can. $	U.K. £
Flambé	125.00	175.00	60.00

**Mouse
Crouching**

Model No.:	1164B		
Height:	Unknown		
Glaze:	Flambé		
Issued:	c.1912		
Varieties:	HN 1090B on Fluted Ashtray		
	HN 1090A on Plain Ashtray		

Glaze	U.S. $	Can. $	U.K. £
Flambé		Rare	

Mouse with a Nut

Model No.:	1164A		
Designer:	Unknown		
Height:	2 ¼", 5.7 cm		
Glaze:	Flambé		
Issued:	c.1912		

Glaze	U.S. $	Can. $	U.K. £
Flambé		Rare	

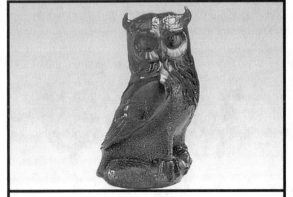

**Owl
Style Two**

Model No.:	2249		
Designer:	Alan Maslankowski		
Height:	12", 30.5 cm		
Glaze:	Flambé		
Issued:	1973-1996		

Glaze	U.S. $	Can. $	U.K. £
Flambé	525.00	800.00	350.00

Panther

Model No.:	111		
Designer:	Charles Noke		
Height:	8 ½" x 9", 21.6 x 22.9 cm		
Glaze:	Flambé		
Issued:	c.1912		

Glaze	U.S. $	Can. $	U.K. £
Flambé		Very Rare	

Note: Model No.: 111 was also used to produce the
Tiger Crouching HN 225.

Parrot on Pillar

Model No.:   45
Height: 6 ½", 16.5 cm
Glaze: Flambé
Issued: c.1913-1936

Glaze	U.S. $	Can. $	U.K. £
Flambé		Very Rare	

Peruvian Penguin on Rock - small

Model No.:   1287
Height: 5", 12.7 cm
Size: Small
Glaze: Flambé
Issued: c.1925-1961

Glaze	U.S. $	Can. $	U.K. £
Flambé	850.00	1,275.00	550.00

Pig
Seated

Model No.:   Unknown
Height: 4 ¼", 10.8 cm
Glaze: Flambé
Issued: Unknown

Glaze	U.S. $	Can. $	U.K. £
Flambé		Very Rare	

Pig
Standing

Model No.:   114
Height: 1 ¼" x 3 ¼", 3.1 x 8.3 cm
Glaze: Flambé
Issued: c.1912

Glaze	U.S. $	Can. $	U.K. £
Flambé		Very Rare	

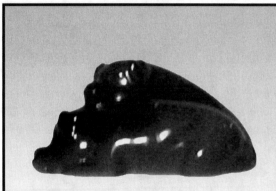

Pig Bowl
Style Two

Model No.:	Unknown
Height:	1 ¾″ x 3 ½″, 4.4 x 8.9 cm
Glaze:	Pink with Sterling silver rim
Issued:	c.1922

Glaze	U.S. $	Can. $	U.K. £
Pink		Only two known	

Pigs
Snoozing - Both Pigs With Ears Down

Model No.:	62
Designer:	Charles Noke
Height:	1 ¾″ x 3 ¾″, 4.4 x 9.5 cm
Glaze:	See below
Issued:	1912-1936

Glaze	U.S. $	Can. $	U.K. £
1. Black		Very Rare	
2. Blue (illustrated)		Very Rare	
3. Orange		Very Rare	

Pigs, Snoozing
One Pig With Ears Down, One With Ears Up

Model No.:	62
Height:	1 ¾″ x 3 ¼″, 4.4 x 8.3 cm
Glaze:	Flambé
Issued:	Unknown

Glaxe	U.S. $	Can. $	U.K. £
Flambé		Very Rare	

Pigs at a Trough

Model No.:	81
Height:	2 ½″ x 4″, 6.4 x 10.1 cm
Glaze:	Flambé
Issued:	c.1931-1936

Glaze	U.S. $	Can. $	U.K. £
Flambé	750.00	1,100.00	500.00

Polar Bear and Cub on base - small

Model No.:	617
Designer:	Charles Noke
Height:	8" x 10", 20.3 x 25.4 cm
Size:	Small
Glaze:	See below
Issued:	c.1929

Glaze	U.S. $	Can. $	U.K. £
1. Chang		Extremely Rare	
2. Sung		Extremely Rare	

Polar Bear on Dish

Model No.:	40
Height:	5", 12.7 cm
Glaze:	Flambé
Issued:	c.1912-1936

Glaze	U.S. $	Can. $	U.K. £
Flambé		Very Rare	

Polar Bears on Ice Floe

Model No.:	54
Height:	3 ½", 8.9 cm
Glaze:	Flambé
Issued:	c.1912-1936

Glaze	U.S. $	Can. $	U.K. £
Flambé		Very Rare	

Quinghai Fu Dogs (Pair) [BAS 34/BA35]

Designer:	Alan Maslankowski
Height:	7 ¼", 18.4 cm
Glaze:	Flambé
Issued:	2002 in a limited edition of 250
Series:	Burslem Artware

Description	U.S. $	Can. $	U.K. £
Quinghai Fu dogs (pair)	1,345.00	2,200.00	750.00

Rabbit
Crouching - Style One
Model No.:   1165A
Height: 3 ½", 8.9 cm
Glaze: Flambé
Issued: c.1912-by 1946

Glaze	U.S. $	Can. $	U.K. £
Flambé		Very Rare	

Photograph not
available
at press time

Rabbit
Crouching - Style Two
Model No.:   1165B
Height: 4", 10.1 cm
Glaze: Sung
Issued: c.1912-by 1946

Glaze	U.S. $	Can. $	U.K. £
Sung		Very Rare	

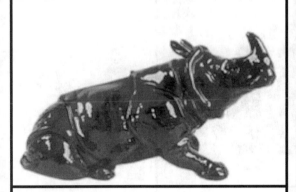

Rhinoceros
Lying
Model No.:   615
Designer: Leslie Harradine
Length: 9 ½", 24.1 cm
Glaze: Flambé
Issued: c.1973-1996

Glaze	U.S. $	Can. $	U.K. £
Flambé	900.00	1,350.00	600.00

Shenlong Dragon (BA 32)
Designer: Alan Maslankowski
Height: 14 ¾", 37.5 cm
Glaze: Flambé
Issued: 2002 in a limited edition of 250
Series: Burslem Artware

Glaze	U.S. $	Can. $	U.K. £
Flambé	1,785.00	2,600.00	1,000.00

Táng Horse (BA 25)

Designer:	Alan Maslankowski
Height:	10 ¼", 25.2 cm
Glaze:	Sung
Issued:	2001 in a limited edition of 250
Series:	Burslem Artware

Glaze	U.S. $	Can. $	U.K. £
Sung	1,950.00	2,600.00	1,000.00

Note: Issued to celebrate the Chinese Year of the Horse, 2002

Tiger on a Rock
Style Four

Designer:	Fred Moore after Charles Noke
Length:	15 ¾", 40.0 cm
Size:	Large
Glaze:	Sung
Issued:	c.1940s

Glaze	U.S. $	Can. $	U.K. £
Sung		Extremely Rare	

Note: Sold at Phillips, London, October 2000, for £4,200.00.

Tortoise - small

Model No.:	101A
Height:	1" x 3", 2.5 x 7.6 cm
Size:	Small
Glaze:	See below
Issued:	c.1912-by 1946

Glaze	U.S. $	Can. $	U.K. £
1. Flambé	750.00	1,100.00	500.00
2. Sung	975.00	1,500.00	650.00

BOOKENDS
BROOCHES
WALL MOUNTS

CHAMPIONSHIP DOG BOOKENDS

The following medium size dog models were available by order as bookends. They were mounted on mahogany and sold by order for 21/10d to 22/- a pair. The bookends utilized the medium size (M/S) dogs in all known cases. The listing below is in alphabetical order cross-referenced with HN numbers for the medium size dogs in question.

Style	HN No.	Colour	Size	U.S. $	Price Can. $	U.K.
Bulldog	HN 1043	Dark brown and white	Medium	1,275.00	1,900.00	850.00
Cairn	HN 1034	Black and grey	Medium	750.00	1,100.00	500.00
Cocker Spaniel	HN 1109	Black and white	Medium	300.00	450.00	200.00
Cocker Spaniel with Pheasant	HN 1028	White and brown dog reddish brown pheasant	Medium	375.00	525.00	250.00
English Setter	HN 2621	Liver and white	Medium	4,000.00	6,000.00	2,700.00
Irish Setter	HN 1055	Reddish brown and black	Medium	375.00	525.00	250.00
Pekinese	HN 1012	Brown and black	Medium	195.00	300.00	130.00
Rough-haired Terrier	HN 1013	White, black and brown	Medium	675.00	1,000.00	450.00
Scottish Terrier	HN 1015	Black	Medium	675.00	1,000.00	450.00
Sealyham	HN 1031	White and brown	Medium	525.00	800.00	350.00

BROOCHES

Produced during the 1930s these china items had pin backs for use as jewellery brooches.

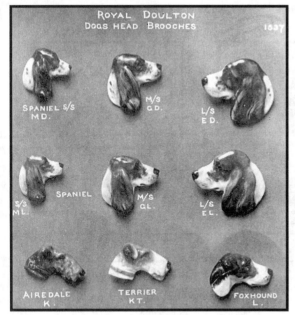

Dogs Head Brooches

Kingfisher Brooch

Butterfly Brooch

Style	Type	Colour	Size	Price U.S. $	Can. $	U.K. £
Dogs	Airedale	Dark brown and black	1″	750.00	1,100.00	500.00
	Cairn	Black and grey	1 ½″	750.00	1,100.00	500.00
	Chow	Golden brown	1″	675.00	1,000.00	450.00
	Cocker Spaniel	Liver and white	1″	675.00	1,000.00	450.00
			1 ½″	675.00	1,000.00	450.00
			2″	675.00	1,000.00	450.00
	Cocker Spaniel	Black and White	1″	675.00	1,000.00	450.00
			1 ½″	675.00	1,000.00	450.00
			2″	675.00	1,000.00	450.00
	Fox Terrier	White and dark brown	1″	750.00	1,100.00	500.00
	Foxhound	Brown and white	1″	750.00	1,100.00	500.00
	Greyhound	Dark brown and white	1 ¼″	1,000.00	1,500.00	675.00
	Pekinese	Brown and black	1″	800.00	1,200.00	525.00
	Pomeranian	Golden brown	1″	1,275.00	1,900.00	850.00
	Sealyham	White and brown	1 ½″	800.00	1,200.00	525.00
	Terrier	White and dark brown	1″	800.00	1,200.00	525.00
Misc.	Butterfly	Pink	N/A	750.00	1,100.00	500.00
		Peach	N/A	750.00	1,100.00	500.00
		Yellow/brown/blue	N/A	750.00	1,100.00	500.00
	Fox	Brown	N/A	750.00	1,100.00	500.00
	Kingfisher	Blue	1 ¼″	750.00	1,100.00	500.00
	Persian Cat	Cream with green eyes	1 ½″	750.00	1,100.00	500.00

* **N/A** - Not Available

WALL MOUNTS

In the 1930s Doulton produced a series of dogs' heads, plain and mounted on oval wooden panels as wall hangings. Similar heads were also mounted for bookends. Ten different models have been recorded, one in two colourways. The heads are numbered SK-21, to SK-31 but (possibly due to size) they show only the "K" and not "SK" resulting in possible confusion with the "K" series. Not all pieces have the Royal Doulton backstamp.

The original issue prices of the models were: Without plinths 5/-; With plinths 6/-; On bookends 8/- each. Prices are shown for a single bookend.

SK 25 Foxhound Plain

SK 31 Pekinese Mounted

804 Fox Mounted

Number	Style	Type	Colour	Size	U.S.$	Price Can. $	U.K. £
SK 21	English Setter	Plain	Black	3 ½"	750.00	1,100.00	500.00
		Mounted	and	8.9 cm	750.00	1,100.00	500.00
		Bookend	white		750.00	1,100.00	500.00
SK 22	Irish Setter	Plain	Reddish	3 ½"	750.00	1,100.00	500.00
		Mounted	brown and	8.9 cm	750.00	1,100.00	500.00
		Bookend	black		750.00	1,100.00	500.00
SK 23	Cocker Spaniel	Plain	Liver	4"	750.00	1,100.00	500.00
		Mounted	and	10.1 cm	750.00	1,100.00	500.00
		Bookend	white		750.00	1,100.00	500.00
SK 24	Cocker Spaniel	Plain	Black	4"	750.00	1,100.00	500.00
		Mounted		10.1 cm	750.00	1,100.00	500.00
		Bookend			750.00	1,100.00	500.00
SK 25	Foxhound	Plain	Brown	3"	750.00	1,100.00	500.00
		Mounted	and	7.6 cm	750.00	1,100.00	500.00
		Bookend	white		750.00	1,100.00	500.00
SK 26	Smooth Haired	Plain	White and	3"	750.00	1,100.00	500.00
	Fox Terrier	Mounted	dark	7.6 cm	750.00	1,100.00	500.00
		Bookend	brown		750.00	1,100.00	500.00
SK 27	Sealyham	Plain	White	3 ½"	750.00	1,100.00	500.00
		Mounted	and	8.9 cm	750.00	1,100.00	500.00
		Bookend	brown		750.00	1,100.00	500.00
SK 28	Airedale	Plain	Brown	3 ½"	750.00	1,100.00	500.00
		Mounted	and	8.9 cm	750.00	1,100.00	500.00
		Bookend	black		750.00	1,100.00	500.00
SK 29	Scottish Terrier	Plain	Black	3"	750.00	1,100.00	500.00
		Mounted		7.6 cm	750.00	1,100.00	500.00
		Bookend			750.00	1,100.00	500.00
SK 30	Cairn	Plain	Black	3 ½"	750.00	1,100.00	500.00
		Mounted	and	8.9 cm	750.00	1,100.00	500.00
		Bookend	grey		750.00	1,100.00	500.00
SK 31	Pekinese	Plain	Brown	4 ¾"	750.00	1,100.00	500.00
		Mounted	and	12.1 cm	750.00	1,100.00	500.00
		Bookend	black		750.00	1,100.00	500.00
804	Fox	Mounted	Reddish	3 ½"	750.00	1,100.00	500.00
			brown and	8.9 cm			
			white				

ADVERTISING ANIMALS

ERVAN LUCAS BOLS DISTILLERS
Bulldog

Type:	Liquor Container
Height:	6", 15.2 cm
Colour:	White with Union Jack - gloss
Issued:	1932

Description	U.S. $	Can. $	U.K. £
Bulldog	600.00	900.00	400.00

ERVAN LUCAS BOLS DISTILLERS
Pekinese

Type:	Liquor Container
Height:	6", 15.2 cm
Colour:	Brown - gloss
Issued:	1940

Description	U.S. $	Can. $	U.K. £
Pekinese	2,000.00	3,000.00	1,250.00

ERVAN LUCAS BOLS DISTILLERS
Salmon

Type:	Liquor Container
Height:	9 ½", 24.0 cm
Colour:	Silver-grey - gloss
Issued:	1940

Description	U.S. $	Can. $	U.K. £
Salmon	450.00	700.00	300.00

FINANCIAL TIMES
Partridge

Type:	Paperweight
Height:	2 ½", 6.4 cm
Colour:	Cream and brown - gloss
Issued:	1988 in a limited edition of 1,200

Description	U.S. $	Can. $	U.K. £
Partridge	300.00	450.00	200.00

GIROLAMA LUXARDO DISTILLERS
Bulldog

Type: Liquor Container
Height: 11", 27.9 cm
Colour: White - gloss
Issued: 1932

Description	U.S. $	Can. $	U.K. £
Bulldog	3,000.00	4,500.00	2,000.00

Photograph not
available
at press time

GIROLAMA LUXARDO DISTILLERS
Bulldog

Type: Anniversary
Height: 10 ½", 26.7 cm
Colour: White - gloss
Issued: 1932

Description	U.S. $	Can. $	U.K. £
Bulldog	3,000.00	4,500.00	2,000.00

Photograph not
available
at press time

GIROLAMA LUXARDO DISTILLERS
Polar Bear

Type: Liquor Container
Height: Unknown
Colour: White - gloss
Issued: 1932

Description	U.S. $	Can. $	U.K. £
Polar bear		Very Rare	

LOUIS WEARDEN & GUYLEE LTD.
Bulldog

Type: Advertising
Height: 3", 7.6 cm
Colour: White bulldog with Union Jack - gloss
Issued: 1932

Description	U.S. $	Can. $	U.K. £
Bulldog	1,000.00	1,500.00	750.00

MATHEW GLOAG
Grouse

Type: Flask
Designer: David Lyttleton
Height: 9 ½", 24.0 cm
Colour: Brown and red - matt
Issued: 1984-1987

Description	U.S. $	Can. $	U.K. £
Grouse	125.00	175.00	75.00

Note: Transferred from Beswick model no. 2798.

NATIONAL DISTILLERS CORP.
Old Crow

Type: Liquor Container
Height: 12 ¾", 32.0 cm
Colour: Black and white - gloss
Issued: 1954

Description	U.S. $	Can. $	U.K. £
Old crow	175.00	250.00	125.00

NATURAL BRANDY OF SOUTH AFRICA
Fish Eagle

Type: Flask
Designer: John G. Tongue
Height: 10 ½", 26.7 cm
Colour: White, dark to light brown - gloss
Issued: 1984

Description	U.S. $	Can. $	U.K. £
Fish Eagle	135.00	225.00	85.00

Note: Modification of Beswick model number 2678, Fish Eagle facing front.

PENGUIN BOOKS
Penguin

Type: Advertising
Height: 4 ½", 11.4 cm
Colour: Black and white - gloss
Issued: 1987

Description	U.S. $	Can. $	U.K. £
Penguin	45.00	65.00	30.00

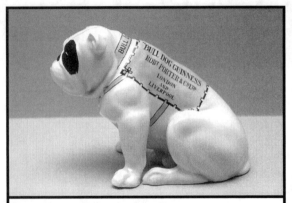

ROBERT PORTER & CO. LTD.
Bulldog

Type:	Advertising
Height:	6", 15.2 cm
Colour:	White, blue and brown - gloss
Issued:	1915

Description	U.S. $	Can. $	U.K. £
Bulldog	1,250.00	1,750.00	850.00

ROYAL DOULTON ANGLING CLUB
Salmon

Type:	Presentation
Height:	9 ½", 24.0 cm
Colour:	Pale green and blue - gloss
Issued:	1985

Description	U.S. $	Can. $	U.K. £
Salmon	400.00	500.00	250.00

STAUFFER & SON CO.
Begging Dog

Type:	Advertising
Height:	8", 20.3 cm
Colour:	Black and white - gloss
Issued:	1929

Description	U.S. $	Can. $	U.K. £
Begging dog	1,000.00	1,250.00	750.00

WHYTE & MACKAY DISTILLERS
Badger

Type:	Flask
Designer:	David Lyttleton
Height:	3", 7.6 cm
Colour:	Black and white - gloss
Issued:	1987-1991

Description	U.S. $	Can. $	U.K. £
Badger flask	25.00	35.00	15.00

Note: Transferred from Beswick model no. 2687.

WHYTE & MACKAY DISTILLERS
Barn Owl

Type:	Flask
Designer:	Graham Tongue
Height:	6 ¾", 17.2 cm
Colour:	Tan-brown and white - gloss
Issued:	1987 to the present

Description	U.S. $	Can. $	U.K. £
Barn owl	125.00	175.00	75.00

Note: Transferred from Beswick model no. 2809.

WHYTE & MACKAY DISTILLERS
Buzzard

Type:	Flask
Designer:	Graham Tongue
Height:	6 ½", 16.5 cm
Colour:	Dark brown and grey - gloss
Issued:	1987 to the present

Description	U.S. $	Can. $	U.K. £
Buzzard	125.00	175.00	75.00

Note: Transferred from Beswick model no. 2640.

WHYTE & MACKAY DISTILLERS
Eagle

Type:	Flask
Designer:	Graham Tongue
Height:	4", 10.1 cm
Colour:	Brown - gloss
Issued:	1987 to the present

Description	U.S. $	Can. $	U.K. £
Eagle	20.00	30.00	15.00

Note: Transferred from Beswick model no. 2104.

WHYTE & MACKAY DISTILLERS
Golden Eagle

Type:	Flask
Designer:	Graham Tongue
Height:	10 ½", 26.7 cm
Colour:	Light and dark brown - gloss
Issued:	1987 to the present

Description	U.S. $	Can. $	U.K. £
Golden eagle	125.00	175.00	75.00

Note: Transferred from Beswick model no. 2678.

WHYTE & MACKAY DISTILLERS
Haggis

Type:	Flask
Designer:	James Haywood
Remodelled:	Albert Hallam
Height:	2 ½", 6.4 cm
Colour:	Brown - gloss
Issued:	1987-1991

Description	U.S. $	Can. $	U.K. £
Haggis	20.00	30.00	15.00

Note: Transferred from beswick model no. 2350.

WHYTE & MACKAY DISTILLERS
Kestrel

Type:	Flask
Designer:	Graham Tongue
Height:	6 ½", 16.5 cm
Colour:	Dark grey and white - gloss
Issued:	1987 to the present

Description	U.S. $	Can. $	U.K. £
Kestrel	95.00	135.00	60.00

Note: Transferred from Beswick model no. 2639.

WHYTE & MACKAY DISTILLERS
Merlin

Type:	Flask
Designer:	Graham Tongue
Height:	6 ½", 16.5 cm
Colour:	Dark grey and white - gloss
Issued:	1987 to the present

Description	U.S. $	Can. $	U.K. £
Merlin	100.00	150.00	65.00

Note: Transferred from Beswick model no. 2641.

WHYTE & MACKAY DISTILLERS
Nessie Flask

Type:	Flask
Designer:	Albert Hallam
Height:	3", 7.6 cm
Colour:	Grey-green - gloss
Issued:	1987 to the present

Description	U.S. $	Can. $	U.K. £
Nessie	25.00	40.00	15.00

Note: Transferred from Beswick model no. 2051.

WHYTE & MACKAY DISTILLERS
Osprey

Type:	Flask
Designer:	David Lyttleton
Height:	7 ¾", 19.7 cm
Colour:	Browns and white - gloss
Issued:	1987 to the present

Description	U.S. $	Can. $	U.K. £
Osprey	125.00	175.00	75.00

Note: Transferred from Beswick model no. 2583.

WHYTE & MACKAY DISTILLERS
Otter

Type:	Flask
Designer:	David Lyttleton
Height:	2 ¼", 5.7 cm
Colour:	Grey and brown - gloss
Issued:	1987-1991

Description	U.S. $	Can. $	U.K. £
Otter	20.00	30.00	15.00

Note: Transferred from Beswick model no. 2686.

WHYTE & MACKAY DISTILLERS
Peregrine Falcon

Type:	Flask
Designer:	Graham Tongue
Height:	6 ½", 16.5 cm
Colour:	Grey - gloss
Issued:	1979

Description	U.S. $	Can. $	U.K. £
Peregrine Falcon	125.00	175.00	75.00

Note: Transferred from Beswick model no. 2642.

WHYTE & MACKAY DISTILLERS
Seal

Type:	Flask
Designer:	Graham Tongue
Height:	3 ½", 8.9 cm
Colour:	Grey - gloss
Issued:	1987-1991

Description	U.S. $	Can. $	U.K. £
Seal	20.00	30.00	15.00

Note: Transferred from Beswick model no. 2693.

WHYTE & MACKAY DISTILLERS
Short Eared Owl

Type:	Flask
Designer:	Graham Tongue
Height:	6 ¾", 17.2 cm
Colour:	Dark and light brown - gloss
Issued:	1987 to the present

Description	U.S. $	Can. $	U.K. £
Short eared owl	125.00	175.00	75.00

Note: Transferred from Beswick model no. 2825.

WHYTE & MACKAY DISTILLERS
Snowy Owl

Type:	Flask
Designer:	Graham Tongue
Height:	6 ½", 16.5 cm
Colour:	White - gloss
Issued:	1987

Description	U.S. $	Can. $	U.K. £
Snowy owl	125.00	175.00	75.00

Note: Transferred from Beswick model no. 2826.

WHYTE & MACKAY DISTILLERS
Squirrel

Type:	Flask
Designer:	David Lyttleton
Height:	3 ½", 8.9 cm
Colour:	Red-brown - gloss
Issued:	1987-1991

Description	U.S. $	Can. $	U.K. £
Squirrel	20.00	30.00	15.00

Note: Transferred from Beswick model no. 2636.

WHYTE & MACKAY DISTILLERS
Tawny Owl

Type:	Flask
Designer:	Graham Tongue
Height:	6 ¼", 15.9 cm
Colour:	Brown - gloss
Issued:	1987 to the present

Description	U.S. $	Can. $	U.K. £
Tawny owl	125.00	175.00	75.00

Note: Transferred from Beswick model no. 2781.

Pride of the Shires and Foal (HN 2518)

INDICES

ALPHABETICAL INDEX TO HN, K, D AND DA SERIES

ALPHABETICAL INDEX TO
STONEWARE SECTION

ALPHABETICAL INDEX TO
ROYAL ADDERLEY BIRD STUDIES

INDEX OF MODEL NUMBERS

MODEL NUMBERS PRE 1910

Model No.	Name
1162	Frog, flambé
1162A	Frog, flambé
1162B	Frog, flambé
1163	Chicks (three), flambé
1163A	Chicks (two), HN 236, flambé, sung
1163B	Chick, HN 274, 282, flambé
1164	Mouse on a cube, HN 255, flambé
1164A	Mouse with a nut, flambé
1164B	Mouse (crouching), flambé; On fluted ashtray HN 1090A, On plain ashtray HN 1090B

Model No.	Name
1165	Lop-eared rabbit, small, flambé On fluted ashtray HN 1091A, On plain ashtray HN 1091B
1165A	Rabbit (crouching - style one), flambé
1165B	Rabbit (crouching - style two), sung
1236	Fledgling (style one), HN 145A, flambé
1237	Fledgling (style five), HN 145C
1238	Fledgling (style two), HN 137B, flambé

MODEL NUMBERS POST 1910

Model No.	Name
1	Apes
2	Duck (preening - style one), HN 235, 298, flambé
3	Duckling (new born), HN 188, 189, 190, flambé
4	Duck (preening - style two), HN 148A, 271, 299, flambé
5	Fish
6	Foxes (curled - Style One), HN 117, 179, flambé, sung, treacle
7	Frog leaping
8	Frog sitting
9	Cat (seated - style one), HN 109, 120, 967, flambé, sung
10	Fish
11	Butterfly
11A	Butterfly
12	Fox (seated - style one), HN 147C, flambé, sung
12A	Fox (seated - style one), HN 147C-1, flambé
14	Fox (seated - style two), HN 147B, flambé, sung
14A	Fox (seated - style two), flambé
15	Fox (curled - style one), HN 147D, flambé, treacle
16	Monkey (hand to ear), HN 156, flambé
17	Cat lying on back, flambé
18	Dog playing
20	Fox bowl, flambé
21	Fox on pedestal, HN 994, flambé
22	Cormorant on rock, flambé
23	Cat asleep, head on paw, HN 210, 227
23A	Cat on cushion
24	Cat asleep on cushion, HN 993
25	Cockerel (crowing), HN 111, flambé
26	Bowl with double fox finial
28	Grotesque
29	Fox (stalking), HN 147E, flambé
29A	Fox (stalking), HN 147A, flambé
29B	Fox (stalking), HN 147A-1, Chinese jade, flambé, sung
30	Cockerel (crouching) HN 124, 178, 180, 267, flambé
33	Butterfly on square base
34	Laughing rabbit

Model No.	Name
35	Lizard
36	Dachshund (standing - style two), HN 970
36A	Dachshund (standing - style one), flambé
37	Owl in a crescent moon-shaped dish, HN 222, flambé
38	Bulldog (seated - style one), flambé
39	Polar bear (seated), HN 121, flambé, sung, titanian
40	Polar bear on dish, flambé
41	Dachshund (begging), flambé
42	Crab, flambé, crystalline
43	Raven, HN 135, flambé
44	Kingfisher on rock (style one), HN 131, 152, flambé
44A	Kingfisher on stand with primroses, HN 862A
44B	Kingfisher on stand with kingcups, HN 862B
45	Parrot on pillar, flambé
46	Fantail pigeons, HN 122, flambé
47	Collie (seated), HN 105, 106, 112, flambé
48	Bloodhound, HN 176, flambé
49	Labrador on base, natural and flambé
50	Cockerel (seated - style one), HN 157
51	Owl box
52	Monkeys, mother and baby, HN 254, flambé, sung
53	Monkey (seated, arms folded), HN 118, 253, flambé, titanian
54	Polar bears on ice floe, flambé
56	Lion seated on rock
57	Comic pig, HN 246, blue
58	Comic brown bear, HN 170, 270, flambé, blue
59	Lion (seated), HN 223, flambé, treacle
61	Pigs (snoozing - both pigs' ears up), HN 213, 238, 802, flambé
62	Pigs (snoozing - both pigs' ears down), flambé
62	Pigs (snoozing - one with Pig with ears down, one with ears up), flambé
64	Lion (lying), flambé
65	Elephant (trunk down, curled), HN 181, 186, flambé, sung
66	Dachshund
67	Polar bear on cube, HN 119, flambé
68	Cockatoo on a rock, HN 185, 191, 192, 200, 877, flambé

A selection of Royal Adderley Birds

INDEX OF BESWICK MODEL NUMBERS

The following Beswick Model Numbers were converted to DA (Doulton Animal) numbers and issued by Royal Doulton.

INDEX OF UNACCOUNTED MODEL NUMBERS

This index lists animal figure subjects by those model numbers assigned by Royal Doulton in their pattern books but subsequently were either not issued or issued but unrecorded.

Some of these model numbers may well exist as HN numbers but have not as yet been identified or cross-referenced with the HN system.

COLLECTING BY SERIES

432

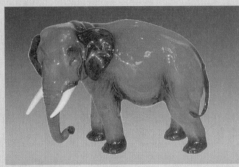

Royal Doulton Shops

ROYAL DOULTON SHOPS – CANADA

C2 - 3625 Shaganappi Trail NW
Calgary, AB
T3A 0E2

West Edmonton Mall
8882 - 170th Street
Edmonton, AB T5T 3J7

Coquitlam Centre
2929 Barnet Highway
Port Coquitlam, BC V3R 5R5

Guildford Town Centre
Surrey, BC
V3R 7C1

Polo Park Shopping Centre
1485 Portage Ave.
Winnipeg, MB R3G 0W4

477 Paul Street
Champlain Place
Dieppe, NB E1A 4X4

1381 Regent Street
Fredericton, NB
E3C 1A2

Micmac Mall
21 Micmac Blvd.
Dartmouth, NS B3A 4K7

White Oaks Mall
1105 Wellington Road
London, ON N6E 1V4

Markville Shopping Centre
5000 Highway #7
Markham, ON L3R 4M9

Pickering Town Centre
1355 Kingston Road
Pickering ON L1V 1B8

Fairview Mall
1800 Sheppard Avenue East
Willowdale, ON M2J 5A7

ROYAL DOULTON FACTORY SHOPS – ENGLAND

Cheshire Oaks Outlet Village, Unit 106
Kinsey Road, Ellesmere Port
Cheshire L65 9LA

167 Picadilly
London
W1V 9DE

Nile Street
Burslem, Stoke-on-Trent
Staffordshire ST6 2AJ

Forge Lane, Etruria
Stoke-on-Trent
Stafffordshire ST1 5NN

Victoria Road
Fenton, Stoke-on-Trent
Staffordshire ST4 2PJ

Lawley Street
Longton, Stoke-on-Trent
Staffordshire ST3 2PH

ROYAL DOULTON SHOPS – UNITED STATES

Dester Hills Premium Outlets
48650 Seminole Dr.
Building C, Suite 152,
Cabazon, CA 92230

Camarillo Premium Outlets
740 Ventura Blvd., Suite 530
Camarillo, CA 93010

Premium Outlets – Gilroy
681 Leavesley Road
Suite B290
Gilroy, CA 95020

Factory Stores at Vacaville
352 Nut Tree Rd.
Vacaville, CA 95687

Clinton Crossing Premium Outlets
20 Killingworth Turnpike, Ste. 530
Clinton, CT 06413

Ocean Outlets
1772 Ocean Outlets
Rehoboth, DE 19971

Gulf Coast Factory Stores
5501 Factory Shops Blvd.
Ellenton, Fl 34222

Miromar Outlets
10801 Corkscrew Rd. Suite 366
Estero, Fl 33928

The Orlando Crossings
5563 International Drive
Orlando, Fl, 32819

Belz Factory Outlet World
500 Belz Outlet Blvd. Suite 80
St. Augustine, Fl 32084

Prime Outlets - Colhoun
455 Belwood Rd., Suite 20
Calhoun, GA 30701

North Georgia Premium Outlets
800 Highway 400, Suite 250
Dawsonville, GA 30534

Lighthouse Place Premium Outlets
403 Lighthouse Place
Michigan City, IN 46360

Kittery Outlet Center
Route 1
Kittery, ME 03904-2505

Prime Outlets - Birch Run
12240 S. Beyer Rd., Suite E80
Birch Run, MI 48415

Shoppes on the Parkway, Ste. 10
Blowing Rock, NC 28605

Factory Stores of America
1209 Industrial Park Drive, Suite 400
Smithfield, NC 27577

Liberty Village Premium Outlets
34 Liberty Village
Flemington, NJ 08822

Belz Factory Outlet World
7400 Las Vegas Blvd. South, Suite 244
Las Vegas, NV 89123

Woodbury Common Premium Outlets
161 Marigold Court
Central Valley, NY 10917

Tanger Outlet Center
Riverhead II, Tanger Drive,
Suite # 1012
Riverhead, NY 11901

Ohio Factory Shops
8150 Factory Shops Blvd.
Jeffersonville, OH 43128

Factory Stores at Lincoln City
1500 SE East Devil's Lake Rd., Ste. 303
Lincoln City, OR 97367

Prime Outlets at Grove City
1911 Leesburg-Grove City Rd.
Suite 210, P.O. Box 1014
Grove City, PA 16127

Tanger Outlet Center
501 Stanley K. Tanger Blvd.
Lancaster, PA 17602-1467

The Crossings Outlet Center
1000 Rte 611, Suite A-23
Tannersville, PA 18372

Myrtle Beach Factory Stores
4638 Factory Stores Blvd. EE 150
Myrtle Beach, SC 29579

Belz Factory Outlet
2655 Teaster Lane, Suite 26
Pigeon Forge, TN 37683

Prime Outlets – Conroe
1111 League Line Rd. Suite 112
Conroe, TX 77303

Tanger Factory Outlet Centre
4015 Interstate 35 South
Suite 402
San Marcos, TX 78666

Potomac Mills
2700 Potomac Mills Circle
Suite 976
Prince William, VA 22192

Prime Outlets - Williamsburg
5699-50 Richmond Rd
Williamsburg, VA 23188

Prime Outlets – Burlington
288 Fashion Way, Store #5
Burlington, WA 98233

ROYAL DOULTON

Visit our website at:
www.royaldoulton.com